THE STATISTICAL THEORY OF NON-EQUILIBRIUM PROCESSES IN A PLASMA

THE STATISTICAL THEORY OF NON-EQUILIBRIUM PROCESSES IN A PLASMA

BY

YU. L. KLIMONTOVICH

TRANSLATED BY

H. S. H. MASSEY

AND O. M. BLUNN

EDITED BY

D. TER HAAR

THE M. I. T. PRESS
Massachusetts Institute of Technology
Cambridge, Massachusetts

First English edition 1967

Library of Congress Catalog Card No. 66–28403

Contents

FOREWORD vii

INTRODUCTION ix

CHAPTER I. MAXWELL EQUATIONS FOR SLOW AND FAST PROCESSES

1. Maxwell equations for slow processes 1
2. Maxwell equations for fast processes 10
3. Magnetohydrodynamic equations 38

CHAPTER II. MICROSCOPIC EQUATIONS FOR A PLASMA. AVERAGING THE MICROSCOPIC EQUATIONS

4. Microscopic equations for a plasma 46
5. Averaging the microscopic equations for a plasma 55

CHAPTER III. EQUATIONS WITH A SELF-CONSISTENT FIELD—VLASOV EQUATIONS

6. Kinetic equations for a plasma in the self-consistent field approximation 68
7. Solution for self-consistent equations for the functions f_a, $\boldsymbol{E}$, $\boldsymbol{B}$ in the linear approximation when there are no external fields 78
8. Propagation of electromagnetic waves in a plasma when there are no external fields 88
9. Propagation of electromagnetic waves in a plasma located in a constant magnetic field 99

CHAPTER IV. CORRELATION FUNCTIONS AND SPECTRAL FUNCTIONS. KINETIC EQUATIONS FOR A PLASMA. LANDAU EQUATIONS

10. Simultaneous correlation functions for a non-relativistic plasma 117
11. Set of kinetic equations for the functions f_a neglecting plasma wave radiation. Landau equations 127

12. Conservation laws taking higher moments into account 139
13. Kinetic equations for a relativistic plasma 145
14. Stationary space–time correlations in a plasma 160
15. Correlation functions and collision integral in the presence of an external magnetic field 180

CHAPTER V. THE KINETIC EQUATIONS AND EXPRESSIONS FOR SPECTRAL FUNCTIONS WHEN THE RADIATION BY PLASMA WAVES IS TAKEN INTO ACCOUNT

16. Non-stationarity. Spectral functions for the radiation region 193
17. Allowing for radiation in the kinetic equations. Set of equations for the first distribution functions and for the spectral field function 207
18. "Quasilinear approximation" for a set of equations with a self-consistent field. Allowing for higher moments 215
19. Quasilinear approximation taking "collisions" into account 231
20. Approximation of "free" and "bound" charges for a plasma. Self-consistent equations for second distribution functions 237

CHAPTER VI. HYDRODYNAMIC DESCRIPTION OF PROCESSES IN A PLASMA

21. Hydrodynamic equations for a heavily ionized plasma neglecting wave radiation 243
22. Taking plasma wave radiation into account in the hydrodynamic equations 258
23. Magnetohydrodynamic equations for a non-isothermic plasma without "collisions" 262
24. Hydrodynamic description of charged particle motion in a weakly ionized plasma 270

REFERENCES 277

INDEX 281

Foreword

THE present monograph attempts to discuss a fairly wide range of questions in the modern statistical theory of non-equilibrium processes in a plasma by a unified method, proceeding from the microscopic equations.

As the starting point we use the closed system of equations:

$$\frac{\partial N_a}{\partial t}+\left(\boldsymbol{v}\cdot\frac{\partial N_a}{\partial \boldsymbol{q}}\right)+e_a\left(\left\{\boldsymbol{E}^{\mathrm{M}}+\frac{1}{c}\,[\boldsymbol{v}\wedge\boldsymbol{H}^{\mathrm{M}}]\right\}\cdot\frac{\partial N_a}{\partial \boldsymbol{p}}\right)=0,$$

$$\operatorname{curl}\boldsymbol{H}^{\mathrm{M}}=\frac{1}{c}\,\frac{\partial \boldsymbol{E}^{\mathrm{M}}}{\partial t}+4\pi\sum_a e_a\int \boldsymbol{v}N_a\,d^3\boldsymbol{p},\qquad \operatorname{div}\boldsymbol{H}^{\mathrm{M}}=0,$$

$$\operatorname{curl}\boldsymbol{E}^{\mathrm{M}}=-\frac{1}{c}\,\frac{\partial \boldsymbol{H}^{\mathrm{M}}}{\partial t};\qquad \operatorname{div}\boldsymbol{E}^{\mathrm{M}}=4\pi\sum_a e_a\int N_a\,d^3\boldsymbol{p},$$

for the microscopic phase densities

$$N_a(\boldsymbol{q},\boldsymbol{p},t)=\sum_{1\leqslant i\leqslant N_a}\delta(\boldsymbol{q}-\boldsymbol{q}_{ia}(t))\,\delta(\boldsymbol{p}-\boldsymbol{p}_{ia}(t))$$

of each component of the plasma a and the microscopic strengths of the electric and magnetic fields $\boldsymbol{E}^{\mathrm{M}}(\boldsymbol{q},t)$, $\boldsymbol{H}^{\mathrm{M}}(\boldsymbol{q},t)$. Under fixed experimental conditions these functions are not determined unambiguously so they must be looked upon as random functions.

With this method of description the problem of the statistical theory of non-equilibrium processes in a plasma can be reduced to determining the first, second and higher moments of these functions. The present book pays most attention to the approximation of the first two moments. Little work has as yet been done on the theory of the higher moments for a plasma.

In the last few years a number of books has appeared about various questions of plasma theory. Amongst them are the well-known books *Propagation of Electromagnetic Waves in a Plasma* by V. L. Ginzburg and *Electromagnetic Properties of a Plasma and Plasma-like Media* by V. P. Silin and A. A. Rukhadze. The first four issues of *Problems in Plasma Theory* have been published under the editorship of M. A. Leontovich and contain papers by a large number of authors. Of non-Russian books R. Balescu's book *Statistical Mechanics of Charged Particles* should be mentioned.

The author hopes that the present book will be a useful addition to what has already been published on plasma theory.

Introduction

PRESENT-DAY statistical theory of a plasma is based on the well-known work by L. D. Landau (1936), A. A. Vlasov (1938) and N. N. Bogolyubov (1962).

Using the Boltzmann equation Landau (1937) was the first to obtain the kinetic equation for a uniform (or quasi-uniform) plasma which allowed for charged particle collisions.

In 1938 Vlasov derived a system of kinetic equations with a self-consistent field—the closed system of equations for the first distribution functions and the Maxwell equations for the average strengths of the electric and magnetic fields. This system of equations is now widely used to describe the processes in a plasma when the characteristic time is much less than the relaxation time (the time taken to establish an equilibrium state).

Bogolyubov's well-known monograph *Problems of Dynamic Theory in Statistical Physics* shows that the kinetic equations of Vlasov and Landau can be derived by approximate solution of the chain of equations for the distribution functions $f_a, f_{ab}, \ldots,$ of one, two or more particles.

Here the distribution functions f_{ab}, f_{abc} are expanded in powers of the interaction energy and the asymptotic solutions are found for the equations for the functions $f_{ab}, f_{abc}, \ldots,$ which are completely determined by the first distribution functions f_a.

The equation with the self-consistent field is in this way the first approximation of perturbation theory, which corresponds to completely neglecting the correlation.

In the second approximation in the case of a spatially uniform plasma we obtain Landau's kinetic equation.

However, using perturbation theory with respect to the small parameter characterizing the ratio of the average interaction energy to the average kinetic energy is insufficient when describing the processes in a plasma. This is manifested in particular in that the "collision" integral in the Landau equation obtained in this way contains a logarithmically divergent integral with respect to the wave numbers.

The divergence at small distances (large wave numbers) cannot be eliminated within the framework of perturbation theory since the interaction energies and correlation functions are not small at small distances. The divergence at large distances is connected with the fact that polarization of the plasma is not allowed for when using perturbation theory with respect to the interaction energy in the collision integral.

Bogolyubov (1962) suggests that plasma polarization be allowed for by an improved perturbation theory method in which the smallness parameter used is the so-called plasma parameter $\varepsilon = (r_{\text{av}}/r_d)^3$. It is defined as the ratio of the cube of the mean distance between the charged particles r_{av} to the cube of the Debye radius r_d which determines the correlation radius of the charged particles for states close to equilibrium.

This parameter is inversely proportional to the mean number of charged particles N_{r_d} in a sphere of radius r_d. For a rarefied plasma the number N_{r_d} is very large so the parameter $\varepsilon \ll 1$.

The presence of this parameter allows us to give the distribution functions f_{ab}, f_{abc}, etc., in the form

$$f_{ab}(\boldsymbol{q}, \boldsymbol{q}', \boldsymbol{p}, \boldsymbol{p}', t) = f_a(\boldsymbol{q}, \boldsymbol{p}, t) f_b(\boldsymbol{q}', \boldsymbol{p}', t) + \varepsilon g_{ab}(\boldsymbol{q}, \boldsymbol{q}', \boldsymbol{p}, \boldsymbol{p}', t),$$

$$f_{abc} = f_a f_b f_c + \varepsilon(g_{ab} f_c + g_{bc} f_a + g_{ca} f_b) + \varepsilon^2 g_{abc}$$

Here the g_{ab} are double correlation functions of the components of the particles a, b and the g_{abc} are triple correlation functions.

In the first approximation with respect to the parameter ε we obtain a closed system of equations for the functions f_a, g_{ab}.

The equation thus obtained for the function g_{ab} differs from the corresponding equation obtained when expanding with respect to smallness of interaction in that polarization is allowed for.

Also in this case it has proved possible to find an asymptotic solution of the equations for the functions g_{ab} in the spatially uniform case when the time dependence of the functions g_{ab} is determined by the time dependence of the first distribution functions f_a. This solution has been obtained by Balescu (1960), Balescu and Taylor (1961), and Lenard (1960) for the classical case and by Konstantinov and Perel (1960), and Silin (1961, 1962) for the quantum case.

The corresponding kinetic equation for the function f_a differs from the Landau equation in that plasma polarization is allowed for more exactly (see § 11).

It is possible, of course, to obtain a more precise solution of the system of equations for the functions f_a, g_{ab}, g_{abc}, ..., when higher approximations with respect to the parameter ε are allowed for (see Silin, 1963a).

Bogolyubov (1962) discusses the case of a Coulomb plasma (a system of charged particles interacting in accordance with Coulomb's law). Bogolyubov's method can, however, also be used in the more general case when it is important to allow not only for the potential electrical field, as in a Coulomb plasma, but also for the rotational electromagnetic field.

In this case instead of the distribution functions that depend on the particle coordinates and momenta we must use the more general distribution functions that depend, apart from the variable particles, on variables characterizing the microstate of the electromagnetic field and use the appropriate equations.

It is convenient to use a different method for giving the microstate to describe the processes in a plasma (see Klimontovich, 1958a, 1958b, 1960a and 1960b). We shall consider that the microscopic state of a system is given if we know the values of the microscopic density of any plasma component

$$N_a = \sum_{1 \leqslant i \leqslant N_a} \delta(\boldsymbol{q}-\boldsymbol{q}_{ia}(t))\, \delta(\boldsymbol{p}-\boldsymbol{p}_{ia}(t))$$

at a given point in time at each point of a six-dimensional phase space $\boldsymbol{q}$, $\boldsymbol{p}$ and the microscopic values $\boldsymbol{E}^{\mathrm{M}}$, $\boldsymbol{H}^{\mathrm{M}}$ of the electrical and magnetic field strengths at any point $\boldsymbol{q}$. In this case we can take the system of equations for the functions N_a, $\boldsymbol{E}^{\mathrm{M}}$, $\boldsymbol{H}^{\mathrm{M}}$ as the initial microscopic equations. This system of equations can be simplified for a Coulomb plasma and becomes a closed system of equations only for the functions $N_a(\boldsymbol{q}, \boldsymbol{p}, t)$. These equations are similar to the operator equations for the wave functions in the Heisenberg representation.

It is this method of describing the microstate of a plasma that is used in the present work. This is dictated by the fact that using the system of equations for the random functions N_a, $\boldsymbol{E}^{\mathrm{M}}$, $\boldsymbol{H}^{\mathrm{M}}$ as the initial one makes possible a considerable simplification of the solution of a number of problems.

This is because we have to solve the comparatively simpler system of equations for the deviations of the random functions N_a, $\boldsymbol{E}^{\mathrm{M}}$, $\boldsymbol{H}^{\mathrm{M}}$ from their average values instead of the very complex equations for the distribution functions of the particle coordinates and momenta and the field oscillator coordinates and momenta.

With this approach the problem of the theory of non-equilibrium processes in a plasma is reduced to determining the moments of the random functions N_a, $\boldsymbol{E}^{\mathrm{M}}$, $\boldsymbol{H}^{\mathrm{M}}$.

The simplest are the first moment $\overline{N}_a = n_a f_a$, $\overline{\boldsymbol{E}}^{\mathrm{M}} = \boldsymbol{E}$, $\overline{\boldsymbol{H}}^{\mathrm{M}} = \boldsymbol{B}$. Here $n_a = N_a/V$ is the average particle concentration of the component a and f_a is the corresponding first distribution function. The bar denotes statistical averaging.

When averaging the system of microscopic equations we do not obtain a closed system of equations for the first moments since the second moments $\overline{e^{\mathrm{M}} N_a}$, $\overline{h^{\mathrm{M}} N_a}$ appear in the equations for the functions $\overline{N}_a$, e, b as well as the first. The third moments appear in the equations for the second moments and so on. The position here is similar to that which occurs with Bogolyubov's method when deriving the chain of equation for the distribution functions or in the Green function method (Zubarev, 1960; Bonch-Bruevich and Tyablikov, 1962; and Abrikosov, Gor'kov and Dzyaloshinskii, 1965).

In those cases when the central moments, starting at the third, can be ignored in the first approximation we obtain a closed system of equations for the first and second central moments of the functions N_a, e^{M}, h^{M}.

For a Coulomb plasma, when the rotational electromagnetic field may be ignored, we obtain in this approximation equations equivalent to the closed system of equations for the functions f_a, g_{ab} which is obtained in the first approximation with respect to the parameter ε.

The microscopic equations for a plasma are discussed in the second chapter. Here we also average the microscopic equations and examine an approximate system of equations for the first and second moments.

The first chapter is of a subsidiary nature. Here we discuss the Maxwell equations for slow and fast processes when dispersion of the medium must be allowed for.

The third chapter discusses the system of equations with a self-consistent field.

In the fourth chapter we investigate the statistical characteristics of a spatially uniform and non-uniform plasma.

To a certain extent this case is the opposite of the self-consistent field approximation. In the self-consistent field approximation of the second moments

$$\overline{N_a e^{\mathrm{M}}} = \bar{N}_a e + \overline{\delta N_a \delta e}\,, \quad \overline{N_a h^{\mathrm{M}}} = \bar{N}_a b + \overline{\delta N_a \delta b},$$

which appear when averaging the microscopic equations for the functions N_a only the first terms expressed by the first moments $\bar{N}_a$, $\boldsymbol{E}, \boldsymbol{B}$ are retained. The second terms, which allow for correlation of the particle and field distribution, are neglected. In the spatially uniform case the correlation terms play a major rôle.

A closed system of equations for the first and second moments is used to describe the processes in a plasma. Even this approximate system of equations is, however, still too complex so the question arises of the conditions under which it can be simplified and to what degree.

If the maximum correlation time of the random disturbances in a plasma is small by comparison with the relaxation time of the first distribution functions f_a, then all the second moments can be expressed by the functions f_a.

Under these conditions we can eliminate the correlation functions from the equations for the functions f_a and obtain closed equations (the kinetic equations) for them. They are discussed in §§ 11, 13 and 14.

Expressions are derived for the spatial and space–time spectral functions for both a Coulomb and a relativistic plasma.

The fifth chapter is devoted to a discussion of the more general case when the correlation time of the perturbations in a plasma can be comparable with or greater than the relaxation time for the first distribution functions.

Then the correlation functions can be expressed by the f_a functions only for the short-wave region of the spectrum ("the collision region"). For the long-wave region of the spectrum ("the radiation region") only the more complex correlation functions can be expressed by the spectral function of the field strengths for the radiation region. Closed equations for the distribution functions f_a (kinetic equations) cannot therefore be obtained. Instead of the kinetic equations we obtain in this case the more general equations for the functions f_a and the spectral functions of the field strengths. This system of equations can be used to describe a definite class of turbulent motions in a plasma.

The equations obtained can be easily generalized for the case when it is necessary to allow for the higher moments of the random functions N_a, $\boldsymbol{E}^{\mathrm{M}}$, $\boldsymbol{H}^{\mathrm{M}}$.

The last chapter is devoted to discussing the various possible methods for a hydrodynamic description of processes in a plasma.

Section 21 derives the hydrodynamic equations for a strongly ionized plasma without allowing for plasma wave emission, when the characteristic dimensions and times are much greater respectively than the relaxation length and relaxation time of the first distribution functions. The kinetic equations for the functions f_a are used as the initial equations. The hydrodynamic equations are obtained by Grad's method.

Section 22 discusses the example of hydrodynamic description of the processes in a spatially uniform plasma allowing for plasma wave emission.

Section 23 discusses the hydrodynamic equations for a "plasma without collisions", when the characteristic dimension of the system is much less than the mean free path (the relaxation length of the function f_a).

Finally, § 24 is devoted to deriving the equations for the

hydrodynamic description of the motion of charged particles in a weakly ionized plasma.

The majority of the material in the present book has been presented in lectures read in the Mechanics and Mathematics Faculty of the Moscow State University.

Lack of space in the book has not permitted the inclusion of a whole series of important and interesting questions in plasma theory. Amongst these are, for example, questions of stability theory, non-linear problems which can be solved on the basis of the equations with a self-consistent field and non-linear problems of a turbulent plasma. Nor is there discussion of questions connected with allowing for inelastic interactions. The author hopes to discuss some of these questions in another monograph.

The list of references covers works used to some degree in the present monograph or which discuss questions not touched on here.

CHAPTER I

Maxwell Equations for Slow and Fast Processes

1. Maxwell Equations for Slow Processes

There are two methods for describing the processes in a plasma, just as in other media such as a gas or a solid: the macroscopic, or thermodynamic, and the statistical.

In the macroscopic description the state of the system is defined by a small number of thermodynamic parameters, such as temperature, density, pressure, internal energy, etc. The thermodynamic parameters are the averaged values of the corresponding microscopic functions.

The thermodynamic description has been developed both for quasistatic (reversible) processes and for slow irreversible processes. In the latter case a closed system of differential equations is established for the thermodynamic functions.

As an example we can take the gas dynamics system of equations which is a closed system of equations for the thermodynamic functions ϱ, T (or p) and the dynamic function $\boldsymbol{u}$ which defines the mean velocity of motion in the gas.

The condition of slowness of the thermodynamic processes in a gas means that the functions $\varrho, T, \boldsymbol{u}$ vary only a little over distances of the order of the mean free path and during the time of free flight. In other words, this means that the thermodynamic description of the processes in a gas is suitable for that stage of the process which follows after local statistical equilibrium has been established, i.e. for the so-called quasi-equilibrium processes.

The gas-dynamics equations can be used to show that the system of equations for describing slow processes can be obtained in two ways.

The first (the phenomenological method) is based on the use of the conservation laws and experimental ratios between the fluxes of heat, momentum and matter and the gradients of the thermodynamic functions. At the same time the equations contain experimental coefficients of, for example, viscosity, thermal conductivity, diffusion, etc.

The statistical description of the thermal processes allows us to determine the validity of the simpler thermodynamic method of description, to establish its limits of applicability and to express the experimental coefficients in terms of the microscopic parameters.

In addition, of course, the use of statistical methods allows us to discuss problems which cannot be solved by the thermodynamic method.

The first two sections will discuss certain questions in the macroscopic theory of electromagnetic processes which are necessary in order to understand the statistical theory.

The present section discusses different ways of writing the Maxwell equations. These equations define the connexion between the average values of the electrical and magnetic field strengths and the average values of the electric current density and charge density.

In their mathematical form the Maxwell equations express the system of basic laws governing electromagnetic processes in an arbitrary medium. When describing slow processes the properties of the medium are characterized by giving a small number of constants: the permittivity, the permeability and the conductivity, whose values are determined by experiment.

The Maxwell equations for fast processes are discussed in the second section.

Let e_i be the electrical charge of a particle with a number i. We define the microscopic charge density and the microscopic current density

$$\varrho_e^M = \sum_i e_i \delta(\boldsymbol{q} - \boldsymbol{q}_i(t)), \quad \boldsymbol{j}^M = \sum_i e_i \boldsymbol{v}_i \delta(\boldsymbol{q} - \boldsymbol{q}_i(t)).$$

Summation is with respect to all the charged particles in the system. The subscript "e" on ϱ will be omitted in the cases when it does not lead to confusion with the particle density ϱ.

The microscopic charge and current densities are extremely complex functions since they depend not only upon the coordinates of the selected point $\boldsymbol{q}$ and the point in time t but also on the coordinates and velocities of all the system's particles.

In the macroscopic description instead of the microscopic functions we use the averaged characteristics

$$\varrho(\boldsymbol{q}, t) = \overline{\varrho^{\mathrm{M}}}, \quad \boldsymbol{j} = \overline{\boldsymbol{j}^{\mathrm{M}}}.$$

The bar indicates averaging with respect to an ensemble of identical systems.

It is frequently convenient to split the average charge and current densities ϱ, $\boldsymbol{j}$ into two parts.

Let us take a flat capacitor as an example.

Let the charge of one of the plates be given as Q and $\sigma = Q/S$ be the charge per unit area of the plate. We shall call the charge Q the external charge. The term "strange" is often used instead of "external". If a dielectric is put between the outer plates, surface charges appear on the capacitor plates due to polarization. We shall call these induced charges. The total surface charge density may therefore be shown in two parts: the surface density of the external charges σ^{e} and the surface density of the induced charges σ^{i}.

Let us take another example. Let a current I flow through a coil. We shall call this given current the external one. Into the coil we put a cylindrical core which is magnetized by the magnetic field produced by the external current. As a result of the magnetization a current flows over the surface; we shall call this the induced current.

Sometimes the charge and current densities are divided not into external and induced but into "free" and "bound". Bound charges are those which can move only over a distance much less than that of the system in question. For example, the charges appearing on the boundary of a dielectric when it is polarized are bound. In the same example $\sigma = Q/S$ is the density of the free charges. The bound currents are the currents produced by the bound charges.

In the examples discussed the two methods of division agree. However, in the case of a completely ionized gas, for example, all the charges may be considered free so the second method of division is no good here, but the charges can be divided into external and induced (see § 7).

We shall therefore assume that the total charge and current density can be divided into two parts:

$$\varrho = \varrho^e + \varrho^i, \quad \boldsymbol{j} = \boldsymbol{j}^e + \boldsymbol{j}^i. \tag{1.1}$$

The strengths of the electrical and magnetic fields can also be defined in two ways.

We can introduce the microscopic strengths of the electrical and magnetic fields. These will be denoted $\boldsymbol{E}^M$ and $\boldsymbol{H}^M$ respectively. These quantities are very complex functions, the value of which at a given point in the field and a given point in time depends on the position and velocities of all the system's charged particles.

At the same time as the microscopic values of the field strengths we shall introduce the averaged values of the electrical and magnetic field strengths as characteristics of the electromagnetic field. We shall denote these by $\boldsymbol{E}$ and $\boldsymbol{B}$. The quantity $\boldsymbol{B}$ is generally called the magnetic flux density. Averaging, as before, is carried out with respect to an ensemble of identical systems.

$\boldsymbol{E}$ is thus the average value of the microscopic field strength $\boldsymbol{E}^M$, which is determined by all the charges, both external and induced.

$\boldsymbol{B}$ is correspondingly the average value of the microscopic magnetic field strength $\boldsymbol{H}^M$, which is determined by all the microscopic currents, i.e.

$$\boldsymbol{E} = \overline{\boldsymbol{E}}^M, \quad \boldsymbol{B} = \overline{\boldsymbol{H}}^M. \tag{1.2}$$

The laws of electromagnetic theory establish the connexion between the *average values* of the charge and current density on the one hand and the strengths of the electrical and magnetic fields on the other.

These laws can be written in the form of the system of differential equations called the Maxwell equations.

The system of Maxwell equations can be written in the form

$$\left.\begin{aligned}
\operatorname{curl}\boldsymbol{B} &= \frac{1}{c}\frac{\partial \boldsymbol{E}}{\partial t}+\frac{4\pi}{c}\boldsymbol{j}; && (1.3)\\
\operatorname{curl}\boldsymbol{E} &= -\frac{1}{c}\frac{\partial \boldsymbol{B}}{\partial t} && (1.4)\\
\operatorname{div}\boldsymbol{B} &= 0; && (1.5)\\
\operatorname{div}\boldsymbol{E} &= 4\pi\varrho. && (1.6)
\end{aligned}\right\} \quad (\mathrm{I})$$

Below we shall sometimes denote eqns. (1.3–6) by the single figure (I).

The first of these expressions expresses the fact that the source of the magnetic field $\boldsymbol{B}$ in a medium is the density of the electric current $\boldsymbol{j}$ of all the charges (both external and induced). In addition an alternating electrical field is a magnetic field source.

The second equation is the differential form of Faraday's law. It expresses the fact that an electrical rotational field appears when the magnetic field strength varies with time. The third equation expresses the fact that the magnetic field is always a rotational field so that the lines of force of the magnetic field strength are closed. Finally, the last equation is the differential form of Gauss's theorem which says that the flux of the electrical field strength vector through a closed surface is proportional to the sum of the charges inside this surface. Gauss's theorem can be proved by using Coulomb's law.

Equations (1.3–6) thus connect the average densities of the charges and currents (both external and induced) with the mean values of the strengths of the electrical and magnetic fields created by these charges and currents.

Equations (1.3–6) are still not enough for determining the electrical and magnetic field strengths.

In actual fact the functions ϱ, $\boldsymbol{j}$ can be written in accordance with formulae (1.1) in the form

$$\varrho = \varrho^{e}+\varrho^{i}, \quad \boldsymbol{j} = \boldsymbol{j}^{e}+\boldsymbol{j}^{i}.$$

The external charges and currents ϱ^{e}, $\boldsymbol{j}^{e}$ can be given but the induced charges and currents themselves depend on the values of the field strengths $\boldsymbol{E}$ and $\boldsymbol{B}$.

There are thus the four unknown functions $\boldsymbol{E}$, $\boldsymbol{B}$, ϱ^{i}, $\boldsymbol{j}^{i}$, three of which are vector functions. Equations (1.3–6) are insufficient for defining these functions with respect to the given external charges and currents.

For the problem to become defined we must have additional data on the system in question which will allow us to establish a connexion between the unknown functions ϱ^{i}, $\boldsymbol{j}^{i}$ and the strengths of the electrical and magnetic fields in the system.

This question will be discussed below. For the moment we will point out that the Maxwell equations in form (I) are not written in the only way possible.

In actual fact if the charge and current densities can be divided into two parts in accordance with formulae (1.1), then the average strengths of the electrical and magnetic fields can accordingly also be divided into two parts.

By $\boldsymbol{D}$ and $\boldsymbol{H}$ we shall denote those parts of the electrical and magnetic field strengths which are created by only the external charges and currents. The vector $\boldsymbol{D}$ is generally called the electrical induction vector and the vector $\boldsymbol{H}$ the magnetic field strength vector.

The remaining components of the electrical and magnetic field strengths, whose source is the induced charges and currents, will be denoted by $4\pi\boldsymbol{P}$ and $4\pi\boldsymbol{M}$ respectively. The vector $\boldsymbol{P}$ is called the polarization vector and the vector $\boldsymbol{M}$ the magnetization vector.

These names are connected with the fact that, for example, for a dielectric inside which there are no charges the vector $\boldsymbol{P}$ is equal to the dipole moment per unit volume of the dielectric. Likewise for magnetics, provided that the total current across the magnetic is equal to zero, the vector $\boldsymbol{M}$ coincides with the magnetic moment of a unit volume of the body (Landau and Lifshitz, 1960) (see, for example, §§ 6, 27).

We can thus express the mean values of the field strengths $\boldsymbol{E}$ and $\boldsymbol{B}$ in the form

$$\boldsymbol{E} = \boldsymbol{D} - 4\pi\boldsymbol{P} \quad \text{and} \quad \boldsymbol{B} = \boldsymbol{H} + 4\pi\boldsymbol{M}. \tag{1.7}$$

Here the minus sign is placed before the term $4\pi \boldsymbol{P}$ on the grounds that the strength of the electrical field always decreases because of the polarization (the appearance of induced charges).

In the case of slowly changing fields the induced current can be represented in the form of three components

$$\boldsymbol{j}^{\mathrm{i}} = \boldsymbol{j}_{\mathrm{cond}} + \frac{\partial \boldsymbol{P}}{\partial t} + c \operatorname{curl} \boldsymbol{M}. \tag{1.8}$$

The first term defines the conductivity current produced by the motion of free charges. The second term defines the polarization current and the third the current that appears upon magnetization. The ratios between these three components of the current $\boldsymbol{j}^{\mathrm{i}}$ are not, of course, the same for different media.

The density of the induced bound charge ϱ_b is defined by the polarization vector

$$\varrho_b = -\operatorname{div} \boldsymbol{P}; \qquad \varrho_b + \varrho_{\mathrm{cond}} = \varrho^{\mathrm{i}}. \tag{1.9}$$

Using formulae (1.7–9) the system of Maxwell equations can be written in the form

$$\left.\begin{aligned}
\operatorname{curl} \boldsymbol{H} &= \frac{1}{c}\frac{\partial \boldsymbol{D}}{\partial t} + \frac{4\pi}{c}\boldsymbol{j}_{\mathrm{cond}} + \frac{4\pi}{c}\boldsymbol{j}^{\mathrm{e}}, && (1.10)\\
\operatorname{curl} \boldsymbol{E} &= -\frac{1}{c}\frac{\partial \boldsymbol{B}}{\partial t}, && (1.11)\\
\operatorname{div} \boldsymbol{B} &= 0, && (1.12)\\
\operatorname{div} \boldsymbol{D} &= 4\pi(\varrho^{\mathrm{e}} + \varrho_{\mathrm{cond}}). && (1.13)
\end{aligned}\right\} \quad \text{(II)}$$

This is the most widely used way of writing the Maxwell equations. In certain cases the first two terms of the right-hand side of (1.10) can be combined into the one $(1/c)\,\partial \boldsymbol{D}/\partial t$ (see § 2).

In eqns. (II) the quantities $\varrho^{\mathrm{e}}, \boldsymbol{j}^{\mathrm{e}}$ are known and the unknowns for $\varrho_{\mathrm{cond}} = 0$ are the vectors $\boldsymbol{B}, \boldsymbol{H}, \boldsymbol{E}, \boldsymbol{D}, \boldsymbol{j}_{\mathrm{cond}}$. In this case as well it is necessary to have additional data about the system to use as a basis for establishing the connexion between these vectors.

If the medium in question is isotropic, i.e. all directions in it are equally likely, then in the case of constant fields there are between the vectors $\boldsymbol{D}, \boldsymbol{E}, \boldsymbol{H}, \boldsymbol{B}, \boldsymbol{j}_{\mathrm{cond}}$, as experiment shows, the relations

$$\boldsymbol{D} = \varepsilon \boldsymbol{E}, \quad \boldsymbol{B} = \mu \boldsymbol{H}, \quad \boldsymbol{j}_{\text{cond}} = \sigma \boldsymbol{E}, \tag{1.14}$$

where ε is the permittivity, μ the permeability and σ the conductivity.

If the first two expressions of (1.14) are substituted in formulae (1.7) we obtain the connexion between the pairs of vectors $\boldsymbol{P}$ and $\boldsymbol{E}$, and $\boldsymbol{M}$ and $\boldsymbol{H}$

$$\boldsymbol{P} = \frac{\varepsilon - 1}{4\pi} \boldsymbol{E} = \alpha \boldsymbol{E}; \qquad \boldsymbol{M} = \frac{\mu - 1}{4\pi} \boldsymbol{H} = \chi \boldsymbol{H}, \tag{1.15}$$

where α is the dielectric susceptibility and χ the magnetic susceptibility.

The coefficient ε is greater than unity in all bodies. The permeability μ may be greater than unity (in paramagnetic and ferromagnetic substances) or less than unity (in diamagnetic substances) but is always positive, i.e. $\mu > 0$.

The coefficients ε, μ, α, χ, σ are functions of the thermodynamic parameters characterizing the state of matter.

In the case of anisotropic media, e.g. crystalline solids or conducting media placed in a strong external magnetic field, the relations (1.14) take the more complex form:

$$D_i = \varepsilon_{ij} E_j, \quad B_i = \mu_{ij} H_j, \quad j_i^{\text{cond}} = \sigma_{ij} E_j. \tag{1.16}$$

Here ε_{ij} is the permittivity tensor, μ_{ij} the permeability tensor and σ_{ij} the electrical conductivity tensor.

If we use the relations (1.14) two unknown vectors, e.g. $\boldsymbol{E}$, $\boldsymbol{H}$, remain in the Maxwell equations (II). Then by solving the Maxwell equations with respect to the given currents and charges $\boldsymbol{j}^{\text{e}}$, ϱ^{e} we can find the strengths of the electrical and magnetic fields. Using formulae (1.7, 14) we can determine the functions $\boldsymbol{B}$, $\boldsymbol{D}$, $\boldsymbol{j}_{\text{cond}}$ and the polarization and magnetization vectors $\boldsymbol{P}$, $\boldsymbol{M}$. Substituting the values of the functions $\boldsymbol{P}$, $\boldsymbol{M}$, $\boldsymbol{j}_{\text{cond}}$ in formulae (1.8, 9) we can find the functions $\boldsymbol{j}^{\text{i}}$, ϱ^{i} which define the distribution of the induced currents and charges.

Equations (1.14) or (1.16) are called the material equations.

In a number of cases it is convenient to have yet another way of writing the Maxwell equations which differs slightly from the equations (II). It can be obtained as follows.

Instead of the electrical induction vector $\boldsymbol{D}$ in eqns. (II) we introduce another vector $\boldsymbol{D}_1$ defined by the relation

$$\frac{\partial \boldsymbol{D}_1}{\partial t} = \frac{\partial \boldsymbol{E}}{\partial t} + 4\pi \boldsymbol{j}^{\mathrm{i}}. \tag{1.17}$$

Thus the expression $(1/4\pi)\,\partial \boldsymbol{D}_1/\partial t$ is the sum of the displacement current caused by the change in the total electrical field $\boldsymbol{E}$ and the induced current $\boldsymbol{j}^{\mathrm{i}}$, i.e. all the current with the exception of the given external current $\boldsymbol{j}^{\mathrm{e}}$.

Using expression (1.17) we obtain the following system of equations instead of eqns. (I):

$$\left.\begin{aligned}
\operatorname{curl} \boldsymbol{B} &= \frac{1}{c}\frac{\partial \boldsymbol{D}_1}{\partial t} + \frac{4\pi}{c}\boldsymbol{j}^{\mathrm{e}}, && (1.18)\\
\operatorname{curl} \boldsymbol{E} &= -\frac{1}{c}\frac{\partial \boldsymbol{B}}{\partial t}, && (1.19)\\
\operatorname{div} \boldsymbol{B} &= 0, && (1.20)\\
\operatorname{div} \boldsymbol{D}_1 &= 4\pi\varrho^{\mathrm{e}}. && (1.21)
\end{aligned}\right\} \text{(III)}$$

As well as the known functions $\boldsymbol{j}^{\mathrm{e}}$, ϱ^{e} the three vectors $\boldsymbol{B}$, $\boldsymbol{E}$, $\boldsymbol{D}_1$ come into eqns. (III). The magnetic field strength vector does not come into the system of eqns. (III). It is therefore sufficient, using the properties of the medium in question, to establish a connexion between any two of them, e.g. between $\boldsymbol{D}_1$ and $\boldsymbol{E}$, for the system of eqns. (III) to suffice to determine the two vectors $\boldsymbol{B}$ and $\boldsymbol{E}$.

The material equations (1.14, 16) occur not only for constant fields but also in those cases when the field strengths are slowly varying functions of time and the coordinates.

For example, the condition for slowness of field variation in time can be written in the form

$$\frac{\partial \boldsymbol{E}}{\partial t} \ll \frac{\boldsymbol{E}}{T}, \quad \frac{\partial \boldsymbol{B}}{\partial t} \ll \frac{\boldsymbol{B}}{T}, \tag{1.22}$$

where T is the characteristic time of the slowest processes in the system in question. Similar relations can also be written for variations in space.

If the conditions (1.22) are not satisfied, the relationships between the vectors $\boldsymbol{D}$ and $\boldsymbol{E}$, $\boldsymbol{H}$ and $\boldsymbol{B}$, and $\boldsymbol{j}_{\text{cond}}$ and $\boldsymbol{E}$ become more complex. This question will be discussed in the next section.

2. Maxwell Equations for Fast Processes

It has been shown in § 1 that it is necessary to find the connexion between the vectors $\boldsymbol{D}$ and $\boldsymbol{E}$, $\boldsymbol{B}$ and $\boldsymbol{H}$, and $\boldsymbol{j}_{\text{cond}}$ and $\boldsymbol{E}$ by proceeding from the properties of the material in question in order to use the Maxwell equations.

In the case of constant or slowly varying fields in an isotropic medium the connexion between these vectors is of the form

$$\boldsymbol{D}(\boldsymbol{q}, t) = \varepsilon \boldsymbol{E}(\boldsymbol{q}, t); \qquad \boldsymbol{B}(\boldsymbol{q}, t) = \mu \boldsymbol{H}(\boldsymbol{q}, t);$$
$$\boldsymbol{j}_{\text{cond}}(\boldsymbol{q}, t) = \sigma \boldsymbol{E}(\boldsymbol{q}, t). \tag{2.1}$$

Instead of the first two relations of (2.1) we can give the connexion between the vectors $\boldsymbol{P}$ and $\boldsymbol{E}$, and $\boldsymbol{M}$ and $\boldsymbol{H}$:

$$\boldsymbol{P}(\boldsymbol{q}, t) = \alpha \boldsymbol{E}(\boldsymbol{q}, t); \qquad \boldsymbol{M}(\boldsymbol{q}, t) = \chi \boldsymbol{H}(\boldsymbol{q}, t). \tag{2.2}$$

By using the formulae

$$\boldsymbol{E} = \boldsymbol{D} - 4\pi \boldsymbol{P}; \qquad \boldsymbol{B} = \boldsymbol{H} + 4\pi \boldsymbol{M}, \tag{2.3}$$

we can establish the connexion between the coefficients ε and α, and μ and χ

$$\varepsilon = 1 + 4\pi\alpha; \qquad \mu = 1 + 4\pi\chi. \tag{2.4}$$

It follows from the formulae (2.2) that the polarization and magnetization vectors at a point $\boldsymbol{q}$ at a time t are determined by the values of the field strengths $\boldsymbol{E}$, $\boldsymbol{H}$ at the same point and time. This is true when there is little variation in the fields at spatial and time intervals characteristic for a given system. In the opposite case the relations (2.2) do not hold and must be replaced by more general relations.

Let us first take a simple example to explain the basic features of the given problem.

We shall discuss the question of the passage of an electromagnetic wave through a dielectric. We give its structure by the following model. We shall assume that the matter consists of atoms having one electron each. When the electrons are displaced from a position of equilibrium an elastic force appears which is proportional to the displacement. The main mass of the atom is connected with its positively charged part.

When a monochromatic electromagnetic wave passes through the medium an alternating electrical field appears at each point which varies in accordance with the law

$$\boldsymbol{E}(t) = \boldsymbol{E}_0 e^{-i\omega t}. \tag{2.5}$$

The frequency of the field's variation is such that only the negatively charged electrons, which have a small mass, are displaced noticeably in the atom during the oscillation cycle.

As a result of the periodic motion of the electron due to the action of the periodic field the atom itself becomes a source of electromagnetic waves, which leads to the electron losing energy. This means that when an electron moves it is acted upon by a frictional force which we consider to be proportional to the electron's velocity of motion. As a result we obtain the following equation of motion of the electron in the atom:

$$m\ddot{\boldsymbol{r}}+\beta\dot{\boldsymbol{r}}+k\boldsymbol{r} = e\boldsymbol{E}(t), \tag{2.6}$$

where β is the friction coefficient and k is the elasticity coefficient.

Equation (2.6) agrees with the equation for a damped harmonic oscillator acted upon by an external periodic force.

We can rewrite eqn. (2.6) in a more convenient form. For this purpose we divide it by m and introduce $2\gamma = \beta/m$ and $\omega_0 = \sqrt{(k/m)}$ (the frequency of the eigen oscillations). As a result eqn. (2.6) becomes

$$\ddot{\boldsymbol{r}}+2\gamma\dot{\boldsymbol{r}}+\omega_0^2\boldsymbol{r} = \frac{e}{m}\boldsymbol{E}(t). \tag{2.7}$$

It must be stressed that the quantity $\boldsymbol{r}$ defined by eqn. (2.7) is the value of the electron's displacement in the atom averaged over a number of atoms since it is not the microscopic electrical field strength in the righthand side of this equation but the averaged electrical field strength that appears in the Maxwell equation.

The frequency ω is not small when compared with the eigenfrequency ω_0. This means that we cannot consider that the process varies slowly with time.

In future we shall use λ to denote the wavelength of an electromagnetic wave in a substance and r_{av} to denote the mean distance between the atoms of the substance. We shall assume that the density of the substance is such that the mean distance between the atoms is much less than the wavelength, i.e.

$$r_{av} \ll \lambda. \tag{2.8}$$

In this case the field strength may be looked upon as a slowly varying function of the coordinates since the field strength varies only a little over distances r_{av}.

As a result it may be assumed that the polarization vector at a point $\boldsymbol{q}$ is determined by the value of the field strength at the same point. Bearing this in mind we shall not generally write the variable $\boldsymbol{q}$ below.

This condition is well satisfied, for example, when an electromagnetic light wave is propagated in a dielectric. In this case the frequencies ω and ω_0 are of the order of 10^{15} sec^{-1}. The wavelength of the light is $\lambda \sim 5\times10^{-5}$ cm and the mean distance between the atoms of the order of 10^{-8} cm.

We thus now have the problem of establishing a connexion between the polarization vector $\boldsymbol{P}(t)$ and the electrical field strength $\boldsymbol{E}(t)$ for the model of the medium in question.

We shall use n to denote the average number of atoms per unit volume. The polarization vector $\boldsymbol{P}$ is equal to the dipole moment $\boldsymbol{p}$ of an individual atom multiplied by n:

$$\boldsymbol{P} = n\boldsymbol{p}. \tag{2.9}$$

In its turn the dipole moment $\boldsymbol{p}$ of the atom is equal to the electron's charge e multiplied by the electron's displacement $\boldsymbol{r}$ from the equilibrium position, i.e. $\boldsymbol{p} = e\boldsymbol{r}$. Substituting this expression in the formula for $\boldsymbol{P}$ we obtain

$$\boldsymbol{P} = en\boldsymbol{r}. \tag{2.10}$$

We have thus connected the polarization vector $\boldsymbol{P}$ and the electron's displacement in the atom $\boldsymbol{r}$, which can be determined by the solution of the differential equation (2.7).

We multiply eqn. (2.7) by *en*. Using formula (2.10) we obtain the differential equation for the polarization vector

$$\ddot{\boldsymbol{P}}+2\gamma\dot{\boldsymbol{P}}+\omega_0^2\boldsymbol{P} = \frac{e^2n}{m}\boldsymbol{E}(t). \tag{2.11}$$

The general solution of eqn. (2.11) can, as is well known, be represented as the sum of two parts. The first of them is of the form

$$\boldsymbol{P}^{\circ}(t) = e^{-\gamma t}(\boldsymbol{C}_1 \cos \omega_1 t+\boldsymbol{C}_2 \sin \omega_1 t),$$

where $\omega_1^2 = \omega_0^2-\gamma^2$.

The constants $\boldsymbol{C}_1$, $\boldsymbol{C}_2$ are determined by the initial values of the polarization vector and its derivative. This part of the solution is fully determined by the initial values of the vector $\boldsymbol{P}$ and its velocity and does not depend upon the strength of the electrical field $\boldsymbol{E}$.

The second part of the solution of eqn. (2.11) is proportional to the field strength $\boldsymbol{E}$ and can be written in the form

$$\boldsymbol{P}^{i}(t) = \frac{e^2n}{m\omega_1}\int_0^t e^{-\gamma(t-t')} \sin \omega_1(t-t')\,\boldsymbol{E}(t')\,dt'. \tag{2.12}$$

Expression (2.12) defines that part of the polarization vector that is not dependent on the initial data.

Using the formula $\boldsymbol{E} = \boldsymbol{D}-4\pi\boldsymbol{P}$ we can write the following expression which connects the induction vector $\boldsymbol{D}$ with the electrical field strength vector $\boldsymbol{E}$:

$$\boldsymbol{D}(t) = \boldsymbol{E}(t) + \frac{4\pi e^2n}{m\omega_1}\int_0^t e^{-\gamma(t-t')} \sin \omega_1(t-t')\,\boldsymbol{E}(t')\,dt'+4\pi p^{\circ}(t). \tag{2.13}$$

The vectors $\boldsymbol{D}$ and $\boldsymbol{E}$ thus become connected through an integral equation in the case of rapidly varying fields.

If we introduce the notation

$$f(t-t') = \frac{4\pi e^2n}{m\omega_1} e^{-\gamma(t-t')} \sin \omega_1(t-t'), \tag{2.14}$$

expression (2.13) can be written in the form

$$\boldsymbol{D}(t) = \boldsymbol{E}(t) + \int_0^t f(t-t')\,\boldsymbol{E}(t')\,dt' + 4\pi \boldsymbol{P}^\circ(t). \tag{2.15}$$

Instead of expression (2.15) we often use the asymptotic expression, which is valid provided that the time interval $t-t_0$ (t_0 is the initial point in time) is greater than the time required for the establishment of steady conditions. In the case under discussion this means that

$$t-t_0 \gg 1/\gamma.$$

In this case we can make the initial point in time in (2.15) approach $-\infty$, thus obtaining the following expression:

$$\boldsymbol{D}(t) = \boldsymbol{E}(t) + \int_{-\infty}^t f(t-t')\,\boldsymbol{E}(t')\,dt', \tag{2.16}$$

which defines the connexion between the vectors $\boldsymbol{D}$ and $\boldsymbol{E}$ for a steady (stationary) process.

For the example under discussion the function f in formulae (2.15, 16) is defined by expression (2.14). However, formulae (2.15, 16) occur in other cases as well since they are the most general form of the linear connexion between the vectors $\boldsymbol{D}$ and $\boldsymbol{E}$.

Formulae (2.15, 16) differ only in the form of the function f for different systems.

Expression (2.16), which defines the connexion of the vectors $\boldsymbol{D}(t)$, $\boldsymbol{E}(t)$, is often written in the form

$$\boldsymbol{D}(t) = \int_{-\infty}^t \varepsilon(t-t')\,\boldsymbol{E}(t')\,dt'. \tag{2.17}$$

By comparing the expressions (2.16, 17) we can find the connexion between the functions f and ε:

$$\varepsilon(t-t') = \delta(t-t') + f(t-t'), \qquad t \geqslant t'. \tag{2.18}$$

Let us find the connexion between the Fourier components of the functions $\boldsymbol{D}(t)$, $\boldsymbol{E}(t)$. To do this we carry out a single-variable Fourier transform with respect to time in (2.17, 18). Using the notations for the Fourier components, for example

$$\boldsymbol{E}(\omega, \boldsymbol{q}) \equiv \boldsymbol{E}_\omega(\boldsymbol{q}) = \int_0^\infty \boldsymbol{E}(\boldsymbol{q}, t)e^{i\omega t}\,dt;$$

$$\omega = \omega' + i\omega'', \quad \omega'' > 0$$

and the similar notations for the other functions we obtain from (2.17, 18)

$$\boldsymbol{D}(\omega) = \varepsilon(\omega)\,\boldsymbol{E}(\omega), \tag{2.19}$$

$$\varepsilon(\omega) = 1 + \int_0^\infty f(t)e^{i\omega t}\,dt = 1 + f(\omega). \tag{2.20}$$

We shall call the function $\varepsilon(t-t')$ the dielectrical constant function and $\varepsilon(\omega)$ the Fourier component of the dielectric constant.

It follows from formula (2.19) that the magnitude of the dielectric constant depends on the frequency, i.e. the ratio of the functions D_ω/E_ω is different for different frequencies.

The frequency dependence of the dielectric constant is called the dielectric-constant dispersion.

Likewise the frequency dependence of the magnetic permeability is called the magnetic permeability dispersion.

Let us examine in greater detail the expression (2.20) for the Fourier component of the dielectric constant $\varepsilon(\omega)$.

The function ε_ω defined by expression (2.20) is complex. Denoting its real and imaginary parts by ε' and ε'' we can write

$$\varepsilon(\omega) = \varepsilon'(\omega) + i\varepsilon''(\omega). \tag{2.21}$$

It follows directly from formula (2.20) that for the real values of ω

$$\varepsilon(-\omega) = \varepsilon^*(\omega)$$

or

$$\varepsilon'(\omega) = \varepsilon'(-\omega), \quad \varepsilon''(\omega) = -\varepsilon''(-\omega). \tag{2.22}$$

Thus the real part of the function ε_ω is an even function of ω and the imaginary part an odd one.

As $\omega \to 0$ the function ε_ω approaches the value of the static dielectric constant ε_0. From formula (2.20) we find the connexion between the functions ε_0 and f:

$$\varepsilon_0 = 1 + \int_0^\infty f(t)\,dt. \tag{2.23}$$

In all real media the integral $\int_0^\infty f(t)\,dt$ is finite. When $\omega \to \infty$, $\varepsilon_\omega \to 1$, since the substance will not have time to be polarized because of inertia.

If we treat the function ε_ω as a function of the complex frequency $\omega = \omega' + i\omega''$ we can establish a number of important properties of the function ε_ω.

It follows from the definition (2.20) that the function ε_ω is finite when $\omega'' > 0$. When $\omega'' < 0$ the integral in expression (2.20) diverges if $|\omega''| > \gamma$.

Remembering the properties of the function $f(t)$ it may be concluded that ε_ω does not become infinite anywhere in the upper half-plane (when $\omega'' > 0$), i.e. it is an analytical function in the upper half-plane.

With a complex frequency we have instead of the condition (2.22)

$$\varepsilon(-\omega) = \varepsilon^*(\omega^*). \tag{2.24}$$

It follows in particular from this that when $\omega = i\omega''$ ($\omega' = 0$), i.e. on the imaginary axis, $\varepsilon(-i\omega'') = \varepsilon^*(-i\omega'')$, i.e. the function ε_ω is real.

On the real axis

$$\varepsilon'' > 0 \quad \text{when} \quad \omega = \omega' > 0 \tag{2.25}$$

$$\text{and} \quad \varepsilon'' < 0 \quad \text{when} \quad \omega' < 0.$$

By using the property of the analytical nature of the function ε_ω in the upper half-plane we can establish important relations between the real and imaginary parts of the function ε_ω as $\omega'' \to 0$.

For this purpose we shall use the expression for the extreme value of the Cauchy integral, namely, if $f(z)$ is a function of the complex variable $z = z' + iz''$ ($z'' > 0$) becoming zero as $z \to \infty$, then the expression

$$f(z) = -\frac{1}{2\pi i}\int_{-\infty}^{\infty} \frac{f(u)}{z-u}\,du$$

defines the function as analytical in the upper half-plane.

It follows from this expression that as $z'' \to 0$

$$f(z') = -\frac{1}{2\pi i}\left\{P\int_{-\infty}^{\infty}\frac{f(u)}{z-u}\,du - i\pi\int_{-\infty}^{\infty}\delta(u-z')f(z')\,du\right\}. \tag{2.26}$$

Using the property of the delta function we find

$$f(z') = \frac{1}{i\pi}P\int_{-\infty}^{\infty}\frac{f(u)}{u-z'}\,du. \tag{2.27}$$

The sign P indicates that we are taking the principal value of the integral.

We can apply formula (2.27) which we have obtained for establishing the connexion between ε'_ω and ε''_ω as $\omega'' \to 0$.

For this we notice that in accordance with what has been said above $\varepsilon_\omega \to 1$ as $\omega \to \infty$, so for the function $\varepsilon_\omega - 1$ we have $\varepsilon_\omega - 1 \to 0$ as $\omega \to \infty$.

Using formula (2.27) for the function $\varepsilon_{\omega'} - 1$ we have

$$\varepsilon_{\omega'} - 1 = \frac{1}{i\pi}P\int_{-\infty}^{\infty}\frac{\varepsilon_u - 1}{u-\omega'}\,du. \tag{2.28}$$

Separating the real and imaginary parts we find

$$\varepsilon'_{\omega'} - 1 = \frac{1}{\pi}P\int_{-\infty}^{\infty}\frac{\varepsilon''_u}{u-\omega'}\,du; \quad \varepsilon''_{\omega'} = -\frac{1}{\pi}P\int_{-\infty}^{\infty}\frac{\varepsilon'_u - 1}{u-\omega'}\,du. \tag{2.29}$$

The relations (2.29) establish the connexion between the real and imaginary parts of the function $\varepsilon_{\omega'}$. They are called the dispersion relations.

Let us find the expression ε_ω for the example given above.

Substituting the formula (2.14) for the function f in expression (2.20) and integrating with respect to t we find for $\omega'' = 0$, $\omega = \omega'$

$$\varepsilon_\omega = 1 + \frac{4\pi e^2 n/m}{\omega_0^2 - \omega^2 - i2\omega\gamma}. \tag{2.30}$$

This expression can be derived more simply if we examine the steady solution of eqn. (2.11) straight away.

From this, separating the real and imaginary parts, we find

$$\varepsilon'_\omega = 1+\frac{4\pi e^2 n}{m}\cdot\frac{\omega_0^2-\omega^2}{(\omega_0^2-\omega^2)^2+4\gamma^2\omega^2}, \tag{2.31}$$

$$\varepsilon''_\omega = \frac{4\pi e^2 n}{m}\cdot\frac{2\gamma\omega}{(\omega_0^2-\omega^2)^2+4\omega^2\gamma^2}. \tag{2.32}$$

This example can be used for an easy check of the properties of the function ε_ω listed above.

As $\omega \to 0$ we obtain from formula (2.31) the expression for ε_0

$$\varepsilon_0 = 1+\frac{4\pi e^2 n}{m\omega_0^2}.$$

For gases the value of ε_0 is almost unity since

$4\pi e^2 n/m \ll \omega_0^2$.

At low frequencies, when $\omega \ll \omega_0$, we have

$$\varepsilon'_\omega = 1+\frac{4\pi e^2 n}{m\omega_0^2}; \qquad \varepsilon''_\omega = \frac{4\pi e^2 n}{m}\cdot\frac{2\gamma\omega}{\omega_0^4}.$$

At high frequencies, when $\omega \gg \omega_0$, we have

$$\varepsilon'_\omega = 1-\frac{\omega_0^2}{\omega^2}, \qquad \varepsilon'' = \frac{4\pi e^2 n}{m}\cdot\frac{\gamma}{\omega^3}.$$

It will be shown below that for a dissipative system the imaginary component is always non-zero and positive.

We shall show now that the absorption coefficient of electromagnetic waves in a medium is proportional to ε''.

For this we recall that the phase velocity of propagation of an electromagnetic wave in the medium at $\mu = 1$ is

$$v_{ph} = \frac{c}{n} = \frac{c}{\sqrt{\varepsilon}}. \tag{2.33}$$

Here n is the refractive index. When ε is complex the refractive index is also a complex quantity. We use the notation $n = n'+in''$.

Since $\varepsilon = n^2$, then

$$\varepsilon' = n'^2-n''^2, \quad \varepsilon'' = 2n'n''. \tag{2.34}$$

Therefore the imaginary part of the refraction coefficient is proportional to the imaginary part of the dielectric constant.

We substitute the expression $n = n'+in''$ in the formula for a plane wave propagated along the z-axis:

$$e^{-i\left(\omega t-\frac{2\pi}{\lambda_0}nz\right)} = e^{-\frac{2\pi n''}{\lambda_0}z-i\left(\omega t-\frac{2\pi}{\lambda_0}n'z\right)}. \tag{2.35}$$

Here λ_0 is the length of the electromagnetic wave in a vacuum.

It follows from formula (2.35) that when $n'' > 0$ (or $\varepsilon'' > 0$, since $n' > 0$) an electromagnetic wave is damped in a medium. The damping coefficient $\beta = 2\pi n''/\lambda_0$ is proportional to the imaginary part of the refractive index.

In the example discussed above where we calculated the dielectric constant it was assumed that the medium consists of neutral atoms (for example, a neutral gas). Such a gas has no electrical conductivity and therefore is a dielectric.

It is also possible to determine the dielectric constant ε_ω for metals. In order to obtain this expression we note that when the frequencies are not too high (less than 10^{15} sec^{-1}, i.e. frequencies in the visible light range) the displacement current $(1/4\pi)\,\partial \boldsymbol{D}/\partial t$ is much less than the conductivity current $\boldsymbol{j}_{\text{cond}}$. This means that in the first Maxwell equation

$$\operatorname{curl} \boldsymbol{H} = \frac{1}{c}\frac{\partial \boldsymbol{D}}{\partial t}+\frac{4\pi}{c}\boldsymbol{j}_{\text{cond}}+\frac{4\pi}{c}\boldsymbol{j}^{\text{e}}$$

we can ignore the first term in the right-hand side by comparison with the second. Therefore for a metal the first Maxwell equation can be written in the form

$$\operatorname{curl} \boldsymbol{H} = \frac{4\pi}{c}(\boldsymbol{j}_{\text{cond}}+\boldsymbol{j}^{\text{e}}).$$

For slow processes in a metal we can use Ohm's law $\boldsymbol{j}_{\text{cond}} = \sigma \boldsymbol{E}$, where σ is the electrical conductivity. When there is no external current we obtain the equation

$$\operatorname{curl} \boldsymbol{H} = \frac{4\pi}{c}\sigma \boldsymbol{E}. \tag{2.36}$$

To determine the dielectric constant of a metal we write eqn. (2.36) in the same form as for a dielectric, i.e.

$$\operatorname{curl} \boldsymbol{H} = \frac{1}{c}\frac{\partial \boldsymbol{D}}{\partial t}. \tag{2.37}$$

Comparing the right-hand sides of eqns. (2.36, 37) we obtain

$$\frac{\partial \boldsymbol{D}}{\partial t} = 4\pi\sigma \boldsymbol{E}. \tag{2.37a}$$

Hence with constant σ for a steady process

$$\boldsymbol{D}(t) = 4\pi\sigma \int_{-\infty}^{t} \boldsymbol{E}(t')dt' \quad \text{or} \quad \boldsymbol{D}(\omega) = i\frac{4\pi\sigma}{\omega}\boldsymbol{E}(\omega). \tag{2.38}$$

Comparing the second equation of (2.38) with eqn. (2.19) we obtain

$$\varepsilon(\omega) = i\,\frac{4\pi\sigma}{\omega}; \quad \omega = \omega' + i\omega''; \quad \omega'' < 0. \tag{2.39}$$

Thus even for slow processes, when the conductivity is constant, the dielectric constant depends upon the frequency.

Ohm's law in the form $\boldsymbol{j}_{\text{cond}}(q, t) = \sigma \boldsymbol{E}(\boldsymbol{q}, t)$ ceases to be valid for rapidly varying processes.

For a steady process the connexion between the current and the field strength $\boldsymbol{E}$ is defined by the expression

$$\boldsymbol{j}_{\text{cond}}(t) = \int_{-\infty}^{t} \sigma(t-t')\,\boldsymbol{E}(t')\,dt'; \quad \boldsymbol{j}(\omega) = \sigma(\omega)\,\boldsymbol{E}(\omega), \tag{2.40}$$

which is similar to expression (2.17).

In this case the conductivity is frequency-dependent and instead of expression (2.39) we have for a metal

$$\varepsilon(\omega) = i\frac{4\pi}{\omega}\sigma(\omega). \tag{2.41}$$

If we make allowance for the displacement current in eqn. (2.36), we obtain the following expression instead of (2.41)

$$\varepsilon(\omega) = 1 + i\frac{4\pi}{\omega}\sigma(\omega). \tag{2.42}$$

It follows from the results obtained that there is no difference in the description of the properties of a dielectric and a metal in the case of rapidly varying processes. In both cases the properties of the medium can be characterized by the complex dielectric constant $\varepsilon(\omega)$. Instead of the dielectric constant we can use the complex conductivity to describe the medium's properties. The connexion between them is defined by relation (2.42).

In the case of rapidly varying processes the connexion between the vectors $\boldsymbol{B}$ and $\boldsymbol{H}$ also varies, of course. Instead of the connexion $\boldsymbol{B} = \mu\boldsymbol{H}$ we then have

$$\boldsymbol{B}(t) = \int_{-\infty}^{t} \mu(t-t')\,\boldsymbol{H}(t')dt'; \quad \boldsymbol{B}(\omega) = \mu(\omega)\,\boldsymbol{H}(\omega). \tag{2.43}$$

When describing processes in a plasma it is best in many cases not to isolate the last term defining the magnetization current from the induced current (1.8).

If the medium can be characterized by an electrical conductivity that determines the connexion of the total induced current and the strength of the electrical field, then the connexion of the total induced current $\boldsymbol{j}^{\mathrm{i}}$ and the field strength $\boldsymbol{E}$ is tensorial, i.e. in a steady state takes the form

$$j_i^{\mathrm{i}}(t) = \int_{-\infty}^{t} \sigma_{ij}(t-t')\,E_j(t')\,dt', \quad j_i^{\mathrm{i}}(\omega) = \sigma_{ij}(\omega)\,E_j(\omega). \tag{2.44}$$

The expression for the total current is defined as usual as

$$\boldsymbol{j} = \boldsymbol{j}^{\mathrm{i}} + \boldsymbol{j}^{\mathrm{e}}, \tag{2.45}$$

where $\boldsymbol{j}^{\mathrm{e}}$ is the external current.

When the state is not steady we must select an initial point in time $t_0 = 0$ and instead of formula (2.44) write

$$j_i^{\mathrm{i}}(t) = \int_{0}^{t} \sigma_{ij}(t-t')\,E_j(t')\,dt'; \quad j_i^{\mathrm{i}}(\omega) = \sigma_{ij}(\omega)\,E_j(\omega). \tag{2.46}$$

The value of the current determined by the initial conditions is included in $\boldsymbol{j}^{\mathrm{e}}$.

If the induced current $\boldsymbol{j}^{\mathrm{i}}$ is combined with the term $(1/c)\partial\boldsymbol{E}/\partial t$ (see (1.17)) and we use the Maxwell equations in form (III), then instead of the conductivity tensor we obtain the dielectric-constant tensor ε_{ij}. The connexion between the vectors $\boldsymbol{D}_1$, $\boldsymbol{E}$

$$D_i(t) = \int_0^t \varepsilon_{ij}(t-t')\,E_j(t')dt', \quad D_i(\omega) = \varepsilon_{ij}(\omega)\,E_j(\omega) \tag{2.47}$$

follows from formulae (1.17) and (2.46).

By comparing the formulae (2.46, 47) we can find the connexion between the tensors ε_{ij}, σ_{ij}. For the Fourier components it is

$$\varepsilon_{ij}(\omega) = \delta_{ij} + i\frac{4\pi}{\omega}\sigma_{ij}(\omega). \tag{2.48}$$

Up to now it has been assumed that the value of, for example, the induced current at a point $\boldsymbol{q}$ at a point in time t, i.e. the quantity $\boldsymbol{j}^{\text{i}}(\boldsymbol{q}, t)$ is determined by the field values at earlier points in time t' (see (2.44)), but at the same point $\boldsymbol{q}$, i.e. by the values of $\boldsymbol{E}(\boldsymbol{q}, t')$. However, when the fields vary appreciably over distances characterizing the medium's properties the value of the induced current $\boldsymbol{j}^{\text{i}}(\boldsymbol{q}, t)$ is determined by the value of the field not only at the point $\boldsymbol{q}$ but also in the region surrounding it (see §§ 7–9).

In this case the connexion between the quantities $\boldsymbol{j}^{\text{i}}$, $\boldsymbol{E}$ and $\boldsymbol{D}$, $\boldsymbol{E}$ becomes more complex. Instead of eqns. (2.46, 47) we shall have the general relations

$$j_i^{\text{i}}(\boldsymbol{q}, t) = \int_0^t \int \sigma_{ij}(t-t', \boldsymbol{q}-\boldsymbol{q}')\,E_j(\boldsymbol{q}', t')\,d^3\boldsymbol{q}'\,dt', \tag{2.49}$$

$$D_i(\boldsymbol{q}, t) = \int_0^t \int \varepsilon_{ij}(t-t', \boldsymbol{q}-\boldsymbol{q}')\,E_j(\boldsymbol{q}', t')\,d^3\boldsymbol{q}'\,dt'. \tag{2.50}$$

In the steady state the lower limit is replaced by $-\infty$.

If the properties of the medium differ at different points, i.e. the medium is spatially non-uniform, then we have $\boldsymbol{q}$, $\boldsymbol{q}'$ in the formulae (2.49, 50) instead of $\boldsymbol{q}-\boldsymbol{q}'$. If the properties of the medium are not uniform in time either, e.g. the mean charged particle concentration varies with time, then we must write t, t' instead of $t-t'$.

Therefore in the most general case (assuming linearity) the formulae (2.49, 50) contain the functions

$$\sigma_{ij}(t, t', \boldsymbol{q}, \boldsymbol{q}'); \quad \varepsilon_{ij}(t, t', \boldsymbol{q}, \boldsymbol{q}'). \tag{2.51}$$

The Maxwell equations (1.18–21), i.e. in form (III), together with the material equation (2.50) make up the closed system of equations for the functions $\boldsymbol{B}, \boldsymbol{E}$. We see that in this case the first and fourth equations of system (III) are integro-differential equations.

It is necessary to know the distribution of the external currents and charges $\boldsymbol{j}^e$, ϱ^e, the initial values of the field strengths $\boldsymbol{B}, \boldsymbol{E}$ and the boundary conditions to solve these equations.

It is important that it be stressed that the data on the state of the system which are not determined by giving the initial values of the fields $\boldsymbol{E}(\boldsymbol{q}, 0)$, $\boldsymbol{B}(\boldsymbol{q}, 0)$ at the initial point in time are included in $\boldsymbol{j}^e$, ϱ^e. The same is true of the boundary conditions.

If there is spatial uniformity in time, when the material equations can be used in the form (2.49, 50), it is simpler to use the Maxwell equations for the Fourier components of the functions $\boldsymbol{E}, \boldsymbol{B}, \boldsymbol{j}^e, \varrho^e$.

We carry out the expansion into the Fourier integral with respect to the time and space variables. We can write the Fourier integral in the form

$$\boldsymbol{E}(\boldsymbol{q}, t) = \frac{1}{(2\pi)^4} \int_{-\infty}^{\infty} \int \boldsymbol{E}(\omega + i\Delta, \boldsymbol{k})\, e^{-i(\omega + i\Delta)t + i(\boldsymbol{k}\cdot\boldsymbol{q})} d\omega\, d^3\boldsymbol{k} \tag{2.52}$$

$$\boldsymbol{E}(\omega + i\Delta, \boldsymbol{k}) \equiv \boldsymbol{E}(\omega, \boldsymbol{k}) = \int_0^{\infty} \int \boldsymbol{E}(\boldsymbol{q}, t)\, e^{-\Delta t + i[\omega t - (\boldsymbol{k}\cdot\boldsymbol{q})]}\, dt\, d^3\boldsymbol{q}. \tag{2.53}$$

Here and below $\omega' + i\omega'' \equiv \omega + i\Delta$; $\omega' \equiv \omega$; $\omega'' = \Delta$. The Fourier coefficients are functions of the complex frequency $\omega + i\Delta$. Similar formulae are also valid for the other functions.

Using the folding theorem we obtain from formulae (2·49, 50) the following relations between the Fourier components of the functions $\boldsymbol{j}^i$ and $\boldsymbol{E}$, and $\boldsymbol{D}$ and $\boldsymbol{E}$:

$$\begin{aligned} j_i^i(\omega, \boldsymbol{k}) &= \sigma_{ij}(\omega, \boldsymbol{k})\, E_j(\omega, \boldsymbol{k}); \\ D_i(\omega, \boldsymbol{k}) &= \varepsilon_{ij}(\omega, \boldsymbol{k})\, E_j(\omega, \boldsymbol{k}). \end{aligned} \tag{2.54}$$

Using these relations and the formulae (1.17) we can find the connexion between the Fourier components of the tensors ε_{ij},

σ_{ij}.

$$\varepsilon_{ij}(\omega, \boldsymbol{k}) = \delta_{ij} + i\frac{4\pi}{\omega + i\Delta}\sigma_{ij}(\omega, \boldsymbol{k}). \tag{2.55}$$

The dependence of the dielectric-constant tensor on the wave number is called the spatial dispersion.

When there is spatial dispersion we have instead of the formulae (2.22)

$$\varepsilon(\omega, \boldsymbol{k}) = \varepsilon^*(-\omega, -\boldsymbol{k}); \quad \varepsilon'(\omega, \boldsymbol{k}) = \varepsilon'(-\omega, -\boldsymbol{k});$$
$$\varepsilon''(\omega, \boldsymbol{k}) = -\varepsilon''(-\omega, -\boldsymbol{k}). \tag{2.56}$$

In the case of a spatially infinite medium the Maxwell equations (1.18–21) can conveniently be written for the Fourier components. Using the formulae (2.53, 54) and the identities

$$\text{curl}\,(\boldsymbol{a}A) = A\,\text{curl}\,\boldsymbol{a} - [\,\boldsymbol{a} \wedge \text{grad}\,A] \tag{2.57}$$

$$\int_0^\infty \left(\frac{\partial}{\partial t}f(t)\right) e^{-\Delta t + i\omega t}\,dt = -i(\omega + i\Delta)f(\omega) - f(0), \tag{2.58}$$

we obtain the following system of equations:

$$i[\boldsymbol{k} \wedge \boldsymbol{B}(\omega, \boldsymbol{k})]_i = -\frac{i}{c}(\omega + i\Delta)\,\varepsilon_{ij}(\omega, \boldsymbol{k})\,E_j(\omega, \boldsymbol{k})$$
$$-\frac{1}{c}E_i(\boldsymbol{k}, 0) + \frac{4\pi}{c}j_i^e(\omega, \boldsymbol{k}), \tag{2.59}$$

$$i[\boldsymbol{k} \wedge \boldsymbol{E}(\omega, \boldsymbol{k})] = \frac{i}{c}(\omega + i\Delta)\,\boldsymbol{B}(\omega, \boldsymbol{k}) + \frac{1}{c}\boldsymbol{B}(\boldsymbol{k}, 0), \tag{2.60}$$

$$(\boldsymbol{k} \cdot \boldsymbol{B}(\omega, \boldsymbol{k})) = 0, \tag{2.61}$$

$$ik_i\varepsilon_{ij}(\omega, \boldsymbol{k})\,E_j(\omega, \boldsymbol{k}) = 4\pi\varrho^e(\omega, \boldsymbol{k}). \tag{2.62}$$

To conclude the present section let us examine the question of the energy of an electromagnetic field, using the Maxwell equations in form (III) for this purpose.

We multiply eqn. (1.18) scalarly by $\boldsymbol{E}$ and eqn. (1.19) by $\boldsymbol{B}$. After this we subtract the second of these equations from the first.

Using the vector identity

$$\text{div}\,[\boldsymbol{E} \wedge \boldsymbol{B}] = (\boldsymbol{B} \cdot \text{curl}\,\boldsymbol{E}) - (\boldsymbol{E} \cdot \text{curl}\,\boldsymbol{B}), \tag{2.63}$$

we obtain

$$\frac{1}{8\pi}\left\{2\left(\boldsymbol{E} \cdot \frac{\partial \boldsymbol{D}}{\partial t}\right) + \frac{\partial \boldsymbol{B}^2}{\partial t}\right\} = -\frac{c}{4\pi}\,\text{div}\,[\boldsymbol{E} \wedge \boldsymbol{B}] - (\boldsymbol{j}^e \cdot \boldsymbol{E}). \tag{2.64}$$

The vector $\boldsymbol{D}$ is connected with the vector $\boldsymbol{E}$ by the material equation (2·50) or the corresponding equation (2.54) for the Fourier components.

The first term in the right-hand side can be written in the form

$$-\operatorname{div} \mathbf{S}, \quad \boldsymbol{S} = \frac{c}{4\pi}[\boldsymbol{E} \wedge \boldsymbol{B}]. \tag{2.65}$$

The vector $\mathbf{S}$ is called the Poynting vector. It defines the flux of electromagnetic energy.

The second term in the right-hand side defines the work done by the external current per unit time.

We integrate eqn. (2.64) over the system's volume

$$\frac{1}{8\pi}\int\left\{2\left(\boldsymbol{E}\cdot\frac{\partial \boldsymbol{D}}{\partial t}\right)+\frac{\partial}{\partial t}\boldsymbol{B}^2\right\}d^3\boldsymbol{q} =$$

$$= -\oint (\mathbf{S}\cdot d^2\mathbf{s}) - \int (\boldsymbol{j}^{\mathrm{e}}\cdot\boldsymbol{E})\, d^3\boldsymbol{q}. \tag{2.66}$$

If the system in question is dispersive, then even if the flux of energy through the surface surrounding the system and the external current are zero the system has no energy integral.

The reason for this is as follows.

It follows from the dispersion relations (2.29) that in a dispersive medium the imaginary component of the dielectric constant $\varepsilon''(\omega)$ is non-zero.

It can be seen from the formulae (2.34, 35) that the imaginary component of the dielectric constant determines the absorption of electromagnetic waves in the medium.

A dispersive medium is thus at the same time an absorbing or dissipative medium. Because of this there is no electromagnetic energy integral since the energy is converted into heat.

If the medium is non-dispersive the connexion of the vectors $\boldsymbol{D}$ and $\boldsymbol{E}$ is defined by the relation $D_i = \varepsilon_{ij}E_j$. The tensor components are real constants.

In this case eqn. (2.66) can be written in the form

$$\frac{\partial W}{\partial t} = -\oint (\mathbf{S}\cdot d^2\mathbf{s}) - \int (\boldsymbol{j}^{\mathrm{e}}\cdot\boldsymbol{E})\, d^3\boldsymbol{q}. \tag{2.67}$$

The quantity W is defined by the expression

$$W = \frac{1}{8\pi} \int \{E_i \varepsilon_{ij} E_j + B^2\}\, d^3\boldsymbol{q}. \tag{2.68}$$

If $\boldsymbol{j}^e = 0$ and the total energy flux through the surrounding surface is zero, then the quantity W is a constant. This allows us to call W the electromagnetic energy of the medium in question.

Proceeding from the Maxwell equations (II) and the material equations (1.14), we obtain for W instead of (2.68) the expression

$$W = \frac{1}{8\pi} \int (\varepsilon \boldsymbol{E}^2 + \mu \boldsymbol{H}^2)\, d^3\boldsymbol{q}.$$

It is also possible to introduce the concept of energy for a dispersive medium provided that the conversion of the energy into heat is a slow process or, in other words, when the medium is weakly dissipative. The condition of "slowness" will be defined below.

Among such systems are, for example, a pendulum or an oscillating circuit with a low damping factor. For example, for a damped oscillating circuit with an eigenfrequency ω_0 we can introduce the energy concept

$$W_{\omega_0} = \frac{LI^2}{2} + \frac{q^2}{2c}; \quad I = \frac{dq}{dt} \tag{2.69}$$

(L is the inductance, C the capacitance, I the current, q the charge) if the damping decrement $\gamma = R/2L$ (R is the resistance) is much less than the oscillation eigenfrequency $\omega_0 = 1\sqrt{(LC)}$. In this case the energy of the circuit's electromagnetic oscillations (the conversion of this energy into heat) decreases as

$$\frac{dW_{\omega_0}}{dt} = -2\gamma W_{\omega_0}. \tag{2.70}$$

We shall show that for a dispersive medium we can obtain a similar equation for the medium's electromagnetic energy.

Let us examine the expression for the spatial Fourier component

$$\boldsymbol{D}(t, \boldsymbol{k}) = \int \boldsymbol{D}(t, \boldsymbol{q}) e^{-i(\boldsymbol{k}\cdot\boldsymbol{q})}\, d^3\boldsymbol{q};$$

$$\boldsymbol{D}(t, \boldsymbol{q}) = \frac{1}{(2\pi)^3} \int \boldsymbol{D}(t, \boldsymbol{k}) e^{i(\boldsymbol{k}\cdot\boldsymbol{q})}\, d^3\boldsymbol{k} \tag{2.71}$$

of the electrical induction vector $\boldsymbol{D}(\boldsymbol{q}, t)$. Using the formulae (2.52–54) we obtain

$$D_i(t, \boldsymbol{k}) = \frac{1}{2\pi}\int_{-\infty}^{\infty} D_i(\omega, \boldsymbol{k}) e^{-i(\omega+i\Delta)t}\, d\omega$$

$$= \frac{1}{2\pi}\int_{-\infty}^{\infty} \varepsilon_{ij}(\omega, \boldsymbol{k})\, E_j(\omega, \boldsymbol{k}) e^{-i(\omega+i\Delta)t}\, d\omega$$

$$= \frac{1}{2\pi}\int_{-\infty}^{\infty} d\omega \int_{0}^{\infty} dt'\, e^{-\Delta(t'-t)+i\omega(t'-t)} \varepsilon_{ij}(\omega, \boldsymbol{k})\, E_j(t', \boldsymbol{k}). \tag{2.72}$$

We shall now define what we understand by a weakly dissipative medium.

We shall use $\omega_1, \omega_2, \ldots$, to denote the eigenfrequencies of the medium in question. In the example taken above the eigenfrequency is the frequency of the electron's oscillations in the atom (see (2.7)).

Let us examine the tensor components $\varepsilon_{ij}(\omega, \boldsymbol{k})$ for frequencies close to $\omega_1, \omega_2, \ldots$. We use ω_l to denote one of the eigenfrequencies. The above condition means that

$$\omega - \omega_l \ll \omega_l. \tag{2.73}$$

When there is spatial dispersion the values of ω_l depend in the general case on the wave number k.

We carry out the expansion of the function $\varepsilon_{ij}(\omega, \boldsymbol{k})$ around the values of ω_l.

$$\varepsilon_{ij}(\omega, \boldsymbol{k}) = \varepsilon_{ij}(\omega_l, \boldsymbol{k}) + \frac{\partial \varepsilon_{ij}(\omega_l, \boldsymbol{k})}{\partial \omega_l}(\omega - \omega_i) + \ldots \tag{2.74}$$

The tensor $\varepsilon_{ij}(\omega, \boldsymbol{k})$ is a complex function of ω_l.

We can write the condition of weak dissipativeness in the form

$$\varepsilon_{ij}(\omega_l, \boldsymbol{k}) = \varepsilon'_{ij}(\omega_l, \boldsymbol{k}) + i\varepsilon''_{ij}(\omega_l, \boldsymbol{k}); \qquad \varepsilon''_{ij} \ll 1. \tag{2.75}$$

We give the field strengths in the form

$$\boldsymbol{E}(\boldsymbol{k}, t) = \sum \boldsymbol{E}_l(t)\, e^{-i\omega_l(\boldsymbol{k})t}; \quad \boldsymbol{B}(\boldsymbol{k}, t) = \sum_l \boldsymbol{B}_l(t)\, e^{-i\omega_l(\boldsymbol{k})t}. \tag{2.76}$$

Here $\boldsymbol{E}$ and $\boldsymbol{B}_l$ are slowly varying functions of the time.

The conditions of slowness of variation of the functions $\boldsymbol{E}_l, \boldsymbol{B}_l$ means that we can choose a time interval T such that

$$\frac{1}{E_l}\frac{\partial E_l}{\partial t} \ll \frac{1}{T} \ll \omega_l^{\min}; \qquad \frac{1}{T} \ll \omega_l - \omega_{l'}, \quad l \neq l', \tag{2.76a}$$

where $\omega_l^{\min}$ is the minimum eigenfrequency.

We substitute expansion (2.76) in formula (2.72). We use the approximate expression (2.74) and instead of ω introduce the variable $\alpha_l = \omega - \omega_l$. After this we obtain

$$D_i(t, \boldsymbol{k}) = \frac{1}{2\pi}\sum_l \int_{-\infty}^{\infty} d\alpha_l \int_0^{\infty} dt'\, e^{-\Delta(t'-t)+i\alpha_l(t'-t)-i\omega_l t} \times \left\{\varepsilon_{ij}(\omega_l, \boldsymbol{k}) + \alpha_l \frac{\partial \varepsilon_{ij}}{\partial \omega_l}\right\} E_j^l(t', \boldsymbol{k}). \tag{2.77}$$

In the second term we integrate by parts with respect to α_l. Using the formula

$$\delta(t-t') = \frac{1}{2\pi}\int_{-\infty}^{\infty} e^{-i\alpha(t'-t)}\, d\alpha,$$

we integrate with respect to α_l and t'. As a result we obtain

$$D_i(t, \boldsymbol{k}) = \sum_l \left\{\varepsilon_{ij}(\omega_l, \boldsymbol{k})\, E_j^l(t, \boldsymbol{k}) + i\frac{\partial \varepsilon_{ij}}{\partial \omega_l}\frac{\partial E_j^l(t, \boldsymbol{k})}{\partial t}\right\} e^{-i\omega_l(\boldsymbol{k})t}. \tag{2.78}$$

A similar expression is required below for the time derivative $\partial \boldsymbol{D}(t, \boldsymbol{k})/\partial t$. Using expression (2.78) we obtain

$$\frac{\partial D_i(t, \boldsymbol{k})}{\partial t} = -i\sum_l \omega_l \varepsilon_{ij}(\omega_l, \boldsymbol{k})\, E_j^l(t, \boldsymbol{k})\, e^{-i\omega_l(\boldsymbol{k})t} + \sum_l \left[\frac{\partial}{\partial \omega_l}(\omega_l \varepsilon'_{ij}(\omega_l, \boldsymbol{k}))\frac{\partial}{\partial t}E_j(t, \boldsymbol{k})\right] e^{-i\omega_l(\boldsymbol{k})t}. \tag{2.79}$$

In the second term of this expression we can eliminate all but the term with ε_{ij}' since, according to eqn. (2.75), $\varepsilon_{ij}'' \ll 1$ so the term containing $\varepsilon_{ij}''\, \partial/\partial t$ is of the second order of smallness.

Let us return to eqn. (2.66) and examine it for the case when the right-hand side is equal to zero.

We expand under the integral the functions $\boldsymbol{E}, \boldsymbol{D}, \boldsymbol{B}$ into Fourier integrals with respect to the coordinates. Using formula (2.71) and the formula

$$\delta(\boldsymbol{k}-\boldsymbol{k}') = \frac{1}{(2\pi)^3}\int e^{i(\boldsymbol{k}-\boldsymbol{k}'\cdot\boldsymbol{q})}\, d^3\boldsymbol{q}, \tag{2.80}$$

we write eqn. (2.66) in the form

$$\frac{1}{8\pi(2\pi)^3}\int\left\{\left(\boldsymbol{E}(t, \boldsymbol{k})\cdot\frac{\partial \boldsymbol{D}^*(t, \boldsymbol{k})}{\partial t}\right)+\left(\boldsymbol{E}^*(\boldsymbol{k}, t)\cdot\frac{\partial \boldsymbol{D}(t, \boldsymbol{k})}{\partial t}\right)\right.$$
$$\left.+\frac{\partial}{\partial t}(\boldsymbol{B}(t, \boldsymbol{k})\cdot\boldsymbol{B}^*(t, \boldsymbol{k}))\right\} d^3\boldsymbol{k} = 0. \tag{2.81}$$

We substitute expression (2.79) in this equation and average with respect to the time interval T.

With the condition (2.76a) we have

$$\frac{1}{T}\int_0^T (\boldsymbol{E}_l(t)\, e^{-i\omega_l t}\cdot\boldsymbol{E}_{l'}^*\, e^{i\omega_{l'} t})\, dt = \delta_{ll'}(\boldsymbol{E}_l\cdot\boldsymbol{E}_l^*). \tag{2.82}$$

We can obtain a similar expression for the integrals containing the amplitudes $\boldsymbol{B}_l$.

By using these formulae, eqn. (2.81) can be written after the above transformations in the form

$$\frac{\partial W}{\partial t} = -Q. \tag{2.83}$$

The right-hand side of this equation is defined by the expression

$$Q = \frac{1}{(2\pi)^3}\int Q_{\boldsymbol{k}}\, d^3\boldsymbol{k};$$

$$Q_{\boldsymbol{k}} = \frac{1}{4\pi}\sum_l \omega_l\, \varepsilon_{ij}''(\omega_l, \boldsymbol{k})\, E_i^l(t, \boldsymbol{k})\, E_j^{l*}(t, \boldsymbol{k}). \tag{2.84}$$

The quantity Q is proportional to the imaginary part of the tensor ε_{ij} and thus defines the conversion of energy into heat in unit time.

The quantity W is defined by the expression

$$W = \frac{1}{8\pi^3}\int W_{\boldsymbol{k}}\, d^3\boldsymbol{k}, \tag{2.85}$$

where

$$W_{\boldsymbol{k}} = \frac{1}{8\pi}\sum_l \left\{\frac{\partial}{\partial\omega_l}(\omega_l \varepsilon'_{ij}(\omega_l, \boldsymbol{k}))\, E_i^l(t, \boldsymbol{k})\, E_j^{*l}(t, \boldsymbol{k}) \right.$$

$$\left. + (\boldsymbol{B}_l(t, \boldsymbol{k})\cdot\boldsymbol{B}_l^*(t, \boldsymbol{k}))\right\}. \tag{2.86}$$

If the medium is not absorbing ($\varepsilon'' = 0$) the quantity W is conserved for a closed system.

Equation (2.83) is similar to eqn. (2.70). We shall call the quantity defined by the formulae (2.85, 86) the electromagnetic energy of a dispersive (dissipative) medium.

If only two frequencies, which are identical but opposite in sign $|\omega_1| = |\omega_2| = \omega_0$, are significant (this means the presence of two waves being propagated in opposite directions), then the expressions for the functions $Q_{\boldsymbol{k}}$, $W_{\boldsymbol{k}}$ become

$$Q_{\boldsymbol{k}} = \frac{1}{2\pi}\omega_0 \varepsilon''_{ij}(\omega_0, \boldsymbol{k})\, E_i^0(t, \boldsymbol{k})\, E_j^{0*}(t, \boldsymbol{k}), \tag{2.87}$$

$$W_{\boldsymbol{k}} = \frac{1}{4\pi}\left\{\frac{\partial}{\partial\omega_0}(\omega_0 \varepsilon'_{ij}(\omega_0, \boldsymbol{k}))\, E_i^0(t, \boldsymbol{k})\, E_j^{0*}(t, \boldsymbol{k}) \right.$$

$$\left. + (\boldsymbol{B}_0(t, \boldsymbol{k})\cdot\boldsymbol{B}_0^*(t, \boldsymbol{k}))\right\}. \tag{2.88}$$

Let us now examine the more general case when the connexion between the vectors $\boldsymbol{D}$ and $\boldsymbol{E}$ is not linear. This occurs with a sufficiently high electrical field strength when the electron's displacement in the atom is so great that the restoring force (see eqn. (2.6)) becomes non-linear so that the connexion between the vectors $\boldsymbol{P}$ and $\boldsymbol{E}$ (or $\boldsymbol{D}$ and $\boldsymbol{E}$) is also non-linear (see Akhmanov and Khokhlov, 1964).

We notice that the expression (2.50) for a steady state can be written in the form

$$D_i^{(1)}(\boldsymbol{q}, t) = \int_0^\infty d\tau_1 \int d^3\boldsymbol{r}_1 \varepsilon_{ij}(\tau_1, \boldsymbol{r}_1)\, E_j(t-\tau_1, \boldsymbol{q}-\boldsymbol{r}_1). \tag{2.89}$$

In order to change from (2.50) to (2.89) we must replace the variables in (2.50) as follows: $t' \to t-\tau_1$, $\boldsymbol{q}' \to \boldsymbol{q}-\boldsymbol{r}_1$. The index "1" in $\boldsymbol{D}^{(l)}$ means that the connexion between the vectors $\boldsymbol{D}$ and $\boldsymbol{E}$ in (2.89) is linear.

When there is a non-linear connexion the vector $\boldsymbol{D}$ can be shown in the form of the sum of two terms

$$\boldsymbol{D} = \boldsymbol{D}^{(l)} + \boldsymbol{D}^{(nl)}. \tag{2.90}$$

The first term (linear) is defined by expression (2.89) and the second (non-linear) by the expression

$$\begin{aligned} D_i^{(nl)}(\boldsymbol{q}, t) &= \int_0^\infty d\tau_1 \int_0^\infty d\tau_2 \int d^3\boldsymbol{r}_1 \int d^3\boldsymbol{r}_2 \chi_{ijk}(\tau_1, \tau_2, \boldsymbol{r}_1, \boldsymbol{r}_2) \\ &\times E_j(t-\tau_1, \boldsymbol{q}-\boldsymbol{r}_1)\, E_k(t-\tau_1-\tau_2, \boldsymbol{q}-\boldsymbol{r}_1-\boldsymbol{r}_2) + \int_0^\infty d\tau_1 \\ &\times \int_0^\infty d\tau_2 \int_0^\infty d\tau_3 \int d^3\boldsymbol{r}_1 \int d^3\boldsymbol{r}_2 \int d^3\boldsymbol{r}_3 \\ &\times \Theta_{ijkl}(\tau_1, \tau_2, \tau_3, \boldsymbol{r}_1, \boldsymbol{r}_2, \boldsymbol{r}_3)\, E_i(t-\tau_1, \boldsymbol{r}-\boldsymbol{r}_1) \\ &\times E_j(t-\tau_1-\tau_2, \boldsymbol{q}-\boldsymbol{r}_1-\boldsymbol{r}_2) \\ &\times E_k(t-\tau_1-\tau_2-\tau_3, \boldsymbol{q}-\boldsymbol{r}_1-\boldsymbol{r}_2-\boldsymbol{r}_3) + \dots \end{aligned} \tag{2.91}$$

Thus in the case of a strong field the medium is characterized not only by the tensor ε_{ij} but also by the more complex tensors χ_{ijk}, Θ_{ijkl}, ...

If the spatial dispersion can be ignored the tensors ε_{ij}, χ_{ijk}, . . ., become

$$\begin{aligned} \varepsilon_{ij}(\tau, \boldsymbol{r}) &= \varepsilon_{ij}(\tau)\, \delta(\boldsymbol{r}), \\ \chi_{ijk}(\tau_1, \tau_2, \boldsymbol{r}_1, \boldsymbol{r}_2) &= \chi_{ijk}(\tau_1, \tau_2)\, \delta(\boldsymbol{r}_1)\, \delta(\boldsymbol{r}_2), \dots \end{aligned} \tag{2.92}$$

When there is no time dispersion either

$$\begin{aligned} \varepsilon_{ij}(\tau, \boldsymbol{r}) &= \varepsilon_{ij} \delta(\tau)\, \delta(\boldsymbol{r}), \\ \chi_{ijk}(\tau_1, \tau_2, \boldsymbol{r}_1, \boldsymbol{r}_2) &= \chi_{ijk} \delta(\tau_1)\, \delta(\tau_2)\, \delta(\boldsymbol{r}_1)\, \delta(\boldsymbol{r}_2), \end{aligned} \tag{2.93}$$

where ε_{ij}, γ_{ijk}, . . ., are constant tensors.

It follows from (2.89, 91, 93) that when there is no dispersion

$$D_i(\boldsymbol{q}, t) = \varepsilon_{ij} E_j(\boldsymbol{q}, t) + \gamma_{ijk} E_j(\boldsymbol{q}, t)\, E_k(\boldsymbol{q}, t) + \dots \tag{2.94}$$

Let us obtain the electromagnetic energy balance equation for a non-linear medium taking spatial dispersion into account.

Let us assume that the spatial and time processes are characterized by fast and slow variations of all the functions and let us give the fields $\boldsymbol{E}$, $\boldsymbol{B}$ in the form (compare (2.76))

$$\boldsymbol{E}(\boldsymbol{q}, t) = \boldsymbol{E}(\mu\boldsymbol{q}, \mu t, \boldsymbol{q}, t), \quad \boldsymbol{B}(\boldsymbol{q}, t) = \boldsymbol{B}(\mu\boldsymbol{q}, \mu t, \boldsymbol{q}, t), \tag{2.95}$$

where μ is a small parameter and $\boldsymbol{q}$, t are fast variables.

We expand into a Fourier integral with respect to the fast variables

$$\boldsymbol{E}(\mu\boldsymbol{q}, \mu t, \boldsymbol{q}, t) = \frac{1}{(2\pi)^4}\int d\omega\, d^3\boldsymbol{k}\, \boldsymbol{E}(\mu\boldsymbol{q}, \mu t, \boldsymbol{k}, \omega)\, e^{-i[\omega t-(\boldsymbol{k}\cdot\boldsymbol{q})]}, \tag{2.96}$$

$$\boldsymbol{B}(\mu\boldsymbol{q}, \mu t, \boldsymbol{q}, t) = \frac{1}{(2\pi)^4}\int d\omega\, d^3\boldsymbol{k} \boldsymbol{B}(\mu\boldsymbol{q}, \mu t, \boldsymbol{k}, \omega)\, e^{-i[\omega t-(\boldsymbol{k}\cdot\boldsymbol{q})]}. \tag{2.97}$$

We can also write the functions $\boldsymbol{D}^{(1)}$, $\boldsymbol{D}^{(\mathrm{nl})}$, $\boldsymbol{j}^{\mathrm{e}}$ . . ., in the form (2.96).

In these formulae the Fourier components themselves are slowly varying functions of the coordinates and time. These expansions are reasonable if the spectral functions are non-zero only at values of ω, k greater than $\omega_{\min}$, $k_{\min}$ such that

$$E(\mu\boldsymbol{q}, \mu t, \omega, \boldsymbol{k})\omega_{\min} \gg \frac{\partial E}{\partial \mu t}, \qquad Ek_{\min} \gg \left|\frac{\partial E}{\partial \mu\boldsymbol{q}}\right|, \qquad \text{etc.} \tag{2.98}$$

Let us obtain the expression for the function $\boldsymbol{D}^{(1)}(\mu\boldsymbol{q}, \mu t, \boldsymbol{k}, \omega)$. For this purpose we substitute the expansion (2.96) in formula (2.89), expand the function $E_j[\mu(t-\tau_1), \mu(\boldsymbol{q}-\boldsymbol{r}_1), \omega, \boldsymbol{k}]$ into a series with respect to τ_1, $\boldsymbol{r}_1$ and limit ourselves to the first two terms of the expansion. As a result we obtain (compare (2.78)):

$$D_i^{(1)}(\mu t, \mu\boldsymbol{q}, \omega, \boldsymbol{k}) = \left(\varepsilon_{ij}(\omega, \boldsymbol{k}) + i\frac{\partial \varepsilon_{ij}}{\partial \omega}\cdot\frac{\partial}{\partial \mu t} - i\left(\frac{\partial \varepsilon_{ij}}{\partial \boldsymbol{k}}\cdot\frac{\partial}{\partial \mu\boldsymbol{q}}\right)\right) E_j(\mu t, \mu\boldsymbol{q}, \omega, \boldsymbol{k}). \tag{2.99}$$

We shall consider that the non-linear terms are small and are of the order of μ, so the dependence of the field on the slow variables can be neglected in (2.91) when deriving the expression for $\boldsymbol{D}^{(\mathrm{nl})}(\mu t, \mu \boldsymbol{q}, \omega, \boldsymbol{k})$. The expression thus obtained for $\boldsymbol{D}^{(\mathrm{nl})}$ can conveniently be written in the form:

$$D_i^{(\mathrm{nl})}(\mu t, \mu \boldsymbol{q}, \omega, \boldsymbol{k})$$
$$= \frac{1}{(2\pi)^4} \int d\omega_1\, d\omega_2\, d^3\boldsymbol{k}_1\, d^3\boldsymbol{k}_2 \delta(\omega-\omega_1-\omega_2)\, \delta(\boldsymbol{k}-\boldsymbol{k}_1-\boldsymbol{k}_2)$$
$$\times \chi_{ijk}(\omega, \boldsymbol{k}, \omega_2, \boldsymbol{k}_2)\, E_j(\omega_1, \boldsymbol{k}_1)\, E_k(\omega_2, \boldsymbol{k}_2)$$
$$+\frac{1}{(2\pi)^8} \int d\omega_1\, d\omega_2\, d\omega_3\, d^3\boldsymbol{k}_1\, d^3\boldsymbol{k}_2\, d^3\boldsymbol{k}_3 \delta(\omega-\omega_1-\omega_2-\omega_3)$$
$$\times \delta(\boldsymbol{k}-\boldsymbol{k}_1-\boldsymbol{k}_2-\boldsymbol{k}_3)\, \Theta_{ijkl}(\omega, \boldsymbol{k}, \omega_2+\omega_3, \boldsymbol{k}_2+\boldsymbol{k}_3, \omega_3, \boldsymbol{k}_3)$$
$$\times E_j(\omega_1, \boldsymbol{k}_1)\, E_k(\omega_2, \boldsymbol{k}_2)\, E_l(\omega_3, \boldsymbol{k}_3). \tag{2.100}$$

Using formulae (2.99, 100) we can find the expression for the Fourier component of the function $\partial \boldsymbol{D}/\partial t$

$$\left(\frac{\partial \boldsymbol{D}}{\partial t}\right)_{\mu t,\, \mu \boldsymbol{q},\, \omega,\, \boldsymbol{k}} = -i\omega(\boldsymbol{D}^{(1)}+\boldsymbol{D}^{(\mathrm{nl})})+\frac{\partial \boldsymbol{D}^{(1)}}{\partial \mu t}(\mu t, \mu \boldsymbol{q}, \omega, \boldsymbol{k}). \tag{2.101}$$

It is easy to obtain the corresponding expressions for all the Fourier components of all the functions in the Maxwell equations. Let us write out the system of equations for the Fourier components of the functions $\boldsymbol{E}, \boldsymbol{B}$. To do this we substitute in the Maxwell equations (1.18–21) the expansions (2.96, 97) for $\boldsymbol{E}$, $\boldsymbol{B}$ and the other functions. As above we shall consider that there is little dissipation ($\varepsilon_{ij}'' \sim \mu$). We shall assume that the functions $\boldsymbol{j}^{\mathrm{e}}$, ϱ^{e} are also of the order of μ. Then in the zero approximation with respect to μ we obtain the following system of equations for the functions $\boldsymbol{E}(\mu t, \mu \boldsymbol{q}, \omega, \boldsymbol{k})$, $\boldsymbol{B}(\mu t, \mu \boldsymbol{q}, \omega, \boldsymbol{k})$:

$$[\boldsymbol{k}\wedge \boldsymbol{B}]_i = -\frac{\omega}{c}\, \varepsilon_{ij}' E_j,\ (\boldsymbol{k}\cdot \boldsymbol{B}) = 0; \tag{2.102}$$

$$[\boldsymbol{k}\wedge \boldsymbol{E}] = \frac{\omega}{c} \boldsymbol{B},\ k_i \varepsilon_{ij}' E_j = 0.$$

Eliminating the vector $\boldsymbol{B}$ we find the system of equations for E_i

$$[\boldsymbol{k}\wedge [\boldsymbol{k}\wedge \boldsymbol{E}]]_i+\frac{\omega^2}{c^2}\, \varepsilon_{ij}' E_j = 0. \tag{2.103}$$

We shall use $\boldsymbol{e}$ to denote a unit vector along the direction of the vector $\boldsymbol{E}$. From (2.103) follows the equation which connects the frequency ω, the wave vector $\boldsymbol{k}$ and the vector $\boldsymbol{e}$ determining the polarization

$$[\boldsymbol{k}\wedge\boldsymbol{e}]^2-\frac{\omega^2}{c^2}e_i\varepsilon_{ij}e_j = 0. \tag{2.104}$$

If the medium is isotropic, the tensor ε_{ij} depends only on the one vector $\boldsymbol{k}$, so can be given in the form

$$\varepsilon_{ij}(\omega, \boldsymbol{k}) = \left(\delta_{ij}-\frac{k_ik_j}{k^2}\right)\varepsilon^{\perp}(\omega, \boldsymbol{k})+\frac{k_ik_j}{k^2}\varepsilon^{\parallel}(\omega, \boldsymbol{k}), \tag{2.105}$$

where $\varepsilon^{\parallel}$, $\varepsilon^{\perp}$ are the longitudinal and transverse permittivity (see § 7).

For an isotropic medium eqn. (2.104) turns into the two dispersion equations

$$\omega^2\varepsilon^{\perp}(\omega, k)-c^2k^2 = 0, \quad \varepsilon^{\parallel}(\omega, k) = 0 \tag{2.106}$$

for transverse and longitudinal waves respectively.

We can now write the equations for the functions $\boldsymbol{E}(\mu t, \mu\boldsymbol{q}$ $\omega, \boldsymbol{k})$, $\boldsymbol{B}(\mu t, \mu\boldsymbol{q}, \omega, \boldsymbol{k})$ in the first approximation with respect to μ:

$$c(\text{curl}_{\mu\boldsymbol{q}}\boldsymbol{B})_i = \frac{\partial}{\partial\omega}(\omega\varepsilon'_{ij})\frac{\partial E_j}{\partial\mu t}-\omega\left(\frac{\partial\varepsilon'_{ij}}{\partial\boldsymbol{k}}\cdot\frac{\partial E_j}{\partial\mu\boldsymbol{q}}\right)-i\omega D_i^{\text{nl}}$$
$$+\omega\varepsilon''_{ij}E_j+4\pi j_i^{\text{e}}; \tag{2.107}$$

$$c(\text{curl}_{\mu\boldsymbol{q}}\boldsymbol{E}) = -\frac{\partial\boldsymbol{B}}{\partial\mu t}; \tag{2.108}$$

$$\left(\frac{\partial}{\partial\mu\boldsymbol{q}}\cdot\boldsymbol{D}\right)_{\mu t,\, \mu\boldsymbol{q},\, \omega, \boldsymbol{k}} = 4\pi\varrho^{\text{e}}; \quad \left(\frac{\partial}{\partial\mu\boldsymbol{q}}\cdot\boldsymbol{B}\right) = 0. \tag{2.109}$$

In order to obtain the energy balance equation we multiply eqn. (2.107) by E_i^* and the complex-conjugate equation (2.108) by $\boldsymbol{B}$ and subtract the second equation from the first. Using the vector identity (2.63) we obtain the equation

$$\frac{1}{8\pi}\frac{\partial}{\partial\mu t}\left(E_i\frac{\partial(\omega\varepsilon'_{ij})}{\partial\omega}E_j^*+\boldsymbol{B}^2\right) = -\frac{c}{4\pi}\text{div}_{\mu\boldsymbol{q}}\,\text{Re}\,[\boldsymbol{E}\wedge\boldsymbol{B}^*]$$

$$+\frac{\omega}{8\pi}\operatorname{div}_{\mu\boldsymbol{q}} E_i \frac{\partial \varepsilon_{ij}}{\partial \boldsymbol{k}} E_j^* - \frac{\omega}{4\pi}\operatorname{Im}(\boldsymbol{D}^{(\mathrm{nl})}\cdot\boldsymbol{E}^*)$$

$$-\frac{\omega}{4\pi} E_i\varepsilon_{ij}'' E^* - \operatorname{Re}(\boldsymbol{j}^{\mathrm{e}}\cdot\boldsymbol{E}^*). \tag{2.110}$$

We can write this equation in a more convenient form.

We introduce the notation for the density of the electromagnetic energy of a dispersive medium appropriate to given ω, $\boldsymbol{k}$:

$$W(\mu t, \mu\boldsymbol{q}, \omega, \boldsymbol{k}) = \frac{1}{8\pi}\left(E_i \frac{\partial(\omega\varepsilon_{ij}')}{\partial\omega} E_j^* + B^2\right). \tag{2.111}$$

The total energy density is defined by the expression

$$W(\mu t, \mu\boldsymbol{q}) = \frac{1}{(2\pi)^4}\int W(\mu t, \mu\boldsymbol{q}, \omega, \boldsymbol{k})\, d\omega\, d^3\boldsymbol{k} \tag{2.112}$$

(compare (2.111, 112) with the expressions (2.85, 86) for a discrete spectrum).

From the zero approximation equations we find

$$\boldsymbol{B} = \frac{c}{\omega}[\boldsymbol{k}\wedge\boldsymbol{E}], \quad [\boldsymbol{E}\wedge\boldsymbol{B}^*] = \frac{c}{\omega}[\boldsymbol{E}\wedge[\boldsymbol{k}\wedge\boldsymbol{E}^*]]. \tag{2.113}$$

Using the first of these formulae we eliminate the vector $\boldsymbol{B}$ from (2.111)

$$W = \left(\frac{c^2}{\omega^2}[\boldsymbol{k}\wedge\boldsymbol{e}]^2 + \frac{\partial}{\partial\omega}(\omega e_i\varepsilon_{ij}' e_j)\right)\frac{E^2}{8\pi}$$

$$\equiv \frac{1}{\omega}\cdot\frac{\partial(\omega^2 e_i\varepsilon_{ij}' e_j)}{\partial\omega}\cdot\frac{E^2}{8\pi}. \tag{2.114}$$

Equation (2.104) is used in the derivation of the second expression of (2.114).

We write the first two terms terms in the right-hand side of (2.110) in the form $-\operatorname{div}_{\mu\boldsymbol{q}}\boldsymbol{S}$, where $\boldsymbol{S}$ is the energy flux vector.

We can write the vector $\boldsymbol{S}$ in the form

$$\boldsymbol{S}(\mu t, \mu\boldsymbol{q}, \omega, \boldsymbol{k}) = \boldsymbol{v}_{\mathrm{gr}} W \equiv \frac{\partial\omega}{\partial\boldsymbol{k}} W, \tag{2.115}$$

where

$$\boldsymbol{v}_{\text{gr}} = \frac{2c^2(\boldsymbol{k}-\boldsymbol{e}(\boldsymbol{k}\cdot\boldsymbol{e}))-\omega^2 \dfrac{\partial}{\partial \boldsymbol{k}} e_i\varepsilon'_{ij}e_j}{\dfrac{\partial}{\partial\omega}(\omega^2 e_i\varepsilon'_{ij}e_j)} \tag{2.116}$$

is the group velocity vector for a dispersive medium. The expression (2.116) can be derived directly from the equation (2.104) if we differentiate it with respect to $\boldsymbol{k}$ and solve the equation obtained for $\partial\omega/\partial\boldsymbol{k}$.

In the case of an isotropic medium we obtain from (2.116) two expressions for the group velocity of the transverse and longitudinal waves

$$\boldsymbol{v}_{\text{gr}}^{\perp} = \frac{2c^2\boldsymbol{k}-\omega^2 \dfrac{\partial}{\partial \boldsymbol{k}} \operatorname{Re} \varepsilon^{\perp}(\omega, \boldsymbol{k})}{\dfrac{\partial}{\partial\omega}(\omega^2 \operatorname{Re} \varepsilon^{\perp}(\omega, \boldsymbol{k}))};$$

$$\boldsymbol{v}_{\text{gr}}^{\parallel} = -\frac{\dfrac{\partial}{\partial \boldsymbol{k}} \operatorname{Re} \varepsilon^{\parallel}(\omega, \boldsymbol{k})}{\dfrac{\partial}{\partial\omega} \operatorname{Re} \varepsilon^{\parallel}(\omega, \boldsymbol{k})}. \tag{2.117}$$

We further introduce the notation for the damping decrement

$$\gamma(\omega, \boldsymbol{k}) = \frac{\omega e_i\varepsilon''_{ij}e_j}{\dfrac{c^2}{\omega^2}[\boldsymbol{k}\wedge\boldsymbol{e}]^2+\dfrac{\partial}{\partial\omega}(\omega e_i\varepsilon'_{ij}e_j)} \equiv \frac{\omega^2 e_i\varepsilon''_{ij}e_j}{\dfrac{\partial}{\partial\omega}(\omega^2 e_i\varepsilon'_{ij}e_j)} \tag{2.118}$$

For an isotropic medium two expressions follow from this for the damping decrements of the transverse and longitudinal waves

$$\gamma^{\perp}(\omega, \boldsymbol{k}) = \frac{\omega^2 \operatorname{Im} \varepsilon^{\perp}}{\dfrac{\partial}{\partial\omega}(\omega^2\varepsilon^{\perp})}; \quad \gamma^{\parallel}(\omega, \boldsymbol{k}) = \frac{\operatorname{Im} \varepsilon^{\parallel}}{\dfrac{\partial\varepsilon^{\parallel}}{\partial\omega}}. \tag{2.119}$$

Using the notations we have introduced we can write eqn. (2.110) in the form

$$\frac{\partial}{\partial\mu t}W+\frac{\partial}{\partial\mu\boldsymbol{q}}(\boldsymbol{v}_{\text{gr}}W) = -2\gamma W-\frac{\omega}{4\pi}\operatorname{Im}(\boldsymbol{D}^{\text{nl}}\cdot\boldsymbol{E}^*) - \operatorname{Re}(\boldsymbol{j}^{\text{e}}\cdot\boldsymbol{E}^*). \tag{2.120}$$

If the medium is linear and the function $\boldsymbol{E}(\mu t, \mu \boldsymbol{q}, \omega, \boldsymbol{k})$ is independent of the coordinates, then eqn. (2.83) follows from (2.120) for a discrete spectrum.

It can be seen from (2.120) that the energy $W(\mu t, \mu \boldsymbol{q}, \omega, \boldsymbol{k})$ may vary because of the presence of an energy flux, dissipation (conversion into heat), work of the external current $\boldsymbol{j}^e$ and, lastly, non-linear interaction between the different waves.

Instead of the function W we can use the distribution function for the quanta:

$$N(\mu t, \mu \boldsymbol{q}, \omega, \boldsymbol{k}) = \frac{W(\mu t, \mu \boldsymbol{q}, \omega, \boldsymbol{k})}{\hbar\omega(2\pi)^4}, \qquad (2.121)$$

where $\hbar\omega$ is the energy of a quantum.

If we ignore the dissipation and consider that $\boldsymbol{j}^e = 0$, then we can obtain from eqn. (2.120) the balance equations for the total number of quanta, the total energy of the quanta and the total momentum of the quanta, i.e. the functions (see Akhmanov and Khokhlov, 1964)

$$\int N\, d\omega\, d^3\boldsymbol{k}, \qquad \int \hbar\omega N\, d\omega\, d^3\boldsymbol{k}, \qquad \int \hbar\boldsymbol{k}\; N\, d\omega\, d^3\boldsymbol{k}. \qquad (2.122)$$

In the derivation of these equations use is made of the following three properties of the non-linear term in eqn. (2.120):

$$\operatorname{Im} \int (\boldsymbol{D}^{\text{nl}} \cdot \boldsymbol{E}^*)\, d\omega\, d^3\boldsymbol{k} = 0,$$

$$\operatorname{Im} \int \omega(\boldsymbol{D}^{\text{nl}} \cdot \boldsymbol{E}^*)\, d\omega\, d^3\boldsymbol{k} = 0;$$

$$\operatorname{Im} \int \boldsymbol{k}(\boldsymbol{D}^{\text{nl}} \cdot \boldsymbol{E}^*)\, d\omega\, d^3\boldsymbol{k} = 0. \qquad (2.123)$$

In the proof of these equations it is essential that the integrands in formula (2.100) for $\boldsymbol{D}^{(\text{nl})}$ should be non-zero only if we can satisfy the conditions

$$\omega = \omega_1 + \omega_2, \qquad \boldsymbol{k} = \boldsymbol{k}_1 + \boldsymbol{k}_2, \qquad (2.124)$$

in the terms that are quadratic and

$$\omega = \omega_1 + \omega_2 + \omega_3, \qquad \boldsymbol{k} = \boldsymbol{k}_1 + \boldsymbol{k}_2 + \boldsymbol{k}_3 \qquad (2.125)$$

in the terms that are cubic with respect to $\boldsymbol{E}$. In quantum language these conditions express the laws of the conservation of energy and momentum during the interaction of three and four waves respectively.

It will be shown below that under certain conditions the equations describing the processes in a plasma can be reduced to the electrodynamic equations. This is possible when we neglect the feedback of the field on the slowly varying distribution functions $f_a(\mu t, \mu \boldsymbol{q}, \boldsymbol{p})$. In the opposite case we obtain a more complex system of equations for the functions f_a, $\boldsymbol{E}(\mu t, \mu \boldsymbol{q}, \omega, \boldsymbol{k})$ (see §§ 17 and 18).

3. Magnetohydrodynamic Equations

We can use a system of gas-dynamics equations to describe the slow processes in a gas when the functions ϱ, $\boldsymbol{u}$, T vary only a little during the time of free flight.

If the gas consists of charged particles, then the gas-dynamics equations are insufficient even to describe the slow processes since it is necessary to know not only the functions ϱ, $\boldsymbol{u}$, T but also the strengths of the electrical and magnetic fields, which are defined by the Maxwell equations, in order to give the system's state thermodynamically.

It is thus to be expected that to describe the slow processes in a gas consisting of charged particles we must use a system of equations both for the density, velocity and temperature of the charged particles and for the strengths of the electrical and magnetic fields.

We give an example of such a system of equations which is valid upon the following assumptions:

1. We are discussing a gaseous or liquid medium which possesses electrical conductivity. At the same time, however, the density of the electric charge is zero at all points in the medium.

2. We place the system under discussion in an external constant magnetic field of magnitude $\boldsymbol{B}_0$. We limit the magnitude of the magnetic field by the following condition. We use λ to denote the mean free path of the charged particles, e.g. electrons, in the system.

Physics tells us that in a constant magnetic field a charged particle describes either a circle or a spiral. The radius of the circle is $r_L = Mcv/eB_0$ and is called the Larmor radius. In this formula v is the particle's velocity, e the charge and M the mass.

We shall consider that the magnitude of the magnetic field strength B_0 is limited by the condition $r_1 \gg \lambda$ or $B_0 \ll Mcv/e\lambda$. This means that there is hardly any distortion of a charged particle's trajectory over its mean free path. With this condition it may therefore be assumed that the coefficients of conductivity σ, viscosity μ and thermal conductivity $\varkappa$ which come into the equations are independent of the magnetic field strength.

3. According to Ohm's law the current density in a medium is proportional to the strength of the electric current, i.e.

$$\boldsymbol{j} = \sigma \boldsymbol{E}. \tag{3.1}$$

We shall assume that variations in the electrical field strength take place so slowly that in the first equation of the system of equations (I) we can neglect the displacement current, i.e.

$$\frac{\partial \boldsymbol{E}}{\partial t} \ll 4\pi\sigma \boldsymbol{E}. \tag{3.2}$$

If the process is periodic the condition (3.2) can be written in the form $\omega < 4\pi\sigma$. For metal conductors this condition is satisfied right up to light frequencies since the magnitude of σ for metals is of the order of 10^{16}–10^{17} sec^{-1}.

For conducting gases the range of frequencies for which the condition (3.2) is valid depends on the degree of ionization of the gas.

4. We shall limit ourselves to discussing the case when the velocity of motion is much less than the velocity of light, i.e. $u \ll c$. If this is so the equations can be discussed in a non-relativistic approximation.

5. We shall assume that the medium's permeability is unity, i.e. $\boldsymbol{B} = \boldsymbol{H}$.

6. We shall discuss only slow processes.

If we use τ to denote the time taken to establish a local equilibrium state in the system under discussion, then the condition of slowness of variation of the functions ϱ, $\boldsymbol{U}$, T, $\boldsymbol{B}$, $\boldsymbol{E}$ can be written in the form†

$$\frac{\partial \boldsymbol{B}}{\partial t} \ll \frac{\boldsymbol{B}}{\tau}; \qquad \frac{\partial \boldsymbol{U}}{\partial t} \ll \frac{\boldsymbol{U}}{\tau} \tag{3.3}$$

with similar conditions for the coordinate derivatives. This means that there is little change in any of the functions during the time taken to establish local equilibrium. For gases the quantity τ is the time of free flight.

Using these limitations we shall first discuss the equations for the strengths of the electrical and magnetic fields. We note that when a conductor moves in a magnetic field an induced electrical field strength $\boldsymbol{E}_i$ appears in it in accordance with Faraday's law resulting in the appearance of an induced e.m.f. at the end of the conductor.

If the velocity of the conductor is $\boldsymbol{U}$, then

$$\boldsymbol{E}_i = \frac{1}{c}[\boldsymbol{U} \wedge \boldsymbol{B}] = \frac{1}{c}[\boldsymbol{U} \wedge \boldsymbol{H}]. \tag{3.4}$$

Here we have allowed for the fact that in the case under discussion $\boldsymbol{B} = \boldsymbol{H}$. An induced field will appear in a conducting medium located in a magnetic field. In this case $\boldsymbol{U}(\boldsymbol{q}, t)$ is the velocity at the point $\boldsymbol{q}$ at the time t. The total strength of the electrical field is $\boldsymbol{E}+(1/c)[\boldsymbol{U} \wedge \boldsymbol{B}]$. Using this result we can write Ohm's law (3.1) for a conducting medium in a magnetic field in the form

$$\boldsymbol{j} = \sigma\left(\boldsymbol{E}+\frac{1}{c}[\boldsymbol{U} \wedge \boldsymbol{B}]\right). \tag{3.5}$$

Hence we can express $\boldsymbol{E}$ in terms of $\boldsymbol{j}$, $\boldsymbol{U}$, $\boldsymbol{B}$

$$\boldsymbol{E} = -\frac{1}{c}[\boldsymbol{U} \wedge \boldsymbol{B}]+\frac{\boldsymbol{j}}{\sigma}. \tag{3.6}$$

† Here and below $\varrho(\boldsymbol{q}, t)\, d^3\boldsymbol{q}$ is the average number of particles in a volume $d^3\boldsymbol{q}$ around the point $\boldsymbol{q}$ at the time t. The mass density is $M\varrho$,where M is the mass of a particle.

The first three Maxwell equations in the approximation under discussion become

$$\operatorname{curl} \boldsymbol{B} = \frac{4\pi}{c}\boldsymbol{j}; \qquad \operatorname{curl} \boldsymbol{E} = -\frac{1}{c}\frac{\partial \boldsymbol{B}}{\partial t}; \qquad \operatorname{div} \boldsymbol{B} = 0.$$

Using expression (3.6) to eliminate $\boldsymbol{E}$ from the second equation and the first equation to eliminate $\boldsymbol{j}$, we obtain, remembering that $\operatorname{div} \boldsymbol{B} = 0$, the following equation for the strength of the magnetic field in the medium:

$$\frac{\partial \boldsymbol{B}}{\partial t} = \operatorname{curl}[\boldsymbol{U} \wedge \boldsymbol{B}] + \frac{c^2}{4\pi\sigma} \nabla^2 \boldsymbol{B}. \tag{3.7}$$

The second equation for $\boldsymbol{B}$ is of the form

$$\operatorname{div} \boldsymbol{B} = 0. \tag{3.8}$$

Equations (3.7, 8) for the magnetic field strength are not closed since the velocity $\boldsymbol{U}(\boldsymbol{q}, t)$ enters into eqn. (3.7).

In order to obtain a closed system of equations we examine the system of equations for the functions ϱ, $\boldsymbol{U}$ and the entropy S.

The continuity equation for a conducting medium is of the previous form:

$$\frac{\partial \varrho}{\partial t} + \operatorname{div} \varrho \boldsymbol{U} = 0. \tag{3.9}$$

In the Navier–Stokes equation we have the additional term

$$\frac{\boldsymbol{F}}{M} = \frac{1}{cM\varrho}[\boldsymbol{j} \wedge \boldsymbol{B}],$$

where $\boldsymbol{F}$ is the force acting on the magnetic field on an element of a conducting medium in which a current $\boldsymbol{j}$ is flowing; M is the mass of a particle. By using the Maxwell equation $\operatorname{curl} \boldsymbol{B} = (4\pi/c)\boldsymbol{j}$ we can eliminate $\boldsymbol{j}$ from the expression for the force. As a result the Navier–Stokes equation becomes

$$\frac{\partial \boldsymbol{U}}{\partial t} + (\boldsymbol{U} \operatorname{grad}) \boldsymbol{U} = -\frac{1}{M\varrho} \operatorname{grad} p - \frac{1}{4\pi\varrho M}[\boldsymbol{B} \wedge \operatorname{curl} \boldsymbol{B}] + \frac{\mu}{M\varrho}\left(\nabla^2 \boldsymbol{U} + \frac{1}{3} \operatorname{grad} \operatorname{div} \boldsymbol{U}\right). \tag{3.10}$$

We can select the equation for the entropy S, for example, as the last equation. It contains an additional dissipative term caused by the generation of Joule heat during the passage of an electric current through the medium in question.

The amount of Joule heat generated per unit time is j^2/σ. Using the Maxwell equation curl $\boldsymbol{B} = (4\pi/c)\boldsymbol{j}$ we can write this expression in the form

$$\frac{c^2}{16\pi^2\sigma}(\text{curl } \boldsymbol{B})^2.$$

As a result we obtain the following equation for the entropy density:

$$\frac{\partial \varrho S}{\partial t} + \text{div } (\varrho \boldsymbol{U} S) = \frac{\mu}{2T}\left(\frac{\partial U_i}{\partial q_j} + \frac{\partial U_j}{\partial q_i} - \frac{2}{3}\delta_{ij}\frac{\partial U_k}{\partial q_k}\right)^2 + \frac{\varkappa}{T}\Delta T + \frac{c^2}{16\pi^2\sigma}(\text{curl } \boldsymbol{B})^2. \quad (3.11)$$

Equations (3.7–11) constitute a closed system of magnetohydrodynamic equations. When $\boldsymbol{B} = 0$ eqns. (3.9–11) agree with the ordinary gas-dynamics equations. We can deal with the question of magnetohydrodynamic waves in a similar way. Let the functions ϱ, $\boldsymbol{B}$, p, $\boldsymbol{U}$ vary only a little from their values ϱ_0, $\boldsymbol{B}_0$, p_0, $\boldsymbol{U}_0$ which they have when there are no disturbances in the medium, i.e.

$$\varrho = \varrho_0 + \varrho_1, \quad \boldsymbol{B} = \boldsymbol{B}_0 + \boldsymbol{h}; \quad p = p_0 + M v_s^2 \varrho_1; \quad \boldsymbol{U} = \boldsymbol{U}_1. \quad (3.12)$$

Here $\boldsymbol{B}_0$ is the external magnetic field and v_s is the velocity of sound in the medium. We shall consider that $\boldsymbol{U}_0 = 0$. Below we shall omit the suffixes 0 and 1 on $\boldsymbol{B}_0$, ϱ_1 and $\boldsymbol{U}_1$ respectively.

We substitute the expressions (3.12) in eqns. (3.7–11), leaving only the linear terms. Omitting the dissipative terms we obtain as a result the following system of equations for the functions ϱ, $\boldsymbol{h}$, $\boldsymbol{U}$:

$$\frac{\partial \boldsymbol{h}}{\partial t} = \text{curl } [\boldsymbol{U} \wedge \boldsymbol{B}], \quad \text{div } \boldsymbol{h} = 0, \quad (3.13)$$

$$\frac{\partial \varrho}{\partial t} + \varrho_0 \operatorname{div} \boldsymbol{U} = 0, \tag{3.14}$$

$$\frac{\partial \boldsymbol{U}}{\partial t} = -\frac{v_s^2}{\varrho_0} \operatorname{grad} \varrho + \frac{1}{4\pi M \varrho_0} [\operatorname{curl} \boldsymbol{h} \wedge \boldsymbol{B}]. \tag{3.15}$$

Using this system we can discuss the problem of the propagation of small disturbances when the effect of the dissipative terms can be ignored.

In order to find the solutions of eqns. (3.13–15) describing the propagation of plane waves with a wave vector $\boldsymbol{k}$ and a frequency ω we shall give the functions ϱ, $\boldsymbol{U}$, $\boldsymbol{h}$ in the form $\sim e^{-[\omega t - (\boldsymbol{k} \cdot \boldsymbol{q})]}$.

In this case the system of eqns. (3.13–15) becomes

$$-\omega \boldsymbol{h} = [\boldsymbol{k} \wedge [\boldsymbol{U} \wedge \boldsymbol{B}]], \quad (\boldsymbol{k} \cdot \boldsymbol{h}) = 0, \tag{3.16}$$

$$\omega \varrho = \varrho_0 (\boldsymbol{k} \cdot \boldsymbol{U}), \tag{3.17}$$

$$\omega \boldsymbol{U} = \frac{v_s^2}{\varrho_0} \varrho \boldsymbol{k} + \frac{1}{4\pi M \varrho_0} [\boldsymbol{B} \wedge [\boldsymbol{h} \wedge \boldsymbol{k}]]. \tag{3.18}$$

Eliminating ϱ from eqns. (3.17, 18) we obtain

$$\omega^2 \boldsymbol{U} = v_s^2 \boldsymbol{k} (\boldsymbol{k} \cdot \boldsymbol{U}) + \frac{\omega}{4\pi M \varrho_0} [\boldsymbol{B} \wedge [\boldsymbol{k} \wedge \boldsymbol{h}]]. \tag{3.19}$$

We shall show firstly that in magnetohydrodynamics there are waves during the propagation of which oscillations occur in the plane of the vectors $\boldsymbol{B}$, $\boldsymbol{k}$.

For this purpose we shall project eqns. (3.16, 19) onto the vectors $\boldsymbol{B}$, $\boldsymbol{k}$. As a result we obtain the following closed system of equations for the functions $(\boldsymbol{h} \cdot \boldsymbol{B})$, $(\boldsymbol{U} \cdot \boldsymbol{B})$, $(\boldsymbol{U} \cdot \boldsymbol{k})$, $[(\boldsymbol{h} \cdot \boldsymbol{k}) = 0$ by virtue of the equation $\operatorname{div} \boldsymbol{h} = 0]$:

$$-\omega (\boldsymbol{h} \cdot \boldsymbol{B}) = \big(\boldsymbol{B} \cdot [\boldsymbol{k} \wedge [\boldsymbol{U} \wedge \boldsymbol{B}]]\big), \tag{3.20}$$

$$\omega^2 (\boldsymbol{k} \cdot \boldsymbol{U}) = v_s^2 k^2 (\boldsymbol{k} \cdot \boldsymbol{U}) + \frac{\omega}{4\pi M \varrho_0} \big(\boldsymbol{k} \cdot [\boldsymbol{B} \wedge [\boldsymbol{k} \wedge \boldsymbol{h}]]\big), \tag{3.21}$$

$$\omega^2 (\boldsymbol{U} \cdot \boldsymbol{B}) = v_s^2 (\boldsymbol{k} \cdot \boldsymbol{B}) (\boldsymbol{U} \cdot \boldsymbol{k}). \tag{3.22}$$

From the condition of solubility of the system of homogeneous equations (3.20–22) for the functions $(\boldsymbol{h} \cdot \boldsymbol{B})$, $(\boldsymbol{U} \cdot \boldsymbol{B})$, $(\boldsymbol{U} \cdot \boldsymbol{k})$ we find the dispersion equation which connects the frequency ω and the wave vector $\boldsymbol{k}$

$$\omega^4-(v_s^2+v_A^2)\omega^2k^2+v_s^2v_A^2k^4\cos^2\theta = 0. \tag{3.23}$$

Here we have introduced the notations $v_A^2 = B^2/4\pi M\varrho$ (the velocity of the magnetohydrodynamic waves) and $\cos\theta = (\boldsymbol{B}\cdot\boldsymbol{k})/Bk$.

From eqn. (3.23) we find

$$\omega_\pm^2 = \frac{1}{2}k^2\{v_s^2+v_A^2\pm\sqrt{[(v_s^2+v_A^2)-4v_A^2v_s^2\cos^2\theta]}\}. \tag{3.24}$$

We have thus obtained two types of wave, during the propagation of which oscillations take place in the plane of the vectors $\boldsymbol{B}$, $\boldsymbol{k}$. It follows from formula (3.24) that the phase velocity of these waves is

$$v_{ph}^\pm = \frac{\omega_\pm}{k} \tag{3.25}$$

and is independent of the magnitude of the wave vector. These waves are called magnetosonic. A wave with a phase velocity of v_{ph}^+ is called accelerated and one with v_{ph}^- retarded.

As $B\to 0$, $v_{ph}^+\to v_s$ and $v_{ph}^-\to 0$. In this extreme case a magnetosonic accelerated wave is the same as an ordinary sonic wave.

It follows from formula (3.24) that in the general case the phase velocity of an accelerated wave can take up values within the limits $v_s^2+v_A^2 \geqslant v_{ph}^{(+)2} \geqslant \text{Max}\,[v_A^2, v_s^2]$.

Accordingly the phase velocity of an accelerated wave when $B\neq 0$ is greater than (or when $\theta=0$, equal to) the velocity of sound.

The phase velocity of a retarded wave is within the limits: $\text{Min}\,[v_A^2\cos^2\theta, v_s^2] \geqslant v_{ph}^{(-)2} \geqslant 0$.

We note further that the variable components of the velocity $\boldsymbol{U}$ and the magnetic field strength have components both along the direction of propagation of the wave (along the vector $\boldsymbol{k}$) and in the direction at right angles to $\boldsymbol{k}$. In the general case, therefore, magnetosonic waves are neither longitudinal nor transverse.

Apart from magnetosonic waves there are other transverse waves that are also called magnetohydrodynamic.

In order to obtain the dispersion equation for them we project eqns. (3.20–22) onto the direction at right angles to the plane formed by the vectors $\boldsymbol{B}, \boldsymbol{k}$. To do this we multiply eqns. (3.16–19) scalarly by the vector $[\boldsymbol{B} \wedge \boldsymbol{k}]$. As a result we obtain two equations for the functions $(\boldsymbol{h} \cdot [\boldsymbol{B} \wedge \boldsymbol{k}])$, $(\boldsymbol{U} \cdot [\boldsymbol{B} \wedge \boldsymbol{k}])$:

$$-\omega(\boldsymbol{h} \cdot [\boldsymbol{B} \wedge \boldsymbol{k}]) = (\boldsymbol{B} \cdot \boldsymbol{k})(\boldsymbol{U} \cdot [\boldsymbol{B} \wedge \boldsymbol{k}]), \tag{3.26}$$

$$-\frac{\omega}{4\pi M \varrho_0}(\boldsymbol{B} \cdot \boldsymbol{k})(\boldsymbol{h} \cdot [\boldsymbol{B} \wedge \boldsymbol{k}]) = \omega^2(\boldsymbol{U} \cdot [\boldsymbol{B} \wedge \boldsymbol{k}]). \tag{3.27}$$

From the solubility condition for these equations we find

$$\omega^2 = v_A^2 k^2 \cos^2 \theta. \tag{3.28}$$

Thus the phase velocity of transverse magnetosonic waves is equal in magnitude to

$$v_{ph} = v_A \cos \theta. \tag{3.29}$$

For these waves the variable density component is $\varrho = 0$. The variable pressure and entropy components are also zero.

In order to obtain the expressions for the damping decrements of the waves in question the dissipative terms must be retained in eqns. (3.7–11).

For example the following expression is obtained for the damping decrement γ of a magnetohydrodynamic wave:

$$\gamma = \frac{\omega^2}{2v_A^2}\left(\frac{\mu}{M\varrho} + \frac{c^2}{4\pi\sigma}\right). \tag{3.30}$$

To conclude the present section we would remark that just as in the case of the gas-dynamics equations we can ask what the statistical foundation is of the magnetohydrodynamic equations for conducting gases, e.g. a plasma.

As a starting point we can take the appropriate kinetic equation for the distribution function of the charged particles in the plasma (see §§ 11, 15).

More can be learnt about the solution of the magnetohydrodynamic equations from other books (Landau and Lifshitz, 1960; Ginzburg, 1964; and Kulikovskii and Lyubimov, 1960).

The magnetohydrodynamic equations for a rarefied plasma (a "plasma without collisions") will be discussed in § 22.

CHAPTER II

Miscroscopic Equations for a Plasma. Averaging the Microscopic Equations

4. Microscopic Equations for a Plasma†

We now come to the discussion of the statistical theory of processes in a plasma.

A plasma is the name given to an ionized gas in which the total charge of the negatively charged particles is equal to the total charge of the positively charged particles. Thus a plasma as a whole is an electrically neutral system.

Neutral gas particles may also exist in a plasma alongside the charged particles, i.e. a plasma may be less than one hundred per cent ionized.

We shall mainly discuss the case when the plasma is a completely ionized gas and consists of two components: negatively charged particles (electrons) and positively charged ions.

We shall denote the charge of an electron by $e (e < 0)$. N_e is the total number of electrons in the plasma. The total charge of the negatively charged particles is eN_e.

We shall denote the charge of an ion by e_i. It may equal one or more electron charges. The ratio of an ion's charge to the electron's charge will be denoted by z. Then $e_i = z|e|$. Furthermore let N_i be the total number of ions in the plasma.

Using these notations the condition of electrical neutrality of the plasma can be written in the form

$$eN_e + e_i N_i = eN_e + z|e|N_i = 0. \tag{4.1}$$

Therefore $N_e = zN_i$.

† Klimontovich (1958a, b; 1960a, b).

We shall also use other notations which will permit considerable simplification in writing the other formulae.

We shall introduce the suffix a to denote whether one or another quantity belongs to a certain plasma component. Thus in the case of a two component electron–ion plasma the suffix takes the two values a = e for the electrons and a = i for the ions.

Using this suffix the electrical neutrality condition can be written in the form

$$\sum_a e_a N_a = 0. \tag{4.2}$$

Here e_a is the charge of a particle of a kind a and N_a is the total number of particles of the same kind.

N_a is normally very large so a plasma is a system consisting of a large number of charged particles.

What are the microscopic equations of motion for such a system?

In the case of a gas consisting of neutral particles the microscopic equations of motion of the gas particles are the system of Hamiltonian equations for all the particles in the system

$$\dot{\boldsymbol{q}}_i = \frac{\partial H}{\partial \boldsymbol{p}_i}, \quad \dot{\boldsymbol{p}}_i = -\frac{\partial H}{\partial \boldsymbol{q}_i}, \qquad (i = 1, 2, \ldots N). \tag{4.3}$$

For example, for a single-component gas when there are no external fields the Hamiltonian function is of the form

$$H = \sum_{1 \leqslant i \leqslant N} \frac{\boldsymbol{p}_i^2}{2m} + \frac{1}{2} \sum_{\substack{1 \leqslant i, j \leqslant N \\ i \neq j}} \Phi(|\boldsymbol{q}_i - \boldsymbol{q}_j|). \tag{4.4}$$

The microscopic state of a gas is defined at a given point in time if the coordinates and momenta of all the system's particles are known. The number of independent variables in this case is $6N$.

The time variation of the state of the system, i.e. the variation of the coordinates and momenta of the system's particles, is defined by the Hamiltonian equations.

For a plasma the situation is more complicated since it consists of charged particles so there are always electrical and magnetic field strengths present in it.

The state of a plasma is defined if as well as the coordinates and momenta of all the charged particles the values of the electrical and magnetic field strengths at each point are also known at a given time.

It follows from this that the microscopic equations for a plasma are a system of equations for all the coordinates and momenta of the charged particles and eqations for the electrical and magnetic fields strengths.

In order to write this system of equations we shall first assume that at a given point in time we know the values of the electrical and magnetic field strengths at each point. We shall denote them $\boldsymbol{E}^{\mathrm{M}}(\boldsymbol{q}, t)$, $\boldsymbol{H}^{\mathrm{M}}(\boldsymbol{q}, t)$.

The index M indicates that we are taking $\boldsymbol{E}^{\mathrm{M}}$, $\boldsymbol{H}^{\mathrm{M}}$ as the precise microscopic values of the electrical and magnetic field strengths as opposed to the averaged values which we were dealing with when studying the Maxwell equations.

If $\boldsymbol{q}_{ai}$ is a coordinate of the ith particle of kind a and $\boldsymbol{v}_{ai}$ its velocity, then the force acting on this particle at a point in time t is defined by the expression

$$\boldsymbol{F}_{ai} = e_a \boldsymbol{E}^{\mathrm{M}}(\boldsymbol{q}_{ai}, t) + \frac{e_a}{c}\left[\boldsymbol{v}_{ai} \wedge \boldsymbol{H}^{\mathrm{M}}(\boldsymbol{q}_{ai}, t)\right]. \tag{4.5}$$

The first term in this expression is the magnitude of the force acting on a charged particle in the electrical field and the second term the force in the magnetic field.

Using expression (4.5) we can write the equation of motion for an "ai" particle:

$$\frac{d\boldsymbol{p}_{ai}}{dt} = \boldsymbol{F}(\boldsymbol{q}_{ai}, t), \quad \boldsymbol{p}_{ai} = m_a \boldsymbol{v}_{ai}. \tag{4.6}$$

Here m_a is the mass of a particle of kind a.

The system of eqns. (4.6) is not closed since the field strengths $\boldsymbol{E}^{\mathrm{M}}$, $\boldsymbol{H}^{\mathrm{M}}$ themselves depend on the coordinates and momenta of the plasma particles. In order to obtain a closed system of equations we have still to write the equations for the field strengths.

Before doing this we note that instead of the system of eqn. (4.5) it is convenient to discuss the equations for the charged particle densities in a six-dimensional phase space which we define as follows:

$$N_a(\boldsymbol{q}, \boldsymbol{p}, t) = \sum_{1 \leqslant i \leqslant N_a} \delta(\boldsymbol{q} - \boldsymbol{q}_{ai}(t))\, \delta(\boldsymbol{p} - \boldsymbol{p}_{ai}(t)). \quad (4.7)$$

With this approach the microscopic state of a plasma at time t will be defined if we know the values of the phase densities $N_a(\boldsymbol{q}, \boldsymbol{p}, t)$ at all points of the six-dimensional phase space and the values of the microscopic strengths of the electrical $\boldsymbol{E}^{\mathrm{M}}(\boldsymbol{q}, t)$ and magnetic $\boldsymbol{H}^{\mathrm{M}}(\boldsymbol{q}, t)$ fields.

Remembering the property of the δ-function $\int_a^b \delta(x - x')\, dx = 1$, if $a \leqslant x' \leqslant b$, we see that $N_a(\boldsymbol{q}, \boldsymbol{p}, t)\, d^3\boldsymbol{q}\, d^3\boldsymbol{p}$ is equal to the number of particles of a kind a whose coordinates and momenta at a point in time t lie around the values of $\boldsymbol{q}, \boldsymbol{p}$ in the range $d^3\boldsymbol{q}\, d^3\boldsymbol{p}$. From the definition of the function $N_a(\boldsymbol{q}, \boldsymbol{p}, t)$ it also follows that

$$\int N_a(\boldsymbol{q}, \boldsymbol{p}, t)\, d^3\boldsymbol{q}\, d^3\boldsymbol{p} = N_a, \quad (4.8)$$

where N_a is the total number of particles of kind a.

We can find the equations for the functions $N_a(\boldsymbol{p}, \boldsymbol{q}, t)$ from the condition

$$\frac{dN_a(\boldsymbol{q}, \boldsymbol{p}, t)}{dt} = \frac{\partial N_a}{\partial t} + \left(\boldsymbol{v} \cdot \frac{\partial N_a}{\partial \boldsymbol{q}}\right) + \left(\dot{\boldsymbol{p}} \cdot \frac{\partial N_a}{\partial \boldsymbol{p}}\right) = 0, \quad (4.9)$$

which is a consequence of the continuity equation in phase space.

Assuming that the variation of the momentum $\boldsymbol{p}$ in a six-dimensional space $\boldsymbol{q}, \boldsymbol{p}$ is defined by a formula similar to (4.5, 6) we obtain the following equation:

$$\frac{\partial N_a}{\partial t} + \left(\boldsymbol{v} \cdot \frac{\partial N_a}{\partial \boldsymbol{q}}\right) + e_a \left(\left\{\boldsymbol{E}^{\mathrm{M}}(\boldsymbol{q}, t) + \frac{1}{c}[\boldsymbol{v} \wedge \boldsymbol{H}^{\mathrm{M}}(\boldsymbol{q}, t)]\right\} \cdot \frac{\partial N_a}{\partial \boldsymbol{p}}\right) = 0, \quad (4.10)$$

where $\boldsymbol{v} = \boldsymbol{p}/m_a$.

For the sake of simplicity we shall omit the arguments of the functions $N_a(\boldsymbol{q}, \boldsymbol{p}, t)$ in those cases when this leads to no difficulties.

Using the functions N_a we can write the expressions for the microscopic density of the charge ϱ_a^{M} and the current density $\boldsymbol{j}_a$ of the component a in the following form:

$$\varrho_a^{\mathrm{M}}(\boldsymbol{q}, t) = \sum_{1 \leq i \leq N_a} e_a \delta(\boldsymbol{q} - \boldsymbol{q}_{ai}(t)) = e_a \int N_a(\boldsymbol{q}, \boldsymbol{p}, t)\, d^3\boldsymbol{p}, \tag{4.11}$$

$$\boldsymbol{j}_a^{\mathrm{M}}(\boldsymbol{q}, t) = \sum_{1 \leq i \leq N_a} e\, v_{ai} \delta(\boldsymbol{q} - \boldsymbol{q}_{ai}(t))$$

$$= e_a \int \frac{\boldsymbol{p}}{m_a} N_a(\boldsymbol{q}, \boldsymbol{p}, t)\, d^3\boldsymbol{p}. \tag{4.12}$$

To derive the equations for the microscopic strengths of the electrical and magnetic fields we note that the Maxwell equations in form (I) hold, as experiment shows, not only for the mean values $\boldsymbol{E} = \overline{\boldsymbol{E}^{\mathrm{M}}}$, $\boldsymbol{B} = \overline{\boldsymbol{H}^{\mathrm{M}}}$, $\boldsymbol{j} = \overline{\boldsymbol{j}^{\mathrm{M}}}$, $\varrho = \overline{\varrho^{\mathrm{M}}}$ but also for the actual functions $\boldsymbol{E}^{\mathrm{M}}$, $\boldsymbol{H}^{\mathrm{M}}$, ϱ^{M}, $\boldsymbol{j}^{\mathrm{M}}$.

Using formulae (4.11, 12) and remembering that the total charge and current densities in a plasma are

$$\varrho = \sum_a \varrho_a; \quad \boldsymbol{j} = \sum_a \boldsymbol{j}_a, \tag{4.13}$$

we can write the microscopic equations for the electrical and magnetic field strengths

$$\operatorname{curl} \boldsymbol{H}^{\mathrm{M}} = \frac{1}{c}\frac{\partial \boldsymbol{E}^{\mathrm{M}}}{\partial t} + \frac{4\pi}{c}\sum_a e_a \int \boldsymbol{v} N_a(\boldsymbol{q}, \boldsymbol{p}, t)\, d^3\boldsymbol{p}, \tag{4.14}$$

$$\operatorname{curl} \boldsymbol{E}^{\mathrm{M}} = -\frac{1}{c}\frac{\partial \boldsymbol{H}^{\mathrm{M}}}{\partial t}, \tag{4.15}$$

$$\operatorname{div} \boldsymbol{H}^{\mathrm{M}} = 0. \tag{4.16}$$

$$\operatorname{div} \boldsymbol{E}^{\mathrm{M}} = 4\pi \sum_a e_a \int N_a(\boldsymbol{q}, \boldsymbol{p}, t)\, d^3\boldsymbol{p}. \tag{4.17}$$

These equations are often called the Lorentz system of equations.

The system of eqns. (4.10, 14–16) composes the closed system of microscopic equations for a plasma.

Instead of the equations for the functions $\boldsymbol{E}^{\mathrm{M}}$, $\boldsymbol{H}^{\mathrm{M}}$ we can use the equations for the microscopic potentials $\boldsymbol{A}^{\mathrm{M}}$, φ^{M}. In this case

$$\boldsymbol{H}^{\mathrm{M}} = \operatorname{curl} \boldsymbol{A}^{\mathrm{M}}, \quad \boldsymbol{E}^{\mathrm{M}} = -\operatorname{grad} \varphi^{\mathrm{M}} - \frac{1}{c} \cdot \frac{\partial \boldsymbol{A}^{\mathrm{M}}}{\partial t}. \tag{4.18}$$

The arbitrary feature in the selection of the potentials permits us to impose an additional relation between them.

It is very important that even in the case of a plasma conditions are possible in which the state of the system at the point in time t can be characterized approximately by giving only the coordinates and momenta of the system's charged particles at the same time.

This is possible if, in the first place, the strengths of the rotational electrical field and the magnetic field in the plasma are low; in the second place, if the temperature of the plasma is such that the mean thermal velocity of the particles is much less than the velocity of light. (When there are no external fields the first condition is a consequence of the second.)

In this case the magnetic field strength, which is proportional to the ratio v/c, is low. The rotational component of the electrical field strength is also low. This follows from eqn. (4.15). It may therefore be assumed that approximately the magnetic field is zero and the electrical field is purely potential, i.e.

$$\boldsymbol{E}^{\mathrm{M}} = -\operatorname{grad} \varphi^{\mathrm{M}}, \quad \operatorname{curl} \boldsymbol{E}^{\mathrm{M}} = 0, \tag{4.19}$$

The equation for φ^{M} is of the form

$$-\operatorname{div} \boldsymbol{E}^{\mathrm{M}} = \nabla^2 \varphi = -4\pi \sum_a e_a \int N_a(\boldsymbol{q}, \boldsymbol{p}, t)\, d^3\boldsymbol{p}, \tag{4.20}$$

whilst the equations for the functions N_a are simplified and become

$$\frac{\partial N_a}{\partial t} + \left(\boldsymbol{v} \cdot \frac{\partial N_a}{\partial \boldsymbol{q}}\right) + e_a \left(\boldsymbol{E}^{\mathrm{M}} \cdot \frac{\partial N_a}{\partial \boldsymbol{p}}\right) = 0 \tag{4.21}$$

and together with eqns. (4.19, 20) make up a closed system of equations for the functions N_a, $\boldsymbol{E}^{\mathrm{M}}$. Solving eqn. (4.20) we find the expression for the potential

$$\varphi^{\mathrm{M}}(\boldsymbol{q}, t) = \sum_b e_b \int \frac{N_b(\boldsymbol{q}', \boldsymbol{p}', t)}{|\boldsymbol{q}-\boldsymbol{q}'|} d^3\boldsymbol{p}'\, d^3\boldsymbol{q}', \tag{4.22}$$

where a is replaced by b.

It follows from this solution that the potential φ^{M} and thus also the electrical field strength at a point in time t are fully defined by giving the coordinates and momenta of the particles at the same point in time. Therefore by using the solution (4.22) we can eliminate the potential from eqns. (4.21) and obtain closed microscopic equations only for the functions $N_a(\boldsymbol{q}, \boldsymbol{p}, t)$

$$\frac{\partial N_a}{\partial t} + \left(\boldsymbol{v}\cdot\frac{\partial N_a}{\partial \boldsymbol{q}}\right) - \sum_b e_a e_b \left(\int \frac{\partial}{\partial \boldsymbol{q}} \frac{1}{|\boldsymbol{q}-\boldsymbol{q}'|} N_b(\boldsymbol{q}', \boldsymbol{p}', t)\, d^3\boldsymbol{p}'\, d^3\boldsymbol{q}'\cdot\frac{\partial N_a}{\partial \boldsymbol{p}}\right) = 0. \tag{4.23}$$

In the case of a two-component electron–ion plasma, eqns. (4.23) are a system of two equations for the functions $N_{\mathrm{e}}(\boldsymbol{q}, \boldsymbol{p}, t)$, $N_{\mathrm{i}}(\boldsymbol{q}, \boldsymbol{p}, t)$ (the phase densities of the electrons and the ions).

Lastly, an even simpler case is possible when the microscopic state of a plasma can be defined by giving the coordinates and momenta of only the electrons.

This is because the mass of an electron m_{e} is much less than the mass of ion m_{i} so when discussing rapidly varying processes we can ignore the displacement of the ions and consider that they are evenly distributed through the whole plasma.

We use $n_{\mathrm{i}} = N_{\mathrm{i}}/V$ to denote the density of the evenly distributed ions. If $z = 1$, then $e_{\mathrm{i}} = |e|$.

Of eqns. (4.23) one equation remains in this approximation for the phase density of the electrons N_{e} since we consider the ion distribution to be given. This equation is of the form

$$\frac{\partial N_{\mathrm{e}}}{\partial t} + \left(\boldsymbol{v}\cdot\frac{\partial N_{\mathrm{e}}}{\partial \boldsymbol{q}}\right) - \left(\int \frac{\partial}{\partial \boldsymbol{q}} \frac{e^2}{|\boldsymbol{q}-\boldsymbol{q}'|} \left\{\int N_{\mathrm{e}}(\boldsymbol{q}', \boldsymbol{p}', t)\, d\boldsymbol{p}' - n_{\mathrm{i}}\right\} d^3\boldsymbol{q}'\cdot\frac{\partial N_{\mathrm{e}}}{\partial \boldsymbol{p}}\right) = 0. \tag{4.24}$$

Equation (4.24) can also act as the initial microscopic equation for describing the processes in a plasma when the ion distribution can be considered to be given.

We can now write the microscopic equations for a relativistic plasma when the particle velocities are so high that the dependence of the mass of the particles on the velocity has to be allowed for.

The quantity

$$N_a(\boldsymbol{q}, \boldsymbol{p}, t)\, d^3\boldsymbol{q}\, d^3\boldsymbol{p} \tag{4.25}$$

defines the number of particles of the component a in the volume $d^3\boldsymbol{q}\, d^3\boldsymbol{p}$ and is an invariant under Lorentz transformations.

An element of the six-dimensional phase volume $d^3\boldsymbol{q}\, d^3\boldsymbol{p}$ remains unchanged during a Lorentz transformation so the function $N_a(\boldsymbol{q}, \boldsymbol{p}, t)$ also remains unchanged (for more detail, see Klimontovich, 1960a, 1960b; and Landau and Lifshitz, 1962).

The system of eqns. (4.10, 14–17) is also invariant under Lorentz transformations if the connexion between the momentum and velocity in it can be defined by the relation

$$\boldsymbol{p} = m_a \gamma \boldsymbol{v}, \quad \gamma = \frac{1}{\sqrt{(1 - v^2/c^2)}}. \tag{4.26}$$

Instead of the functions $N_a(\boldsymbol{q}, \boldsymbol{p}, t)$ we can use functions of eight variables: the four-dimensional vector $q_i(\boldsymbol{q}, ict)$ and the four-dimensional vector $p_i(\boldsymbol{p}, i\varepsilon/c)$, where ε is the energy of a particle.

We can define these functions as follows:

$$N_a(q_i, p_i) = \sum_{1 \le l \le N_a} \frac{1}{\gamma_l}\, \delta(\boldsymbol{q} - \boldsymbol{q}_l(t))\, \delta(p_i - p_{i(l)}(t)), \tag{4.27}$$

$$\delta(p_i - p_{i(l)}(t)) = \delta(\boldsymbol{p} - \boldsymbol{p}_l(t))\, \delta(\varepsilon - \varepsilon_l(t)).$$

In this definition the expression

$$N_a(q_i, p_i)\, \gamma\, d^3\boldsymbol{q}\, d^3\boldsymbol{p}\, d\varepsilon \tag{4.28}$$

is the number of particles of kind a whose world lines intersect an element of the hypersurface orientated along the time axis, and whose momenta lie in the range $d^3\boldsymbol{p}\, d\varepsilon$ around p_i.

The expression (4.28) can be written in the explicitly relativistically invariant form proposed by R. L. Stratonovich

$$N_a(q_i, p_i) = \sum_{1\leq l\leq N_a} \int \delta(q_i - q_{i(l)}(s_l))\, \delta(p_i - p_{i(l)}(s_l))\, ds_l. \tag{4.29}$$

Here s_l is the eigentime of a particle with a number l.

Instead of the system of eqns. (4.10, 14–17) in this description we must use the system of equations for the functions $N_a(q_i, p_i)$ and the electromagnetic tensor F^{M}_{ik} whose components are the microscopic field strengths $\boldsymbol{E}^{\mathrm{M}}, \boldsymbol{H}^{\mathrm{M}}$.

This system of equations is as follows:

$$U_i \frac{\partial}{\partial q_i} N_a(q_i, p_i) + \frac{e_a}{c} F^{\mathrm{M}}_{ik} U_k \frac{\partial}{\partial p_i} N_a(q_i, p_i) = 0. \tag{4.30}$$

$$\frac{\partial F^{\mathrm{M}}_{ik}}{\partial q_k} = 4\pi \sum_a e_a \int U_i N_a(q_i, p_i)\, d^3\boldsymbol{p}\, d\varepsilon, \tag{4.31}$$

$$\frac{\partial F^{\mathrm{M}}_{ik}}{\partial q_l} + \frac{\partial F^{\mathrm{M}}_{kl}}{\partial q_i} + \frac{\partial F^{\mathrm{M}}_{li}}{\partial q_k} = 0, \quad (i, k, l = 1, 2, 3, 4), \tag{4.32}$$

where $U_i(\gamma\boldsymbol{v}, ic\gamma)$ is the four-dimensional velocity.

The relativistic invariance of eqns. (4.30–32) is self-evident.

The microscopic equations for a plasma can be obtained from a variational principle.

It is well known (see, for example, Landau and Lifshitz, 1962) that the expression for the action S of a system of charged particles can be written in the form

$$S = \sum_a \sum_{1\leq l\leq N_a} \left\{ -m_a c \int \sqrt{(-U^2_{i(l)})}\, ds_l + \frac{e_a}{c} \int A^{\mathrm{M}}_i U_{i(l)}\, ds_l + \frac{i}{16\pi c} \int F^{\mathrm{M}^2}_{ik}\, d^4q, \right. \tag{4.33}$$

where $A_i(\boldsymbol{A}, i\varphi)$ is the four-dimensional potential.

Using the functions (4.27, 29) and remembering that $ds = dt/\gamma$ we can write expression (4.33) in the form

$$S = \sum_a \int \left\{ -m_a c \sqrt{(-U^2_i)} + \frac{e_a}{c} A^{\mathrm{M}}_i U_i \right\} \times N_a(q_i, p_i)\, d^3\boldsymbol{q}\, d^3\boldsymbol{p}\, dt\, d\varepsilon + \frac{i}{16\pi c} \int F^{\mathrm{M}^2}_{ik}\, d^4q. \tag{4.34}$$

We find the equations of motion of particles of kind a from (4.34) as follows:

$$P_i = \frac{\partial}{\partial U_i} \cdot \frac{\delta S}{\delta N_a(q_i, p_i)} = p_i + \frac{e_a}{c} A_i^{\mathrm{M}}, \tag{4.35}$$

$$\frac{dP_i}{ds} = \frac{\partial}{\partial q_i} \cdot \frac{\delta S}{\delta N_a(q_i, p_i)} = \frac{e_a}{c} \cdot \frac{\partial}{\partial q_i}(A_k^{\mathrm{M}} U_k). \tag{4.36}$$

Remembering that

$$\frac{dA_i^{\mathrm{M}}}{ds} = U_k \frac{\partial A_i^{\mathrm{M}}}{\partial q_k}; \qquad \frac{\partial}{\partial q_i}(A_k^{\mathrm{M}} U_k) = U_k \frac{\partial A_i^{\mathrm{M}}}{\partial q_k} + F_{ik}^{\mathrm{M}} U_k, \tag{4.37}$$

we can write the equation of motion of a particle of the kind a in the usual form

$$m_a \frac{dU_i}{ds} = \frac{e_a}{c} F_{ik}^{\mathrm{M}} U_k. \tag{4.38}$$

Using the last equation we obtain the expression (4.30) for the function $N_a(q_i, p_i)$. We obtain the equations for F_{ij}^{M} by the usual method (Landau and Lifshitz, 1962), carrying out variation with respect to A_i^{M}.

5. Averaging the Microscopic Equations for a Plasma

It is very difficult to make direct use of the microscopic equations for a plasma, just as in the case of a gas, because of their extreme complexity. We shall therefore proceed to a discussion of the averaging of the microscopic equations (see Klimontovich, 1958a, b; 1960a, b).

We shall start with the simplest case when the microscopic state of the plasma at a certain time t is completely defined by giving the coordinates and momenta of the plasma's charged particles.

In this approximation we can proceed from the system of eqns. (4.23) for the phase densities

$$\frac{\partial N_a}{\partial t}+\left(\boldsymbol{v}\cdot\frac{\partial N_a}{\partial \boldsymbol{q}}\right)-\sum_b e_a e_b$$
$$\times\left(\int\frac{\partial}{\partial \boldsymbol{q}}\frac{1}{|\boldsymbol{q}-\boldsymbol{q}'|}N_b(\boldsymbol{q}',\boldsymbol{p}',t)\,d^3q'\,d^3p'\cdot\frac{\partial N_a}{\partial \boldsymbol{p}}\right)=0. \tag{5.1}$$

We remember that $N_a(\boldsymbol{q}, \boldsymbol{p}, t)$ is a dynamic function of the coordinates $\boldsymbol{q}_{ai}$ and the momenta $\boldsymbol{p}_{ai}$ of all the charged particles of the kind a and is defined by the expression

$$N_a(\boldsymbol{q}, \boldsymbol{p}, t)=\sum_{1\leqslant i\leqslant N_a}\delta(\boldsymbol{q}-\boldsymbol{q}_{ai}(t))\,\delta(\boldsymbol{p}-\boldsymbol{p}_{ai}(t)), \tag{5.2}$$

where N_a is the total number of particles of the kind a.

Since the microscopic state in this approximation is defined by giving the coordinates and momenta of the particles, the statistical properties of such a system are given fully by the distribution function f_N of the coordinates and momenta of all the $N=\sum_a N_a$ particles in the system. This function is introduced so that the expression $f_N\prod_a d^3\boldsymbol{q}_{a1}\ldots d^3\boldsymbol{q}_{aN_a}d^3\boldsymbol{p}_{a1}\ldots d^3\boldsymbol{p}_{aN_a}$ defines the probability that at a time t the coordinates and momenta of the particles of the kind a have the values $\boldsymbol{q}_{a1},\ldots,\boldsymbol{q}_{aN_a},\boldsymbol{p}_{a1},\ldots,\boldsymbol{p}_{aN_a}$ in the ranges $d^3\boldsymbol{q}_{a1},\ldots,d^3\boldsymbol{q}_{aN_a},d^3\boldsymbol{p}_{a1},\ldots,d^3\boldsymbol{p}_{aN_a}$.

We shall use the symbol $\boldsymbol{x}_{ai}$ to denote the combination of the coordinates $\boldsymbol{q}_{ai}, \boldsymbol{p}_{ai}$ of a particle of kind a. The letter $\boldsymbol{x}$ without a suffix is the combination of the coordinates and momenta $\boldsymbol{q}, \boldsymbol{p}$ of a point in a six-dimensional phase space.

Therefore

$$\boldsymbol{x}_{ai}=(\boldsymbol{q}_{ai}, \boldsymbol{p}_{ai}),\quad \boldsymbol{x}=(\boldsymbol{q}, \boldsymbol{p}). \tag{5.3}$$

With these notations the expressions for function (5.2) become

$$N_a(\boldsymbol{x}, t)=\sum_{1\leqslant i\leqslant N_a}\delta(\boldsymbol{x}-\boldsymbol{x}_{ai}(t)). \tag{5.4}$$

Using the distribution function f_N we can find the mean value of the phase density $N_a(\boldsymbol{x}, t)$.

We denote statistical averaging by a bar on top. Since the particles of one kind are identical

$$\overline{N_a}(\boldsymbol{x}, t) = \int \sum_{1 \leqslant i \leqslant N_a} \delta(\boldsymbol{x}-\boldsymbol{x}_{ai}) f_N \prod_a d^6\boldsymbol{x}_{a1} \dots d^6\boldsymbol{x}_{a_{N_a}}$$
$$= N_a \int \delta(\boldsymbol{x}-\boldsymbol{x}_{a1}) f_N \prod_a d^6\boldsymbol{x}_{a1} \dots d^6\boldsymbol{x}_{a_{N_a}}. \tag{5.5}$$

We define the distribution function of one particle of kind a:

$$f_a(\boldsymbol{x}_{a1}, t) = V \int f_N \, d^6\boldsymbol{x}_{a2} \dots d^6\boldsymbol{x}_{a_{N_a}} \prod_{b \neq a} d^6\boldsymbol{x}_{b1} \dots d^6\boldsymbol{x}_{b_{N_b}}, \tag{5.6}$$

where V is the volume of the particle. Using this function the expression (5.5) can be written in the form

$$\overline{N_a}(\boldsymbol{q}, \boldsymbol{p}, t) = n_a f_a(\boldsymbol{q}, \boldsymbol{p}, t). \tag{5.7}$$

Here n_a is the mean concentration of particles of the kind a.

In a similar way we can connect the mean value of the products of the phase densities N_a, N_b, N_c, . . ., at different points in a phase space with the distribution functions.

Splitting the double sum

$$\sum_{1 \leqslant i \leqslant N_a} \sum_{1 \leqslant j \leqslant N_b} \delta(\boldsymbol{x}-\boldsymbol{x}_{ai}) \, \delta(\boldsymbol{x}'-\boldsymbol{x}_{bj})$$

into the two parts

$$\sum_{1 \leqslant i \leqslant N_a} \sum_{\substack{1 \leqslant j \leqslant N_b \\ \boldsymbol{x}_{ai} \neq \boldsymbol{x}_{bj} \text{ when } a=b}} \delta(\boldsymbol{x}-\boldsymbol{x}_{ai}) \, \delta(\boldsymbol{x}'-\boldsymbol{x}_{bj})$$
$$+ \delta_{ab} \sum_{1 \leqslant i \leqslant N_a} \delta(\boldsymbol{x}-\boldsymbol{x}_{ai}) \delta(\boldsymbol{x}-\boldsymbol{x}'),$$

we obtain, neglecting unity when compared with N_a, the following expression for the mean value of the product of the two functions

$$\overline{N_a(\boldsymbol{x}, t) N_b(\boldsymbol{x}', t)} = n_a n_b f_{ab}(\boldsymbol{x}, \boldsymbol{x}' \, t)$$
$$+ \delta_{ab} n_a \delta(\boldsymbol{x}-\boldsymbol{x}') f_a(\boldsymbol{x}, t), \tag{5.8}$$

where f_{ab} is the distribution function of two particles of kinds a and b. In terms of f_N it is defined as

$$f_{ab}(\boldsymbol{x}_{1a}, \boldsymbol{x}_{1b}, t) = V^2 \int f_N \, d^6\boldsymbol{x}_{a2} \ldots d^6\boldsymbol{x}_{aN_a} \, d^6\boldsymbol{x}_{b2} \ldots \ldots d^6\boldsymbol{x}_{bN_b} \prod_{c \neq a,\, b} d^6\boldsymbol{x}_{c1} \ldots d^6\boldsymbol{x}_{cN} \, . \tag{5.9}$$

Likewise we obtain

$$\begin{aligned}\overline{N_a(\boldsymbol{x}, t) N_b(\boldsymbol{x}', t) N_c(\boldsymbol{x}'', t)} &= n_a n_b n_c f_{abc}(\boldsymbol{x}, \boldsymbol{x}', \boldsymbol{x}'', t) \\ &+ \delta_{ab} n_a n_c \delta(\boldsymbol{x}-\boldsymbol{x}') f_{ac}(\boldsymbol{x}, \boldsymbol{x}'', t) \\ &+ \delta_{ac} n_a n_b \delta(\boldsymbol{x}-\boldsymbol{x}'') f_{ab}(\boldsymbol{x}, \boldsymbol{x}', t) \\ &+ \delta_{bc} n_a n_c \delta(\boldsymbol{x}'-\boldsymbol{x}'') f_{ac}(\boldsymbol{x}, \boldsymbol{x}'', t) \\ &+ \delta_{ab} \delta_{bc} \delta(\boldsymbol{x}-\boldsymbol{x}') \, \delta(\boldsymbol{x}'-\boldsymbol{x}'') f_a(\boldsymbol{x}, t)\end{aligned} \tag{5.10}$$

and so on.

Apart from the distribution functions use is made below of the correlation functions $g_{ab}(\boldsymbol{x}, \boldsymbol{x}', t)$ of two, $g_{abc}(\boldsymbol{x}, \boldsymbol{x}', \boldsymbol{x}'', t)$ of three . . ., particles.

The second and third correlation functions are defined by the formulae

$$f_{ab}(\boldsymbol{x}, \boldsymbol{x}', t) = f_a(\boldsymbol{x}, t) f_b(\boldsymbol{x}', t) + g_{ab}(\boldsymbol{x}, \boldsymbol{x}', t), \tag{5.11}$$

$$\begin{aligned}f_{abc}(\boldsymbol{x}, \boldsymbol{x}', \boldsymbol{x}'', t) &= f_a(\boldsymbol{x}, t) f_b(\boldsymbol{x}', t) f_c(\boldsymbol{x}'', t) \\ &+ f_a(\boldsymbol{x}, t) \, g_{bc}(\boldsymbol{x}', \boldsymbol{x}'', t) \\ &+ f_b(\boldsymbol{x}', t) \, g_{ac}(\boldsymbol{x}, \boldsymbol{x}'', t) \\ &+ f_c(\boldsymbol{x}'', t) \, g_{ab}(\boldsymbol{x}, \boldsymbol{x}', t) \\ &+ g_{abc}(\boldsymbol{x}, \boldsymbol{x}', \boldsymbol{x}'', t).\end{aligned} \tag{5.12}$$

It is sufficient to know the first and second distribution functions f_a, f_{ab} in order to determine the thermodynamic functions, the fluctuations and the gas-dynamics functions.

It follows from the formulae (5.7, 8) that the functions f_a, f_{ab} can be expressed in terms of the first $\overline{N_a(\boldsymbol{x}, t)}$ and second $\overline{N_a(\boldsymbol{x}, t) \, N_b(\boldsymbol{x}', t)}$ simultaneous moments of the random functions.

We obtain the equations for the moments of the function $N_a(\boldsymbol{x}, t)$.

Direct averaging of eqns. (4.23) gives the equations for the first moments

$$\frac{\partial \overline{N_a}}{\partial t}+\left(\boldsymbol{v}\cdot\frac{\partial \overline{N_a}}{\partial \boldsymbol{q}}\right)-\left(\sum_b\int\frac{\partial}{\partial \boldsymbol{q}}\frac{e_a e_b}{|\boldsymbol{q}-\boldsymbol{q}'|}\cdot\frac{\partial}{\partial \boldsymbol{p}}\overline{N_b(\boldsymbol{q}',\boldsymbol{p}',t)N_a(\boldsymbol{q},\boldsymbol{p},t)}\,d^3\boldsymbol{q}'\,d^3\boldsymbol{p}'\right)=0. \tag{5.13}$$

This system of equations is not closed since it contains the second moments as well as the first.

Equation (5.13) can conveniently be written in a different form, using

$$\delta N_a(\boldsymbol{q},\boldsymbol{p},t)=N_a(\boldsymbol{q},\boldsymbol{p},t)-\overline{N_a(\boldsymbol{q},\boldsymbol{p},t)} \tag{5.14}$$

to denote the deviation of the random function N_a from its mean.

At the same time as using the moments of the function N_a we shall use the central moments $\overline{\delta N_a\,\delta N_b}$, $\overline{\delta N_a\,\delta N_b\,\delta N_c}$, etc.

It follows from definition (5.14) that

$$\overline{N_a(\boldsymbol{x},t)N_b(\boldsymbol{x}',t)}=\overline{N_a}(\boldsymbol{x},t)\overline{N_b}(\boldsymbol{x}',t)+\overline{\delta N_a(\boldsymbol{x},t)\,\delta N_b(\boldsymbol{x}',t)}. \tag{5.15}$$

From formulae (5.8, 11, 15) we obtain the connexion between the function $\overline{\delta N_a\,\delta N_b}$ and g_{ab}

$$\overline{\delta N_a(\boldsymbol{x},t)\,\delta N_b(\boldsymbol{x}',t)}=n_a n_b g_{ab}(\boldsymbol{x},\boldsymbol{x}',t)+\delta_{ab}\delta(\boldsymbol{x}-\boldsymbol{x}')n_a f_a. \tag{5.16}$$

Taking into account that $\overline{N_a}=n_a f_a$, and using (5.15) and (5.13), the resulting equation for the first distribution function f_a is:

$$\begin{aligned}\frac{\partial f_a}{\partial t}&+\left(\boldsymbol{v}\cdot\frac{\partial f_a}{\partial \boldsymbol{q}}\right)-\sum_b n_b\left(\frac{\partial}{\partial \boldsymbol{q}}\int\frac{e_a e_b}{|\boldsymbol{q}-\boldsymbol{q}'|}f_b(\boldsymbol{q}',\boldsymbol{p}',t)\,d^3\boldsymbol{q}'\,d^3\boldsymbol{p}'\cdot\frac{\partial f_a}{\partial \boldsymbol{p}}\right)\\&=\frac{1}{n_a}\sum_b\int\left(\frac{\partial}{\partial \boldsymbol{q}}\frac{e_a e_b}{|\boldsymbol{q}-\boldsymbol{q}'|}\cdot\frac{\partial}{\partial \boldsymbol{p}}\overline{\delta N_a(\boldsymbol{q},\boldsymbol{p},t)\,\delta N_b(\boldsymbol{q}',\boldsymbol{p}',t)}\right)d^3\boldsymbol{q}'\,d^3\boldsymbol{p}'\\&\equiv S_a(\boldsymbol{q},\boldsymbol{p},t).\end{aligned} \tag{5.17}$$

The equations for the functions f_a contain the second central moments $\overline{\delta N_a\,\delta N_b}$. $S_a(\boldsymbol{q}, \boldsymbol{p}, t)$ is the notation for the right-hand side of eqn. (5.17).

If we use formula (5.16) and remember that the integral

$$\int \frac{\partial}{\partial \boldsymbol{q}} \frac{1}{|\boldsymbol{q}-\boldsymbol{q}'|}\,\delta(\boldsymbol{q}-\boldsymbol{q}')\,d^3\boldsymbol{q}' = 0,$$

then the right-hand side of eqn. (5.17) can be expressed in terms of the correlation functions g_{ab}

$$S_a(\boldsymbol{q}, \boldsymbol{p}, t) = \sum_b n_b \int \left(\frac{\partial}{\partial \boldsymbol{q}} \frac{e_a e_b}{|\boldsymbol{q}-\boldsymbol{q}'|} \cdot \frac{\partial}{\partial \boldsymbol{p}} g_{ab}(\boldsymbol{q}, \boldsymbol{p}, \boldsymbol{q}', \boldsymbol{p}', t)\right) d^3\boldsymbol{q}'\,d^3\boldsymbol{p}'. \tag{5.18}$$

Thus we must use the functions $\overline{\delta N_a\,\delta N_b}$ or the functions g_{ab} to define the first distribution functions f_a.

Before doing this we shall write eqn. (5.17) in a more convenient form, noting that, in accordance with formula (4.22), the expression

$$\begin{aligned}\boldsymbol{E}^{\mathrm{M}} &= -\operatorname{grad}\varphi^{\mathrm{M}} \\ &= -\frac{\partial}{\partial \boldsymbol{q}} \sum_b e_b \int \frac{1}{|\boldsymbol{q}-\boldsymbol{q}'|} N_b(\boldsymbol{q}', \boldsymbol{p}', t)\,d^3\boldsymbol{q}'\,d^3\boldsymbol{p}'\end{aligned} \tag{5.19}$$

defines the microscopic strength of a longitudinal electrical field in a plasma.

Denoting the deviation of the field from the mean by

$$\delta\boldsymbol{E}(\boldsymbol{q}, t) = \boldsymbol{E}^{\mathrm{M}}(\boldsymbol{q}, t) - \boldsymbol{E}(\boldsymbol{q}, t), \tag{5.20}$$

we write eqn. (5.17) in the form

$$\begin{aligned}&\frac{\partial f_a}{\partial t} + \left(\boldsymbol{v}\cdot\frac{\partial f_a}{\partial \boldsymbol{q}}\right) + e_a\left(\boldsymbol{E}\cdot\frac{\partial f_a}{\partial \boldsymbol{p}}\right) = -\frac{e_a}{n_a}\left(\frac{\partial}{\partial \boldsymbol{p}}\cdot\overline{\delta N_a\,\delta\boldsymbol{E}}\right) \\ &\equiv S_a(\boldsymbol{q}, \boldsymbol{p}, t); \\ &\operatorname{div}\boldsymbol{E} = 4\pi\sum_a e_a n_a \int f_a\,d^3\boldsymbol{p}; \quad \operatorname{curl}\boldsymbol{E} = 0.\end{aligned} \tag{5.21}$$

Therefore to find the functions f_a we must know the correlation $\overline{\delta N_a(\boldsymbol{q}, \boldsymbol{p}, t)\,\delta\boldsymbol{E}(\boldsymbol{q}, t)}$.

In order to find the equation for the function $\overline{\delta N_a\, \delta N_b}$ contained in eqn. (5.17) we first examine the equations for the functions δN_a, $\delta \boldsymbol{E}$.

From eqns. (4.21), (5.21), remembering that $\overline{\boldsymbol{E}^{\mathrm{M}} N_a} = \boldsymbol{E}\overline{N}_a + \overline{\delta \boldsymbol{E}}\, \overline{N}_a + \boldsymbol{E}\delta N_a + \overline{\delta \boldsymbol{E} \delta N_a}$ and $\overline{N}_a = n_a f_a$, we obtain the equation for δN_a

$$\frac{\partial \delta N_a}{\partial t} + \left(\boldsymbol{v} \cdot \frac{\partial \delta N_a}{\partial \boldsymbol{q}}\right) + e_a n_a \left(\delta \boldsymbol{E} \cdot \frac{\partial f_a}{\partial \boldsymbol{p}}\right) + e_a \left(\boldsymbol{E} \cdot \frac{\partial \delta N_a}{\partial \boldsymbol{p}}\right)$$
$$+ e_a \left(\frac{\partial}{\partial \boldsymbol{p}} \cdot (\delta \boldsymbol{E} \delta N_a - \overline{\delta \boldsymbol{E} \delta N_a})\right) = 0. \qquad (5.22)$$

We obtain the equation for $\delta \boldsymbol{E}$ by subtracting the second eqn. (5.21) from eqn. (4.20)

$$\operatorname{div} \delta \boldsymbol{E} = 4\pi \sum_a e_a \int \delta N_a\, d^3\boldsymbol{p}, \quad \operatorname{curl} \delta \boldsymbol{E} = 0. \qquad (5.23)$$

It is now easy to obtain the equations for the second moments.

The most general simultaneous second moment for the case under discussion is

$$\overline{\delta N_a(\boldsymbol{q}, \boldsymbol{p}, t)\, \delta N_b(\boldsymbol{q}', \boldsymbol{p}', t)}. \qquad (5.24)$$

If this function is known, we can find the expressions for the simpler functions, e.g.

$$\overline{\delta N_a(\boldsymbol{q}, \boldsymbol{p}, t)\, \delta \boldsymbol{E}(\boldsymbol{q}', t)}, \quad \overline{(\delta \boldsymbol{E}(\boldsymbol{q}, t) \cdot \delta \boldsymbol{E}(\boldsymbol{q}', t))} \quad \text{etc.}$$

In order to obtain the equation for the function (5.24) we notice that

$$\frac{\partial}{\partial t} \overline{\delta N_a(\boldsymbol{x}, t)\, \delta N_b(\boldsymbol{x}', t)}$$
$$= \overline{\frac{\partial \delta N_a(\boldsymbol{x}, t)}{\partial t} \cdot \delta N_b(\boldsymbol{x}', t) + \delta N_a(\boldsymbol{x}, t) \frac{\partial \delta N_b(\boldsymbol{x}', t)}{\partial t}}.$$

In this we substitute the derivative $\partial\, \delta N_a / \partial t$ from eqn. (5.22) and the derivative $\partial \delta N_b / \partial t$ from the corresponding equation for the function $\delta N_b(\boldsymbol{q}', \boldsymbol{p}', t)$ [it is obtained from (5.22) by making the substitutions $a \to b$; $\boldsymbol{q}, \boldsymbol{p} \to \boldsymbol{q}', \boldsymbol{p}'$] to obtain the unknown equation. This equation is not closed either since the means of three products such as, e.g. $\overline{\delta N_a \delta N_b \delta \boldsymbol{E}}$, will appear in it.

Thus the third moments appear in the equations for the second moments. In the same way we find that the fourth moments appear in the equations for the third and so on, i.e. we obtain a chain of coupled equations.

Using the connexion between the distribution functions f_a, f_{ab}, etc., and the central moments we can obtain a corresponding chain of equations for the distribution functions $f_{ab}, f_{abc}, \ldots,$ or a chain of equations for the functions f_a and the correlation functions $g_{ab}, g_{abc}, \ldots.$

The solution of these chains of equations is just as complicated as the precise solution of the original microscopic equations. Therefore, just as in the kinetic theory of gases, the question arises of the possibility of breaking the chain of equations and obtaining closed equations for a small number of the first moments.

In the case of rarefied gases the possibility of breaking the chain of equations for the functions f_a, g_{ab}, g_{abc} is based on the following. The radius r_0 of the sphere of action of the molecular forces in the gases is small ($r_0 \sim 10^{-8}$–10^{-7} cm). Therefore in rarefied gases the simultaneous approach to a distance of the order of r_0 of three or more molecules is a rare occurrence. This permits us to neglect the triple correlation functions g_{abc} and use a closed system of equations for the functions f_a, g_{ab}.

With certain assumptions it is possible to find a solution of the equations for the functions g_{ab} which is independent of the initial values of the functions g_{ab} and is wholly determined by the form of the first distribution functions f_a.

After substituting this solution in the equations for f_a we obtain a closed system of equations for the first distribution functions f_a—the Boltzmann system of kinetic equations.

In the case of a plasma it is also possible to break the chain of equations for the moments or distribution functions. The possibility of this cut-off is, however, conditioned by other causes. The interaction of the charged particles in a plasma proceeds according to Coulomb's law, so it decreases comparatively slowly as the distance between them increases. In the case of gases the effective radius of the sphere of action is the same in order of magnitude as the radius of the molecule. We shall see below that the quantity determining the effective radius of action of the charged particles in a plasma is the so-called Debye radius r_d, which can be defined by the formula

$$\frac{1}{r_d^2} = \sum_a \frac{4\pi e_a^2 n_a}{\varkappa T_a}, \tag{5.25}$$

where T_a, n_a are the temperature and concentration of particles of the component a and $\varkappa$ is the Boltzmann constant.

Let us estimate the magnitude of the Debye radius and compare it with the radius of action of the molecular forces in a gas.

We shall take the following characteristic data for the plasma parameters: $n_a = 10^{10}$ cm^{-3}, $T_a = 3\times 10^4$ degrees. Such values occur, for example, in the positive column of a glow discharge.

Remembering that $|e| \approx 5\times 10^{-10}$ esu, $\varkappa = 1{\cdot}4\times 10^{-16}$ erg/degree, we obtain $r_d \approx 10^{-2}$ cm.

Under these conditions the mean distance between charged particles is $r_{av} \approx 5\times 10^{-4}$ cm. Therefore $r_{av} \ll r_d$, i.e. in a plasma the radius of the sphere of action may be considerably greater than the mean distance between the particles, whilst in a rarefied gas, on the other hand, $r_0 \ll r_{av}$.

We introduce for a plasma the non-dimensional parameter

$$\varepsilon = \frac{r_{av}^3}{r_d^3}. \tag{5.26}$$

The quantity $1/\varepsilon$ is proportional to the number of particles in a sphere with radius r_d. For the example discussed above $\varepsilon \ll 1$. This means that there is a very large number of particles in a sphere of radius r_d. We shall use this fact.

We introduce a physically infinitely small volume dV_{ph} such that

$$r_{av}^3 \ll dV_{ph} \leqslant r_d^3. \tag{5.27}$$

This is possible if $\varepsilon \ll 1$.

It may then be expected that the central moments $\overline{\delta N_a \, \delta N_b}$ and the correlation functions g_{ab} will be small when compared with $\overline{N}_a \overline{N}_b$ and f_a, f_b respectively. This assumption is confirmed by the solution obtained below of the equations for the correlation functions.

The expressions (5.11), (5.15) in this case can be written in the form

$$f_{ab}(\boldsymbol{x}, \boldsymbol{x}', t) = f_a(\boldsymbol{x}, t) f_b(\boldsymbol{x}', t) + \varepsilon g_{ab}(\boldsymbol{x}, \boldsymbol{x}', t), \tag{5.28}$$

$$\overline{N_a(\boldsymbol{x}, t) N_b(\boldsymbol{x}', t)} = \bar{N}_a(\boldsymbol{x}, t) \bar{N}_b(\boldsymbol{x}', t) + \varepsilon \overline{\delta N_a(\boldsymbol{x}, t)\, \delta N_b(\boldsymbol{x}', t)}. \tag{5.29}$$

It can therefore be assumed under the above conditions that the second distribution function deviates only a little from the product of the first distribution functions.

In its turn the third distribution function differs little from the product of the first functions

$$f_{abc}(\boldsymbol{x}, \boldsymbol{x}', \boldsymbol{x}'', t) = f_a f_b f_c + \varepsilon(g_{ab} f_c + g_{ac} f_b + g_{bc} f_a) + \varepsilon^2 g_{abc}, \tag{5.30}$$

where g_{abc} is a triple correlation function of the order of ε^2.

Accordingly, the expression for $\overline{N_a N_b N_c}$ contains, if we substitute in it $N_a = \bar{N}_a + \delta N_a$, the mean of the triple deviations $\overline{\delta N_a\, \delta N_b\, \delta N_c}$, likewise of the order of ε^2.

By dropping the terms proportional to ε^2 we can obtain a closed system of equations for the first and second moments or for the functions f_a, g_{ab}.

We notice that in this approximation we can omit in eqn. (5.22) the non-linear terms $\delta \boldsymbol{E} \delta N_a$, $\overline{\delta \boldsymbol{E} \delta N_a}$ since it is they that lead to the appearance of the third moments in the equations for the second moments.

As a result in the "second moments approximation" we obtain the following system of equations for the functions δN_a, $\delta \boldsymbol{E}$:

$$\frac{\partial \delta N_a}{\partial t} + \left(\boldsymbol{v} \cdot \frac{\partial \delta N_a}{\partial \boldsymbol{q}}\right) + e_a \left(\boldsymbol{E} \cdot \frac{\partial \delta N_a}{\partial \boldsymbol{p}}\right) + e_a n_a \left(\delta \boldsymbol{E} \cdot \frac{\partial f_a}{\partial \boldsymbol{p}}\right) = 0, \tag{5.31}$$

$$\operatorname{div} \delta \boldsymbol{E} = 4\pi \sum_b e_b \int \delta N_b \, d^3\boldsymbol{p}, \quad \operatorname{curl} \delta \boldsymbol{E} = 0.$$

From the next two equations we find

$$\delta \boldsymbol{E} = -\sum_b e_b \frac{\partial}{\partial \boldsymbol{q}} \int \frac{\delta N_b(\boldsymbol{q}', \boldsymbol{p}', t)}{|\boldsymbol{q} - \boldsymbol{q}'|} d^3\boldsymbol{q}' \, d^3\boldsymbol{p}'. \tag{5.32}$$

Using this expression the system of eqns. (5.31) can be written in the form

$$\frac{\partial \delta N_a}{\partial t} + \left(\boldsymbol{v} \cdot \frac{\partial \delta N_a}{\partial \boldsymbol{q}}\right) + e_a \left(\boldsymbol{E} \cdot \frac{\partial \delta N_a}{\partial \boldsymbol{p}}\right)$$
$$- n_a \sum_b \left(\frac{\partial}{\partial \boldsymbol{q}} \int \frac{e_a e_b}{|\boldsymbol{q}-\boldsymbol{q}'|} \, \delta N_b(\boldsymbol{q}', \boldsymbol{p}', t) \, d^3q' \, d^3p' \cdot \frac{\partial f_a}{\partial \boldsymbol{p}}\right)$$
$$= 0. \tag{5.33}$$

We multiply the first equation of (5.31) by $\delta N_b(\boldsymbol{q}', \boldsymbol{p}', t)$ and the corresponding equation for the function $\delta N_b(\boldsymbol{q}', \boldsymbol{p}', t)$, by $\delta N_a(\boldsymbol{q}, \boldsymbol{p}, t)$, add the two equations and average. As a result we obtain for the function $\overline{\delta N_a(\boldsymbol{q}, \boldsymbol{p}, t) \, \delta N_b(\boldsymbol{q}', \boldsymbol{p}', t)}$:

$$\left[\frac{\partial}{\partial t} + \left(\boldsymbol{v} \cdot \frac{\partial}{\partial \boldsymbol{q}}\right) + \left(\boldsymbol{v}' \cdot \frac{\partial}{\partial \boldsymbol{q}'}\right)\right] \overline{\delta N_a \delta N_b}$$
$$+ \left[e_a \left(\boldsymbol{E} \cdot \frac{\partial}{\partial \boldsymbol{p}}\right) + e_b \left(\boldsymbol{E} \cdot \frac{\partial}{\partial \boldsymbol{p}'}\right)\right] \overline{\delta N_a \delta N_b}$$
$$+ e_a n_a \left(\overline{\delta \boldsymbol{E}(\boldsymbol{q}, t) \, \delta N_b} \cdot \frac{\partial f_a}{\partial \boldsymbol{p}}\right)$$
$$+ e_b n_b \left(\overline{\delta N_a \, \delta \boldsymbol{E}(\boldsymbol{q}', t)} \cdot \frac{\partial f_b}{\partial \boldsymbol{p}'}\right) = 0. \tag{5.34}$$

Using formula (5.32) we can express the functions $\overline{\delta \boldsymbol{E} \delta N_b}$, $\overline{\delta N_a \, \delta \boldsymbol{E}}$ in terms of $\overline{\delta N_a \, \delta N_b}$.

The system of eqns. (5.17, 34) [or (5.21, 34)] is a closed system of equations for the first and second moments.

Instead of eqns. (5.34) we can use the equations for the correlation functions g_{ab}. Using formula (5.16) and the equation for f_a we obtain

$$\left(\frac{\partial}{\partial t} + \left(\boldsymbol{v} \cdot \frac{\partial}{\partial \boldsymbol{q}}\right) + \left(\boldsymbol{v}' \cdot \frac{\partial}{\partial \boldsymbol{q}'}\right)\right) g_{ab}$$
$$+ \left(e_a \left(\boldsymbol{E} \cdot \frac{\partial}{\partial \boldsymbol{p}}\right) + e_b \left(\boldsymbol{E} \cdot \frac{\partial}{\partial \boldsymbol{p}'}\right)\right) g_{ab}$$

$$-\sum_c n_c\left(\frac{\partial}{\partial \boldsymbol{q}}\int\frac{e_a e_c}{|\boldsymbol{q}-\boldsymbol{q}''|}g_{cb}\,d^3\boldsymbol{q}''\,d^3\boldsymbol{p}''\cdot\frac{\partial f_a}{\partial \boldsymbol{p}}\right)$$

$$-\sum_c n_c\left(\frac{\partial}{\partial \boldsymbol{q}'}\int\frac{e_b e_c}{|\boldsymbol{q}'-\boldsymbol{q}''|}g_{ac}\,d^3\boldsymbol{q}''\,d^3\boldsymbol{p}''\cdot\frac{\partial f_b}{\partial \boldsymbol{p}'}\right)$$

$$=\left(\frac{\partial}{\partial \boldsymbol{q}}\frac{e_a e_b}{|\boldsymbol{q}-\boldsymbol{q}'|}\cdot\left\{\frac{\partial f_a}{\partial \boldsymbol{p}}f_b-\frac{\partial f_b}{\partial \boldsymbol{p}'}f_a\right\}\right). \tag{5.35}$$

Equations (5.35) and (5.17) with the right-hand side of (5.18) also make up a closed system of equations for the functions f_a, g_{ab}.

We must bear in mind that the set of equations (5.34, 35) is not completely equivalent: while in eqn. (5.34) we neglected the third central moments, in eqn. (5.35) the ternary correlation functions are neglected.

Let us lastly discuss the most general case when for the characteristic of the microscopic state of a plasma we have to know not only the coordinates and momenta of the plasma's charged particles but also the strengths of the electrical and magnetic fields. In this case we can proceed from eqns. (4.10) for the functions $N_a(\boldsymbol{q}, \boldsymbol{p}, t)$ and eqns. (4.14–17) for the microscopic field strengths $\boldsymbol{E}^{\mathrm{M}}$, $\boldsymbol{H}^{\mathrm{M}}$.

Averaging these equations we obtain

$$\frac{\partial \overline{N}_a}{\partial t}+\left(\boldsymbol{v}\cdot\frac{\partial \overline{N}_a}{\partial \boldsymbol{p}}\right)$$
$$+e_a\overline{\left(\left\{\boldsymbol{E}^{\mathrm{M}}(\boldsymbol{q},t)+\frac{1}{c}\left[\boldsymbol{v}\wedge\boldsymbol{H}^{\mathrm{M}}(\boldsymbol{q},t)\right]\right\}\cdot\frac{\partial N_a}{\partial \boldsymbol{p}}\right)}=0, \tag{5.36}$$

$$\operatorname{curl}\boldsymbol{B}=\frac{1}{c}\frac{\partial \boldsymbol{E}}{\partial t}+\frac{4\pi}{c}\sum_a e_a\int \boldsymbol{v}N_a(\boldsymbol{q},\boldsymbol{p},t)\,d^3\boldsymbol{p}, \tag{5.37}$$

$$\operatorname{curl}\boldsymbol{E}=-\frac{1}{c}\frac{\partial \boldsymbol{B}}{\partial t}, \tag{5.38}$$

$$\operatorname{div}\boldsymbol{B}=0. \tag{5.39}$$

$$\operatorname{div}\boldsymbol{E}=4\pi\sum_a e_a\int \overline{N_a}(\boldsymbol{q},\boldsymbol{p},t)\,d^3\boldsymbol{p}. \tag{5.40}$$

Here $\boldsymbol{E} = \overline{\boldsymbol{E}^{\mathrm{M}}}, \boldsymbol{E} = \overline{\boldsymbol{H}^{\mathrm{M}}}$ are the mean values of the electrical and magnetic field strengths.

The system of averaged eqns. (5.36–40) is not closed since the averages of the product of the functions N_a and the microscopic field strengths $\boldsymbol{E}^{\mathrm{M}}, \boldsymbol{H}^{\mathrm{M}}$ are in it as well as the mean values of the functions $N_a, \boldsymbol{E}^{\mathrm{M}}, \boldsymbol{H}^{\mathrm{M}}$.

Thus we also have a coupled chain of equations for the moments here as well.

In the second moments approximation we obtain from (4.10, 14–17), (5.36–40) the following system of equations for the random deviations:

$$\delta N_a, \quad \delta \boldsymbol{E}, \quad \delta \boldsymbol{B} = \boldsymbol{H}^{\mathrm{M}} - \boldsymbol{B};$$

$$\frac{\partial \delta N_a}{\partial t} + \left(\boldsymbol{v} \cdot \frac{\partial \delta N_a}{\partial \boldsymbol{q}}\right) + e_a \left(\left\{\boldsymbol{E} + \frac{1}{c}\,[\boldsymbol{v} \wedge \boldsymbol{B}]\right\} \cdot \frac{\partial \delta N_a}{\partial \boldsymbol{p}}\right)$$

$$+ e_a n_a \left(\left\{\delta \boldsymbol{E} + \frac{1}{c}\,[\boldsymbol{v} \wedge \delta \boldsymbol{B}]\right\} \cdot \frac{\partial f_a}{\partial \boldsymbol{p}}\right) = 0. \quad (5.41)$$

$$\operatorname{curl} \delta \boldsymbol{B} = \frac{1}{c} \cdot \frac{\partial \delta \boldsymbol{E}}{\partial t} + \frac{4\pi}{c} \sum_a e_a \int \boldsymbol{v}\, \delta N_a \, d^3\boldsymbol{p}, \quad \operatorname{div} \delta \boldsymbol{B} = 0; \quad (5.42)$$

$$\operatorname{curl} \delta \boldsymbol{E} = -\frac{1}{c} \cdot \frac{\partial \delta \boldsymbol{B}}{\partial t}, \quad \operatorname{div} \delta \boldsymbol{E} = 4\pi \sum_a e_a \int \delta N_a \, d^3\boldsymbol{p}. \quad (5.43)$$

These equations permit us to obtain the equations for the second moments.

CHAPTER III

Equations with a Self-consistent Field—Vlasov Equations

6. Kinetic Equations for a Plasma in the Self-consistent Field Approximation

For an electron-ion plasma, just as for a gas, we can introduce the concept of the relaxation time τ_r—the time taken to establish statistical equilibrium. This quantity is different for the electrons and the ions. For the time being it is important that the relaxation time and the corresponding length for the electrons are in order of magnitude

$$\tau_r \sim \frac{1}{\omega_L \varepsilon}, \quad \lambda_r \sim \frac{r_d}{\varepsilon} = \frac{V_T}{\omega_L \varepsilon} = V_T \tau_r, \tag{6.1}$$

where ε is a quantity which is inversely proportional to the number of charged particles in a sphere with the Debye radius (defined by formula (5.27)) and ω_L is the frequency of the plasma oscillations. In a rarefied plasma the quantity ε is small so the relaxation time is considerably longer than the period of the plasma oscillations and the relaxation length is far greater than the Debye radius.

If the characteristic times T of a process in a plasma, e.g. the period of the oscillations in the plasma, the oscillation damping time or the time of flight of charged particles through the plasma, are much less than the relaxation time and likewise the characteristic linear dimension L is much less than the relaxation length, i.e.

$$T \ll \tau_r, \quad L \ll \lambda_r, \tag{6.2}$$

then the equations given in the preceding section can be considerably simplified. In actual fact, the first two terms in the left-hand side of eqn. (5.17) are in order of magnitude equal to f_a/T.

It is shown in § 11 that the term on the right-hand side of eqn. (5.17) is in order of magnitude equal to f_a/τ_r, so that when the conditions (6.2) are satisfied in the zero approximation with respect to the parameter T/τ_r we can neglect the term on the right-hand side of eqn. (5.17). As a result we obtain the following equation

$$\frac{\partial f_a}{\partial t}+\left(\boldsymbol{v}\cdot\frac{\partial f_a}{\partial \boldsymbol{q}}\right)-\sum_b n_b \times\left(\frac{\partial}{\partial \boldsymbol{q}}\int\frac{e_a e_b}{|\boldsymbol{q}-\boldsymbol{q}'|}f_b(\boldsymbol{q}',\boldsymbol{p}',t)\,d^3q'\,d^3p'\cdot\frac{\partial f_a}{\partial \boldsymbol{p}}\right)=0. \quad (6.3)$$

If instead of eqn. (5.17) we use the system of equations (5.21), then in the zero approximation with respect to T/τ_r we obtain a system of equations for the functions f_a, $\boldsymbol{E}$

$$\frac{\partial f_a}{\partial t}+\left(\boldsymbol{v}\cdot\frac{\partial f_a}{\partial \boldsymbol{q}}\right)+e_a\left(\boldsymbol{E}\cdot\frac{\partial f_a}{\partial \boldsymbol{p}}\right)=0;$$

$$\operatorname{div}\boldsymbol{E}=4\pi\sum_a e_a n_a\int f_a\,d^3p;\qquad \operatorname{curl}\boldsymbol{E}=0. \quad (6.4)$$

Equations (6.3, 4) are called equations with a self-consistent field.

It is important to stress that the equations with a self-consistent field are obtained from the corresponding chains of equations for the moments of the functions N_a or the equations for f_a, g_{ab}, g_{abc}, if the higher moments (starting with the second) or all the correlation functions g_{ab}, g_{abc}, . . ., in them are completely neglected.

This means that instead of the formulae (5.11, 12, 15) in the self-consistent field approximation

$$f_{ab}(\boldsymbol{x},\boldsymbol{x}',t)=f_a(\boldsymbol{x},t)f_b(\boldsymbol{x}',t);\qquad f_{abc}=f_af_bf_c,$$
$$\overline{N_a(\boldsymbol{x},t)N_b(\boldsymbol{x}',t)}=\overline{N_a}(\boldsymbol{x},t)\overline{N_b}(\boldsymbol{x}',t)\quad\text{etc.} \quad (6.5)$$

In other words, the approximation leading to the equations with a self-consistent field is based on the assumption of the complete independence of the phase densities at different points in six-dimensional phase space.

Equations (6.3, 4) relate to the case when we can neglect the transverse electromagnetic field.

In the general case the system of equations in the self-consistent field approximation can be obtained from the system of eqns. (5.36–40) if we neglect the correlation between the values of the phase densities and the microscopic strengths of the electrical and magnetic fields, i.e.

$$\overline{N_a \boldsymbol{E}^{\mathrm{M}}} = \bar{N}_a \boldsymbol{E} = n_a f_a \boldsymbol{E}, \tag{6.6}$$

$$\overline{N_b \boldsymbol{H}^{\mathrm{M}}} = \bar{N}_a \boldsymbol{B} = n_a f_a \boldsymbol{B}. \tag{6.7}$$

As a result we obtain the following system of self-consistent equations for the functions f_a and the average electrical and magnetic field strengths:

$$\frac{\partial f_a}{\partial t} + \left(\boldsymbol{v}\cdot\frac{\partial f_a}{\partial \boldsymbol{q}}\right) + e_a\left(\left\{\boldsymbol{E}(\boldsymbol{q}, t) + \frac{1}{c}[\boldsymbol{v}\wedge \boldsymbol{B}(\boldsymbol{q}, t)]\right\}\cdot\frac{\partial f_a}{\partial \boldsymbol{p}}\right) = 0, \tag{6.8}$$

$$\operatorname{curl} \boldsymbol{B} = \frac{1}{c}\frac{\partial \boldsymbol{E}}{\partial t} + \frac{4\pi}{c}\sum_a e_a n_a \int \boldsymbol{v} f_a(\boldsymbol{q}, \boldsymbol{p}, t)\, d^3\boldsymbol{p}, \tag{6.9}$$

$$\operatorname{curl} \boldsymbol{E} = -\frac{1}{c}\frac{\partial \boldsymbol{B}}{\partial t}, \tag{6.10}$$

$$\operatorname{div} \boldsymbol{B} = 0, \tag{6.11}$$

$$\operatorname{div} \boldsymbol{E} = 4\pi \sum_a e_a n_a \int f_a(\boldsymbol{q}, \boldsymbol{p}, t)\, d^3\boldsymbol{p}. \tag{6.12}$$

The system of equations with a self-consistent field for a plasma was first studied by Vlasov (1938, 1950) and it is called the Vlasov system of equations after him.

Equations (6.8–12) are still valid in the relativistic case, provided that $\boldsymbol{p} = m_a \gamma \boldsymbol{v}$.

Let us examine the conservation laws for a system of equations with a self-consistent field.

We use the definition of the density ϱ_a and the mean velocity $\boldsymbol{U}_a$ of the component a

$$\varrho_a(\boldsymbol{q}, t) = n_a \int f_a \, d^3\boldsymbol{p}; \qquad \boldsymbol{U}_a(\boldsymbol{q}, t) = \frac{n_a}{\varrho_a} \int \boldsymbol{v} f_a \, d^3\boldsymbol{p}, \tag{6.13}$$

where $n_a = N_a/V$ is the mean number of particles of the component a per unit volume.

We integrate eqn. (6.8) over $\boldsymbol{p}$ and sum over a. Remembering that

$$f_a(\boldsymbol{q}, \boldsymbol{p}, t) = 0 \quad \text{when} \quad p_i = \pm\infty \qquad (i = 1, 2, 3) \tag{6.14}$$

and

$$\left([\boldsymbol{v} \wedge \boldsymbol{B}] \cdot \frac{\partial f_a}{\partial \boldsymbol{p}}\right) = \left(\frac{\partial}{\partial \boldsymbol{p}} \cdot [\boldsymbol{v} \wedge \boldsymbol{B}] f_a\right), \quad \text{since}$$

$$\left(\frac{\partial}{\partial \boldsymbol{p}} \cdot [\boldsymbol{v} \wedge \boldsymbol{B}]\right) = 0, \tag{6.15}$$

we obtain the equation

$$\frac{\partial \sum\limits_a \varrho_a}{\partial t} + \frac{\partial \sum\limits_a \varrho_a \boldsymbol{U}_a}{\partial \boldsymbol{q}} = 0. \tag{6.16}$$

We proceed as follows in order to obtain the equation that expresses the law of conservation of momentum.

We multiply eqn. (6.8) by $n_a \boldsymbol{p} = n_a m_a \boldsymbol{v}$, integrate over $\boldsymbol{p}$ and sum over a.

In accordance with (6.13)

$$\sum_a m_a n_a \int \boldsymbol{v} f_a \, d^3\boldsymbol{p} = \sum_a m_a \varrho_a \boldsymbol{U}_a \tag{6.17}$$

is the total momentum density of the plasma particles.

We introduce the following notation for the tensor of the momentum flux density:

$$\Pi_{ij} = \sum_a m_a n_a \int v_i v_j f_a \, d^3\boldsymbol{p}. \tag{6.18}$$

From this we split off the part determined by the average velocity

$$\Pi_{ij} = \sum_a m_a \varrho_a U_i^a U_j^a + P_{ij}. \tag{6.19}$$

The stress tensor P_{ij} is defined by the expression

$$P_{ij} = \sum_a P_{ij}^a = \sum_a m_a n_a \int \delta v_i \, \delta v_j f_a \, d^3\boldsymbol{p}, \tag{6.20}$$

where $\delta v_i = v_i - U_i^a$ is the deviation of the ith component of the velocity from its mean.

Finally, we use the notation for the electric charge density

$$\varrho_{\text{el}} = \sum_a e_a n_a \int f_a \, d^3\boldsymbol{p} \tag{6.21}$$

and the electric current density

$$\boldsymbol{j} = \sum_a e_a n_a \int \boldsymbol{v} f_a \, d^3\boldsymbol{p}. \tag{6.22}$$

Using these notations we obtain from eqn. (6.8), after multiplying by $n_a m_a v_i$, integrating over $\boldsymbol{p}$ and summing over a, the following equation:

$$\frac{\partial}{\partial t}\sum_a m_a \varrho_a U_i^a + \frac{\partial}{\partial q_j}\sum_a (m_a \varrho_a U_i^a U_j^a + P_{ij}^a) = \varrho_{\text{el}} E_i + \frac{1}{c}[\boldsymbol{j} \wedge \boldsymbol{B}]_i. \tag{6.23}$$

We transform the right-hand side of the equation. Using the Maxwell equations (6.9–12) we obtain

$$\begin{aligned} \varrho_{\text{el}}\boldsymbol{E} + \frac{1}{c}[\boldsymbol{j} \wedge \boldsymbol{B}] &= \frac{1}{4\pi}\operatorname{div}(\boldsymbol{E}\cdot\boldsymbol{E}) + \frac{1}{4\pi}[\operatorname{curl}\boldsymbol{B} \wedge \boldsymbol{B}] \\ &\quad - \frac{1}{4\pi c}\left[\frac{\partial \boldsymbol{E}}{\partial t} \wedge \boldsymbol{B}\right] = \frac{1}{4\pi}[\operatorname{div}(\boldsymbol{E}\cdot\boldsymbol{E}) + \operatorname{div}(\boldsymbol{B}\cdot\boldsymbol{B})] \\ &\quad + \frac{1}{4\pi}([\operatorname{curl}\boldsymbol{B} \wedge \boldsymbol{B}] + [\operatorname{curl}\boldsymbol{E} \wedge \boldsymbol{E}]) \\ &\quad - \frac{1}{4\pi c}\cdot\frac{\partial}{\partial t}[\boldsymbol{E} \wedge \boldsymbol{B}], \end{aligned} \tag{6.24}$$

where the zero term $\operatorname{div}\boldsymbol{B} = 0$ is added.

We make use of the vector identity

$$A_x \operatorname{div} \boldsymbol{A}+[\operatorname{curl} \boldsymbol{A}\wedge\boldsymbol{A}]_x = \frac{\partial\left(A_x^2-\frac{1}{2}A^2\right)}{\partial q_x}+\frac{\partial A_xA_y}{\partial q_y}+\frac{\partial A_xA_z}{\partial q_z}.$$

Then, by putting $A_i = E_i+B_i$, we can write the expression (6.24) in the form

$$\varrho_{\text{el}}E_i+\frac{1}{c}[\boldsymbol{j}\wedge\boldsymbol{B}]_i = -\frac{1}{4\pi c}\cdot\frac{\partial}{\partial t}[\boldsymbol{E}\wedge\boldsymbol{B}]_i-\frac{\partial T_{ij}}{\partial q_j}. \tag{6.25}$$

The tensor T_{ij} is defined by the expression

$$T_{ij} = -\frac{1}{4\pi}\left(E_iE_j+B_iB_j-\delta_{ij}\frac{E^2+B^2}{2}\right) \tag{6.26}$$

and is called the electromagnetic stress tensor (or the Maxwell stress tensor).

Using the relations (6.25) we can write eqn. (6.23) in the form

$$\frac{\partial}{\partial t}\left\{\sum_a n_a\varrho_aU_i^a+\frac{1}{4\pi c}[\boldsymbol{E}\wedge\boldsymbol{B}]_i\right\}= -\frac{\partial}{\partial q_i}\{\Pi_{ij}+T_{ij}\}. \tag{6.27}$$

It expresses the law of conservation of the total momentum of a plasma. In fact, by integrating this equation with respect to the whole volume using Gauss's theorem, we obtain

$$\frac{\partial}{\partial t}\int\left\{\sum_a e_an_a U_i^a+\frac{1}{4\pi c}[\boldsymbol{E}\wedge\boldsymbol{B}]_i\right\}d^3\boldsymbol{q} = -\oint\{\Pi_{ij}+T_{ij}\}\,d^2s_j. \tag{6.28}$$

On the left-hand side is the variation in unit time of the ith component of the total plasma momentum

$$\boldsymbol{G} = \int\left\{\sum_a e_an_a\boldsymbol{U}_a+\frac{1}{4\pi c}[\boldsymbol{E}\wedge\boldsymbol{B}]\right\}d^3\boldsymbol{q}. \tag{6.29}$$

It consists of two parts: the momentum of the plasma's charged particles and the momentum of the electromagnetic field.

The right-hand side of eqn. (6.28) is the amount of total momentum "flowing out" per unit time through the surface bounding the plasma.

We shall call the tensor

$$\Pi_{ij}+T_{ij} \tag{6.30}$$

the total momentum flux density tensor.

In the case of a closed system the right-hand side of eqn. (6.28) is equal to zero and the total momentum $\boldsymbol{G}$ remains constant, i.e.

$$\boldsymbol{G} = \int \left\{ \sum_a e_a n_a \boldsymbol{U}_a + \frac{1}{4\pi c}[\boldsymbol{E}\wedge\boldsymbol{B}] \right\} d^3\boldsymbol{q} = \text{const.} \tag{6.31}$$

If we take eqns. (6.4) as our starting point, which takes into account only the longitudinal electrical field $\boldsymbol{E}$, then instead of eqn. (6.27) we obtain

$$\frac{\partial}{\partial t}\sum_a e_a n_a U_i^a = -\frac{\partial}{\partial q_j}(\Pi_{ij}+T_{ij}^e). \tag{6.32}$$

Here

$$T_{ij}^e = -\frac{1}{4\pi}\left(E_i E_j - \delta_{ij}\frac{\boldsymbol{E}^2}{2}\right) \tag{6.33}$$

is the electrical stress tensor and the total momentum

$$\boldsymbol{G} = \int \sum_a e_a n_a \boldsymbol{U}^a \, d^3\boldsymbol{q} \tag{6.34}$$

is determined by the momenta of the plasma's charged particles.

Let us now examine the plasma energy balance equation.

We multiply eqn. (6.8) by $n_a \boldsymbol{p}^2/2m_a$, sum over a and integrate over $\boldsymbol{p}$.

In this case the first term in eqn. (6.8) becomes

$$\sum_a n_a \int \frac{\boldsymbol{p}^2}{2m_a} f_a \, d^3\boldsymbol{p}$$
$$= \sum_a \frac{m_a \varrho_a \boldsymbol{U}_a^2}{2} + \sum_a n_a m_a \int \frac{\delta v^2}{2} f_a \, d^3\boldsymbol{p}. \tag{6.35}$$

We now introduce the definition of the temperature of the component a plasma particles

$$\frac{3}{2}\varkappa T_a = \frac{n_a}{\varrho_a}\int \frac{m_a(\delta v)^2}{2} f_a \, d^3\boldsymbol{p}. \tag{6.36}$$

Using this definition we can write expression (6.35) in the form

$$\sum_a n_a \int \frac{\boldsymbol{p}^2}{2m_a} f_a \, d^3\boldsymbol{p} = \sum_a \frac{m_a \varrho_a \boldsymbol{U}_a^2}{2} + \frac{3}{2} \sum_a \varrho_a \varkappa T_a. \tag{6.37}$$

Thus the total kinetic energy of the charged particles consists of the kinetic energy determined by the mean velocities and the energy of random motion.

The expression

$$\sum_a n_a \int v_i \frac{\boldsymbol{p}^2}{2m_a} f_a \, d^3\boldsymbol{p} \tag{6.38}$$

defines the ith component of the flux vector for the kinetic energy of all the system's particles.

Remembering that the last term in eqn. (6.8) drops out in these transformations, since $(\boldsymbol{v} \cdot [\boldsymbol{v} \wedge \boldsymbol{B}]) = 0$, and using the definition (6.22) for the electric current density we obtain the equation

$$\frac{\partial}{\partial t} \sum_a n_a \int \frac{\boldsymbol{p}^2}{2m_a} f_a \, d^3\boldsymbol{p} = -\frac{\partial}{\partial q_i} \sum_a n_a \int v_i \frac{\boldsymbol{p}^2}{2m_a} f_a \, d^3\boldsymbol{p} + (\boldsymbol{j} \cdot \boldsymbol{E}). \tag{6.39}$$

We now use the Maxwell equations (6.9–12).

We form the scalar products of eqn. (6.9) and the vector $\boldsymbol{E}$, and of eqn. (6.10) and the vector $\boldsymbol{B}$. After doing this we subtract the second equation from the first and using the vector identity

$$\operatorname{div}[\boldsymbol{E} \wedge \boldsymbol{B}] = (\boldsymbol{B} \cdot \operatorname{curl} \boldsymbol{E}) - (\boldsymbol{E} \cdot \operatorname{curl} \boldsymbol{B}), \tag{6.40}$$

we write the result in the form

$$\frac{1}{8\pi} \frac{\partial}{\partial t} (E^2 + B^2) = -\frac{c}{4\pi} \operatorname{div} [\boldsymbol{E} \wedge \boldsymbol{B}] - (\boldsymbol{j} \cdot \boldsymbol{E}) \tag{6.41}$$

This is the energy balance equation of an electromagnetic field whose energy density is

$$W = \frac{1}{8\pi} (E^2 + B^2). \tag{6.42}$$

$$\boldsymbol{S} = \frac{c}{4\pi} [\boldsymbol{E} \wedge \boldsymbol{B}] \tag{6.43}$$

is the vector of the electromagnetic field energy flux (the Poynting vector).

The last term in eqns. (6.39, 41) $(\boldsymbol{j}\cdot\boldsymbol{E})$ describes the exchange of energy between the electromagnetic field and the charged particles of the plasma.

We eliminate this term from eqns. (6.39, 41). As a result we obtain the equation

$$\frac{\partial}{\partial t}\left\{\sum_a n_a \int \frac{p^2}{2m_a} f_a \, d^3\boldsymbol{p} + \frac{1}{8\pi}(E^2+B^2)\right\}$$
$$= -\operatorname{div}\left\{\sum_a n_a \int \boldsymbol{v}\frac{p^2}{2m_a} f_a \, d^3\boldsymbol{p} + \frac{c}{4\pi}[\boldsymbol{E}\wedge\boldsymbol{B}]\right\}. \tag{6.44}$$

The left-hand side of this equation expresses the change per unit time of the total energy of the charged particles and the electromagnetic field. The right-hand side defines the flux of the total energy of the particles and the field.

In the case of a closed system the total energy of the plasma is conserved, i.e.

$$\sum_a n_a \int \frac{p^2}{2m_a} f_a(\boldsymbol{q}, \boldsymbol{p}, t)\, d^3\boldsymbol{q}\, d^3\boldsymbol{p} + \frac{1}{8\pi}\int (E^2+B^2)\, d^3\boldsymbol{q} = \text{const.} \tag{6.45}$$

If we use eqns. (6.4) as the initial equations, then there are no terms containing the magnetic field strength $\boldsymbol{B}$ in eqns. (6.41, 44) or formula (6.45).

We shall show that in the self-consistent field approximation, i.e. in the case of complete neglect of the correlation, the entropy of all the plasma's charged particles remains unchanged if the system is closed.

This will mean that dissipative processes are not taken into consideration in the self-consistent field approximation.

In this sense the self-consistent field approximation is analogous to the "ideal liquid approximation" in hydrodynamics.

We can define the total entropy of the charged particles by the expression

$$S(t) = -\varkappa \sum_a n_a \int f_a \ln f_a \, d^3\boldsymbol{q}\, d^3\boldsymbol{p}. \tag{6.46}$$

We multiply eqn. (6.8) by $-\varkappa n_a \ln f_a$, sum over a and integrate over $\boldsymbol{p}$ and $\boldsymbol{q}$.

We take into consideration the fact that

$$\sum_a n_a \int \ln f_a \frac{\partial f_a}{\partial t} \, d^3\boldsymbol{q} \, d^3\boldsymbol{p} = \frac{\partial}{\partial t} \sum_a n_a \int f_a \ln f_a \, d^3\boldsymbol{q} \, d^3\boldsymbol{p}$$

$$- \sum_a n_a \int f_a \frac{\partial \ln f_a}{\partial t} \, d^3\boldsymbol{q} \, d^3\boldsymbol{p}. \tag{6.47}$$

The second term here is equal to zero since

$$\frac{\partial}{\partial t} \sum_a n_a \int f_a \, d^3\boldsymbol{q} \, d^3\boldsymbol{p} = \frac{\partial}{\partial t} \sum_a n_a = 0.$$

Integrating by parts, we obtain from the second term of eqn. (6.8)

$$\sum_a n_a \int \ln f_a \frac{\partial}{\partial q_i} v_i f_a \, d^3\boldsymbol{q} \, d^3\boldsymbol{p}$$

$$= \sum_a n_a \int \left\{ \frac{\partial}{\partial q_i} (v_i f_a \ln f_a) - \left(\boldsymbol{v} \cdot \frac{\partial f_a}{\partial \boldsymbol{q}} \right) \right\} d^3\boldsymbol{q} \, d^3\boldsymbol{p} = 0. \tag{6.48}$$

Finally, the last term of eqn. (6.8) gives

$$\sum_a e_a n_a \int \ln f_a \left(\frac{\partial}{\partial \boldsymbol{p}} \cdot \left\{ \left(\boldsymbol{E} + \frac{1}{c} [\boldsymbol{v} \wedge \boldsymbol{B}] f_a \right) \right\} \right) d^3\boldsymbol{p} \, d^3\boldsymbol{q}$$

$$= \sum_a e_a n_a \int \left(\frac{\partial}{\partial \boldsymbol{p}} \cdot \left\{ (f_a \ln f_a - f_a) \left(\boldsymbol{E} + \frac{1}{c} [\boldsymbol{v} \wedge \boldsymbol{B}] \right) \right\} \right) d^3\boldsymbol{q} d^3\boldsymbol{p}$$

$$= 0. \tag{6.49}$$

This expression vanishes since $f_a(\boldsymbol{q}, \boldsymbol{p}, t) = 0$ when any of the components of the momentum is equal to $\pm \infty$.

Using formulae (6.47–49) we obtain

$$\frac{dS(t)}{dt} = 0, \tag{6.50}$$

i.e. the total entropy of the plasma's charged particles remains constant provided that the whole system is closed.

Let us now take a look at the solution of the system of eqns. (6.8–12) in a linear approximation.

7. Solution for Self-consistent Equations for the Functions f_a, E, B in the Linear Approximation when there are no External Fields

The system of self-consistent equations for the functions f_a and the field strengths $\boldsymbol{E}$, $\boldsymbol{B}$ discussed in the previous section is a complex non-linear system of equations.

We can, however, immediately produce a special solution of this system of equations:

$$f_a(\boldsymbol{q}, \boldsymbol{p}, t) = f_a^0(|p|), \quad \boldsymbol{E} = 0, \quad \boldsymbol{B} = 0.$$

Here (we are omitting the suffix "el" of ϱ)

$$\varrho = 4\pi \sum e_a n_a \int f_a^0 \, d^3\boldsymbol{p} = 4\pi \sum_a e_a n_a = 0 \tag{7.1}$$

by virtue of the condition (4.2) for neutrality of the plasma, and

$$\boldsymbol{j} = 4\pi \sum_a e_a n_a \int \boldsymbol{v} f_a^0 \, d^3\boldsymbol{p} = 0 \tag{7.2}$$

because

$$f_a^0 = f_a(|p|).$$

Let us examine a solution which differs only a little from this special solution.

We shall assume that

$$f_a(\boldsymbol{q}, \boldsymbol{p}, t) = f_a^0(|p|) + f_a^1(\boldsymbol{q}, \boldsymbol{p}, t); \quad f_a^1 \ll f_a^0, \tag{7.3}$$

$$\boldsymbol{E} = \boldsymbol{E}^1, \quad \boldsymbol{B} = \boldsymbol{B}^1, \tag{7.4}$$

and consider that the functions f_a^1, $\boldsymbol{E}^1$, $\boldsymbol{B}^1$ are small, so that when the expressions (7.3, 4) are substituted in the system of eqns. (6.8–12) we can neglect the quadratic terms in the functions f_a^1, $\boldsymbol{E}^1$, $\boldsymbol{B}^1$.

As a result we obtain the following system of equations for the functions f_a^1, $\boldsymbol{E}^1$, $\boldsymbol{B}^1$

$$\frac{\partial f_a^1}{\partial t} + \left(\boldsymbol{v} \cdot \frac{\partial f_a^1}{\partial \boldsymbol{q}}\right) + e_a \left(E^1(\boldsymbol{q}, t) \cdot \frac{\partial f_a^0}{\partial \boldsymbol{p}}\right) = 0, \tag{7.5}$$

$$\operatorname{curl} \boldsymbol{B}^1 = \frac{1}{c} \frac{\partial \boldsymbol{E}^1}{\partial t} + \frac{4\pi}{c} \sum_a e_a n_a \int \boldsymbol{v} f_a^1 \, d^3\boldsymbol{p}, \tag{7.6}$$

$$\operatorname{curl} \boldsymbol{E}^1 = -\frac{1}{c}\frac{\partial \boldsymbol{B}^1}{\partial t}, \tag{7.7}$$

$$\operatorname{div} \boldsymbol{B}^1 = 0, \tag{7.8}$$

$$\operatorname{div} \boldsymbol{E}^1 = 4\pi \sum_a e_a n_a \int f_a^1 \, d^3\boldsymbol{p}. \tag{7.9}$$

We have allowed for the fact that in the equation for f_a^1 the term

$$\frac{e_a}{c}\left([\boldsymbol{v} \wedge \boldsymbol{B}^1] \cdot \frac{\partial f_a^0}{\partial \boldsymbol{p}}\right) = 0,$$

since

$$\frac{\partial f_a^0}{\partial \boldsymbol{p}} = \boldsymbol{p} \frac{\partial f_a^0}{\partial \dfrac{p^2}{2}} \quad \text{and} \quad ([\boldsymbol{v} \wedge \boldsymbol{B}] \cdot \boldsymbol{v}) = 0.$$

In future we shall omit the index 1 of the functions f_a^1, $\boldsymbol{E}^1$, $\boldsymbol{B}^1$. This will not lead to confusion.

We shall show that the system of eqns. (7.5–9) can be reduced to the Maxwell equations for the electrical and magnetic field strengths $\boldsymbol{E}$, $\boldsymbol{B}$.

We shall use the Maxwell equations in the form (III) (see § 1) but taking into account dispersion in time and space.

In the case of an infinite plasma it can be reduced to the system of eqns. (2.59–62) for the Fourier components $\boldsymbol{E}(\omega, \boldsymbol{k})$, $\boldsymbol{B}(\omega, \boldsymbol{k})$. We must obtain the expression for the tensor $\varepsilon_{ij}(\omega, \boldsymbol{k})$ and the functions $\boldsymbol{j}^e(\omega, \boldsymbol{k})$, $\varrho^e(\omega, \boldsymbol{k})$ from the equation for the distribution function f_a.

Equation (7.5) can be written in the form

$$\frac{\partial f_a}{\partial t} + \left(\boldsymbol{v} \cdot \frac{\partial f_a}{\partial \boldsymbol{q}}\right) = -e_a\left(\boldsymbol{E} \cdot \frac{\partial f_a^0}{\partial \boldsymbol{p}}\right) \tag{7.10}$$

and its right-hand side looked upon as a non-uniform term. Then the expression for f_a can be given in the form of two parts: the solution of the homogeneous equation that satisfies the initial condition

$$f_a(\boldsymbol{q}, \boldsymbol{p}, t) = f_a(\boldsymbol{q}, \boldsymbol{p}, 0), \quad \text{when} \quad t = 0$$

and the special solution of the non-uniform equation. As a

result we obtain

$$f_a(\boldsymbol{q}, \boldsymbol{p}, t) = f_a(\boldsymbol{q}-\boldsymbol{v}t, \boldsymbol{p}, 0) - e_a \int_0^t \left(\boldsymbol{E}(\boldsymbol{q}-\boldsymbol{v}(t-t'), t')dt' \cdot \frac{\partial f_a^0}{\partial \boldsymbol{p}}\right). \tag{7.11}$$

It is easy to check by direct differentiation that eqn. (7.11) is equivalent to eqns. (7.5) for the functions f_a.

Let us examine the waves in an infinite plasma. In this case it is convenient by virtue of the linearity of eqns. (7.5–9) to expand all the functions in a Fourier integral with respect to the coordinates and write the equations for the Fourier components.

We can give the expansion in a Fourier integral in the form

$$f_a = \frac{1}{(2\pi)^3} \int f_a(\boldsymbol{k}, \boldsymbol{p}, t) e^{i(\boldsymbol{k}\cdot\boldsymbol{q})}\, d^3\boldsymbol{k}, \tag{7.12}$$

$$\begin{aligned} \boldsymbol{E} &= \frac{1}{(2\pi)^3} \int \boldsymbol{E}(\boldsymbol{k}, t) e^{i(\boldsymbol{k}\cdot\boldsymbol{q})}\, d^3\boldsymbol{k}, \\ \boldsymbol{B} &= \frac{1}{(2\pi)^3} \int \boldsymbol{B}(\boldsymbol{k}, t) e^{i(\boldsymbol{k}\cdot\boldsymbol{q})}\, d^3\boldsymbol{k}. \end{aligned} \tag{7.13}$$

We shall denote the Fourier components by the same letters.

Substituting the expressions (7.12, 13) in eqn. (7.11) we obtain the following equation for the Fourier components of the functions f_a

$$f_a(\boldsymbol{k}, \boldsymbol{p}, t) = f_a(\boldsymbol{k}, \boldsymbol{p}, 0) e^{-i(\boldsymbol{k}\cdot\boldsymbol{v}t)} - e_a \int_0^t \left(\boldsymbol{E}(\boldsymbol{k}, t') e^{-i(\boldsymbol{k}\cdot\boldsymbol{v}(t-t'))}\, dt' \cdot \frac{\partial f_a^0}{\partial \boldsymbol{p}}\right). \tag{7.14}$$

We multiply (7.14) by $e_a n_a$, sum over a and integrate over $\boldsymbol{p}$. As a result we obtain the expression for the Fourier components of the electrical charge density

$$\varrho(\boldsymbol{k}, t) = \sum_a e_a n_a \int f_a(\boldsymbol{k}, \boldsymbol{p}, 0) e^{-i(\boldsymbol{k}\cdot\boldsymbol{v}t)}\, d^3\boldsymbol{p} - \sum_a e_a^2 n_a \int_0^t \int \left(\boldsymbol{E}(\boldsymbol{k}, t') e^{-i(\boldsymbol{k}\cdot\boldsymbol{v}(t-t'))} \cdot \frac{\partial f_a^0}{\partial \boldsymbol{p}}\right) dt'\, d^3\boldsymbol{p}. \tag{7.15}$$

It can be seen from the formula obtained that the total charge density consists of two parts. The first part is wholly determined by the initial distribution function and is therefore a known function of the coordinates and time. In accordance with the terminology adopted in § 1 we shall denote this part of the charge density by ϱ^e (the density of the "external" charges). The second part of the charge density, which is proportional to the electrical field strength, is determined by the induced charge density ϱ^i. Therefore the expression (7.15) can be written in the form

$$\varrho(\boldsymbol{k}, t) = \varrho^e(\boldsymbol{k}, t) + \varrho^i(\boldsymbol{k}, t). \tag{7.16}$$

We now multiply the expression (7.14) by $e_a n_a \boldsymbol{v}$, sum over a and integrate over $\boldsymbol{p}$. We then obtain the expression for the electric current density

$$\boldsymbol{j}(\boldsymbol{k}, t) = \sum_a e_a n_a \int \boldsymbol{v} f_a(k, \boldsymbol{p}, 0) e^{-i(\boldsymbol{k}\cdot\boldsymbol{v}t)}\, d^3\boldsymbol{p}$$
$$-\sum_a e_a^2 n_a \int_0^t \int \boldsymbol{v} e^{-i[(\boldsymbol{k}\cdot\boldsymbol{v}(t-t')]} \left(\boldsymbol{E}(\boldsymbol{k}, t')\cdot \frac{\partial f_a^0}{\partial \boldsymbol{p}}\right) dt'\, d^3\boldsymbol{p}. \tag{7.17}$$

The expression for the current density can also be represented as the sum of the "external" (or "strange") and induced currents

$$\boldsymbol{j}(\boldsymbol{k}, t) = \boldsymbol{j}^e(\boldsymbol{k}, t) + \boldsymbol{j}^i(\boldsymbol{k}, t). \tag{7.18}$$

The Fourier component of the "external" current is defined by the first term of expression (7.17) and that of the induced current by the second term.

Just as in § 2 we use a single-variable Fourier transform with respect to time

$$\boldsymbol{E}(\omega, \boldsymbol{k}) = \int_0^\infty E(\boldsymbol{k}, t) e^{-\Delta t + i\omega t}\, dt. \tag{7.19}$$

In the same way we determine the functions $\boldsymbol{B}(\omega, \boldsymbol{k})$, $\boldsymbol{j}(\omega, \boldsymbol{k})$, $\varrho(\omega, \boldsymbol{k})$, ...

Using the folding theorem and remembering that the integral

$$-i\int_0^\infty e^{-\Delta t + i[\omega - (\boldsymbol{k}\cdot\boldsymbol{v})]t}\, dt = \frac{1}{\omega - (\boldsymbol{k}\cdot\boldsymbol{v}) + i\Delta}, \tag{7.20}$$

we find from the expressions (7.15–18)

$$\varrho^{e}(\omega, \boldsymbol{k}) = i\sum_{a} e_a n_a \int \frac{f_a(\boldsymbol{k}, \boldsymbol{p}, 0)}{\omega-(\boldsymbol{k}\cdot\boldsymbol{v})+i\Delta}\, d^3\boldsymbol{p};$$

$$\boldsymbol{j}^{e}(\omega, \boldsymbol{k}) = i\sum_{a} e_a n_a \int \frac{\boldsymbol{v} f_a(\boldsymbol{k}, \boldsymbol{p}, 0)}{\omega-(\boldsymbol{k}\cdot\boldsymbol{v})+i\Delta}\, d^3\boldsymbol{p}; \tag{7.21}$$

$$\varrho^{i}(\omega, \boldsymbol{k}) = -i\sum_{a} e_a^2 n_a \int \frac{\left(\boldsymbol{E}\cdot\frac{\partial f_a^0}{\partial \boldsymbol{p}}\right)}{\omega-(\boldsymbol{k}\cdot\boldsymbol{v})+i\Delta}\, d^3\boldsymbol{p};$$

$$\boldsymbol{j}^{i}(\omega, \boldsymbol{k}) = -i\sum_{a} e_a^2 n_a \int \frac{\boldsymbol{v}\left(\boldsymbol{E}(\omega, \boldsymbol{k})\cdot\frac{\partial f_a^0}{\partial \boldsymbol{p}}\right)}{\omega-(\boldsymbol{k}\cdot\boldsymbol{v})+i\Delta}\, d^3\boldsymbol{p}. \tag{7.22}$$

We notice that the second equation (7.22) can be considered as Ohm's law for a plasma which defines the connexion between the Fourier components $\boldsymbol{j}^{i}(\omega, \boldsymbol{k})$ and $\boldsymbol{E}(\omega, \boldsymbol{k})$.

If we use $\sigma_{ij}(\omega, \boldsymbol{k})$ to denote the conductivity tensor, then Ohm's law for a plasma will become

$$j_i^{i}(\omega, \boldsymbol{k}) = \sigma_{ij}(\omega, \boldsymbol{k})\, E_j(\omega, \boldsymbol{k}). \tag{7.23}$$

Comparing the expressions (7.22, 23) we obtain the formula for the conductivity tensor

$$\sigma_{ij}(\omega, \boldsymbol{k}) = -i\sum_{a} e_a^2 n_a \int \frac{v_i \frac{\partial f_a^0}{\partial p_j}}{\omega-(\boldsymbol{k}\cdot\boldsymbol{v})+i\Delta}\, d^3\boldsymbol{p}. \tag{7.24}$$

We now introduce, just as we did in § 2, the induction vector

$$D_i(\omega, \boldsymbol{k}) = E_i(\omega, \boldsymbol{k}) + i\frac{4\pi}{\omega+i\Delta}\sigma_{ij}E_j(\omega, \boldsymbol{k}) = \varepsilon_{ij}(\omega, \boldsymbol{k})E_j, \tag{7.25}$$

where $\varepsilon_{ij}(\omega, \boldsymbol{k})$ is the tensor of the plasma's dielectric constant which is connected with the conductivity tensor by the relation (2.55)

$$\varepsilon_{ij}(\omega, \boldsymbol{k}) = \delta_{ij} + i\frac{4\pi}{\omega+i\Delta}\sigma_{ij}(\omega, \boldsymbol{k}). \tag{7.26}$$

By using the formula (7.24) we obtain the expression for the dielectric constant tensor

$$\varepsilon_{ij}(\omega, \boldsymbol{k}) = \delta_{ij} + \sum_a \frac{4\pi e_a^2 n_a}{\omega + i\Delta} \int \frac{v_i \dfrac{\partial f_a^0}{\partial p_j}}{\omega - (\boldsymbol{k}\cdot\boldsymbol{v}) + i\Delta}\, d^3\boldsymbol{p}. \quad (7.27)$$

The formulae (7.21, 27) define the functions $\varrho^e(\omega, \boldsymbol{k})$, $\boldsymbol{j}^e(\omega, \boldsymbol{k})$, $\varepsilon_{ij}(\omega, \boldsymbol{k})$ for a plasma in the linear approximation and in the absence of external fields. Accordingly the problem of determining the field strengths $\boldsymbol{E}, \boldsymbol{B}$ is reduced to the system of Maxwell equations (2.59–62).

It must be stressed that in the case under discussion the quantities $\boldsymbol{j}^e$, ϱ^e are determined by the initial values of the distribution functions $f_a(\boldsymbol{q}, \boldsymbol{p}, 0)$.

It follows from the Poisson equation for the Fourier components when $t = 0$,

$$i(\boldsymbol{k}\cdot\boldsymbol{E}(\boldsymbol{k}, 0)) = 4\pi \sum_a e_a n_a \int f_a(\boldsymbol{k}, \boldsymbol{p}, 0)\, d^3\boldsymbol{p}, \qquad (7.28)$$

that the initial values of the functions f_a also determine the initial value of the projection of the vector $\boldsymbol{E}(\boldsymbol{k}, t)$ onto the vector $\boldsymbol{k}$.

We shall split the vector $\boldsymbol{E}(\boldsymbol{k}, t)$ into transverse and longitudinal parts with respect to the vector $\boldsymbol{k}$

$$\boldsymbol{E}(\boldsymbol{k}, t) = \boldsymbol{E}^{\|} + \boldsymbol{E}^{\perp}, \quad [\boldsymbol{k} \wedge \boldsymbol{E}^{\|}] = 0, \quad (\boldsymbol{k}\cdot\boldsymbol{E}^{\perp}) = 0.$$

Using this division we can see from (7.28) that the initial value of the functions f_a determines the initial value of the longitudinal electrical field.

Therefore in the Maxwell equations (2.59–62) we need to know the initial value only of the transverse component of the electrical field strength in order to determine the field strengths $\boldsymbol{E}$, $\boldsymbol{B}$. The magnetic field is always transverse since $(\boldsymbol{k}\cdot\boldsymbol{B}) = 0$

The actual expression (7.27) for the tensor $\varepsilon_{ij}(\omega, \boldsymbol{k})$ is derived with the proviso that the function f_a^0 depends only on the modulus of the momentum, i.e. for the isotropic case.

Since in this case the dielectric constant tensor depends on the single vector $\boldsymbol{k}$, it can always be represented in the form

$$\varepsilon_{ij}(\omega, \boldsymbol{k}) = \left(\delta_{ij} - \frac{k_i k_j}{k^2}\right) \varepsilon^{\perp}(\omega, \boldsymbol{k}) + \frac{k_i k_j}{k^2} \varepsilon^{||}(\omega, \boldsymbol{k}). \qquad (7.29)$$

The functions $\varepsilon^{||}$, $\varepsilon^{\perp}$, which depend on the magnitude of the vector $\boldsymbol{k}$, will be called respectively the "longitudinal" and the "transverse" dielectric constant. The meaning of these names is that the functions $\varepsilon^{||}$, $\varepsilon^{\perp}$, as we shall see below, determine respectively the longitudinal $\boldsymbol{E}^{||}$ and the transverse $\boldsymbol{E}^{\perp}$ components of the electrical field strength vector in the plasma.

It follows from formula (7.29) that

$$\varepsilon^{||} = \varepsilon_{ij} \frac{k_i k_j}{k^2}; \qquad 2\varepsilon^{\perp} = \left(\delta_{ij} - \frac{k_i k_j}{k^2}\right) \varepsilon_{ij}. \qquad (7.30)$$

Substituting in the expressions (7.30) the formula (7.27) for the tensor ε_{ij} we obtain the explicit form of the functions $\varepsilon^{||}$, $\varepsilon^{\perp}$

$$\varepsilon^{||}(\omega, \boldsymbol{k}) = 1 + \sum_a \frac{4\pi e_a^2 n_a}{k^2(\omega + i\Delta)} \int \frac{(\boldsymbol{k}\cdot\boldsymbol{v})\left(\boldsymbol{k}\cdot\dfrac{\partial f_a^0}{\partial \boldsymbol{p}}\right)}{\omega - (\boldsymbol{k}\cdot\boldsymbol{v}) + i\Delta}\, d^3\boldsymbol{p}, \qquad (7.31)$$

$$\varepsilon^{\perp}(\omega, \boldsymbol{k}) = 1 + \sum_a \frac{2\pi e_a^2 n_a}{k^2(\omega + i\Delta)} \int \frac{\left([[\boldsymbol{k}\wedge\boldsymbol{v}]\wedge\boldsymbol{k}]\cdot\dfrac{\partial f_a^0}{\partial \boldsymbol{p}}\right)}{\omega - (\boldsymbol{k}\cdot\boldsymbol{v}) + i\Delta}\, d^3\boldsymbol{p}. \qquad (7.32)$$

The expressions (7.31, 32) are often written in a different form. In the expression (7.31) we take into account the fact that $(\boldsymbol{k}\cdot\boldsymbol{v})\,[\omega - (\boldsymbol{k}\cdot\boldsymbol{v}) + i\Delta]^{-1} = -1 + (\omega + i\Delta)/[\omega - (\boldsymbol{k}\cdot\boldsymbol{v}) + i\Delta]$ and in the expression (7.32) we integrate by parts. As a result we obtain the following formulae:

$$\varepsilon^{||}(\omega, \boldsymbol{k}) = 1 + \sum_a \frac{4\pi e_a^2 n_a}{k^2} \int \frac{\left(\boldsymbol{k}\cdot\dfrac{\partial f_a^0}{\partial \boldsymbol{p}}\right)}{\omega - (\boldsymbol{k}\cdot\boldsymbol{v}) + i\Delta}\, d^3\boldsymbol{p}, \qquad (7.33)$$

$$\varepsilon^{\perp}(\omega, \boldsymbol{k}) = 1 - \sum \frac{4\pi e_a^2 n_a}{m_a(\omega + i\Delta)} \int \frac{f_a^0}{\omega - (\boldsymbol{k}\cdot\boldsymbol{v}) + i\Delta}\, d^3\boldsymbol{p}. \qquad (7.34)$$

Let us return to the system of eqns. (2.59–62). By using eqn. (2.60) we can eliminate the vector $\boldsymbol{B}$. Then we obtain the system of equations

$$i\left([\boldsymbol{k}\wedge[\boldsymbol{k}\wedge\boldsymbol{E}]]+\frac{\omega^2}{c^2}\boldsymbol{D}\right)=\frac{4\pi\omega}{c^2}\boldsymbol{j}^{\mathrm{e}}-\frac{\omega}{c^2}\boldsymbol{E}(\boldsymbol{k},0)+\frac{1}{c}[\boldsymbol{k}\wedge\boldsymbol{B}(\boldsymbol{k},0)]; \tag{7.35}$$

$$i(\boldsymbol{k}\cdot\boldsymbol{D})=4\pi\varrho^{\mathrm{e}};\qquad D_i=\varepsilon_{ij}E_j. \tag{7.36}$$

We can represent the vector $\boldsymbol{E}$ in the form of the sum of the longitudinal and transverse components

$$\boldsymbol{E}=\boldsymbol{E}^{\perp}+\boldsymbol{E}^{\parallel};\quad \boldsymbol{E}^{\perp}=\boldsymbol{E}-\frac{\boldsymbol{k}(\boldsymbol{k}\cdot\boldsymbol{E})}{k^2};$$

$$\boldsymbol{E}^{\parallel}=\boldsymbol{k}\,\frac{(\boldsymbol{k}\cdot\boldsymbol{E})}{k^2}. \tag{7.37}$$

Using eqns. (7.35, 36) and the expression (7.29) for the tensor ε_{ij} we obtain the equations of the functions $\boldsymbol{E}^{\parallel}$, $\boldsymbol{E}^{\perp}$

$$i\varepsilon^{\parallel}(\omega,\boldsymbol{k})\,(\boldsymbol{k}\cdot\boldsymbol{E}^{\parallel})=4\pi\varrho^{\mathrm{e}};\quad [\boldsymbol{k}\wedge\boldsymbol{E}^{\parallel}]=0, \tag{7.38}$$

$$i\left(\frac{\omega^2}{c^2}\,\varepsilon^{\perp}-k^2\right)\boldsymbol{E}^{\perp}=\frac{4\pi\omega}{c^2}\boldsymbol{j}_{\mathrm{e}}^{\perp}-\frac{\omega}{c^2}\boldsymbol{E}^{\perp}(\boldsymbol{k},0)+\frac{1}{c}[\boldsymbol{k}\wedge\boldsymbol{B}(\boldsymbol{k},0)];\quad (\boldsymbol{k}\cdot\boldsymbol{E}^{\perp})=0. \tag{7.39}$$

From these equations we find

$$\boldsymbol{E}^{\parallel}(\omega,\boldsymbol{k})=-i\frac{\boldsymbol{k}}{k^2}\cdot\frac{4\pi\varrho^{\mathrm{e}}}{\varepsilon^{\parallel}(\omega,\boldsymbol{k})}, \tag{7.40}$$

$$\boldsymbol{E}^{\perp}(\omega,\boldsymbol{k})=\frac{-i4\pi\omega\boldsymbol{j}_{\mathrm{e}}^{\perp}+i\omega\boldsymbol{E}^{\perp}(\boldsymbol{k},0)-ic[\boldsymbol{k}\wedge\boldsymbol{B}(\boldsymbol{k},0)]}{(\omega+i\Delta)^2\,\varepsilon^{\perp}(\omega,\boldsymbol{k})-c^2k^2}. \tag{7.41}$$

In the expressions (7.39, 41) the vector

$$\boldsymbol{j}_{\mathrm{e}}^{\perp}=\boldsymbol{j}^{\mathrm{e}}-\frac{\boldsymbol{k}(\boldsymbol{k}\cdot\boldsymbol{j}^{\mathrm{e}})}{k^2} \tag{7.42}$$

is the transverse component of the external current.

The magnetic field strength can be determined by the formula

$$\boldsymbol{B} = \frac{c}{\omega + i\Delta}[\boldsymbol{k} \wedge \boldsymbol{E}^{\perp}] + \frac{i}{\omega + i\Delta}\boldsymbol{B}(\boldsymbol{k}, 0). \tag{7.43}$$

The transverse and longitudinal components of the electrical field as functions of the coordinates and momenta are defined by the formulae

$$\boldsymbol{E}^{\parallel}(\boldsymbol{q}, t) = \frac{1}{(2\pi)^4}\int_{-\infty}^{\infty}\int \boldsymbol{E}^{\parallel}(\omega, \boldsymbol{k})\, e^{\Delta t - i[\omega t - (\boldsymbol{k}\cdot\boldsymbol{q})]}\, d\omega\, d^3\boldsymbol{k}, \tag{7.44}$$

$$\boldsymbol{E}^{\perp}(\boldsymbol{q}, t) = \frac{1}{(2\pi)^4}\int_{-\infty}^{\infty}\int \boldsymbol{E}^{\perp}(\omega, \boldsymbol{k})\, e^{\Delta t - i[\omega t - (\boldsymbol{k}\cdot\boldsymbol{q})]}\, d\omega\, d^3\boldsymbol{k}. \tag{7.45}$$

It follows from these formulae and the formulae (7.40, 41) that the electrical and magnetic field strengths in a plasma are determined by two factors. In the first place by the form of the initial distribution functions $f_a(\boldsymbol{q}, \boldsymbol{p}, 0)$ and, hence, by the external currents and charges $\boldsymbol{j}^e$, ϱ^e and also the initial values of the fields $\boldsymbol{E}^{\perp}$, $\boldsymbol{B}$. In the second place by the functions $\varepsilon^{\parallel}(\omega, \boldsymbol{k})$, $\varepsilon^{\perp}(\omega, \boldsymbol{k})$ which are characteristics of the properties of an isotropic plasma in the linear approximation.

It follows from the expressions (7.40, 41, 44, 45) that we must find the zeros of the denominators of the expressions (7.40, 41) in order to calculate the functions $\boldsymbol{E}^{\parallel}(\boldsymbol{q}, t), \boldsymbol{E}^{\perp}(\boldsymbol{q}, t)$, i.e. we must solve the equations

$$\varepsilon^{\parallel}(\omega, \boldsymbol{k}) = 0, \; (\omega + i\Delta)^2 \varepsilon^{\perp}(\omega, \boldsymbol{k}) - c^2 k^2 = 0. \tag{7.46}$$

By using expressions (7.33, 34) we can write these equations in the expanded form

$$1 + \sum \frac{4\pi e_a^2 n_a}{k^2}\int \frac{\left(\boldsymbol{k}\cdot\dfrac{\partial f_a^0}{\partial \boldsymbol{p}}\right)}{\omega - (\boldsymbol{k}\cdot\boldsymbol{v}) + i\Delta}\, d^3\boldsymbol{p} = 0, \tag{7.47}$$

$$(\omega + i\Delta)^2\left(1 - \sum_a \frac{4\pi e_a^2 n_a}{m_a(\omega + i\Delta)}\int \frac{f_a^0}{\omega - (\boldsymbol{k}\cdot\boldsymbol{v}) + i\Delta}\, d^3\boldsymbol{p}\right) - c^2 k^2 = 0. \tag{7.48}$$

Equations (7.47, 48) define the dependence of the complex frequency on the wave vector for longitudinal and transverse waves respectively in a plasma and are therefore called the dispersion relations. These equations were first derived by Vlasov (1938, 1950). In the next section we shall discuss the solution of these equations for different forms of the distribution functions $f_a^0(|\boldsymbol{p}|)$.

For a given distribution f_a^0 we can find the most exact solution of the initial equations with a self-consistent field by using the perturbation theory method (the method of successive approximations). In this case the initial equations can also be reduced to the electrodynamic equations of a dispersive medium which are, however, non-linear (see § 2). In the non-linear approximation the plasma is characterized not by the single tensor ε_{ij} but by the combination of tensors ε_{ij}, $\varkappa_{ijk}$, Θ_{ijkl}, . . . (see § 2) defining the connexion between the vectors $\boldsymbol{D}$, $\boldsymbol{E}$ in a non-linear medium. The position here is similar to that which occurs in non-linear optics (see Akhmanov and Khokhlov, 1964).

With this approach no allowance is made for the inverse effect of the electromagnetic waves on the form of the distribution functions f_a^0. If this inverse effect is significant the equations with a self-consistent field can no longer be reduced to the electrodynamic equations. In this case, however, we can under certain conditions simplify the initial system of equations with a self-consistent field and reduce it to the simpler system of equations for the smoothed distribution functions $f_a(\mu t, \mu \boldsymbol{q}, \mu \boldsymbol{p})$ and equations for the slowly varying spectral functions of the electrical and magnetic field strengths. This approximation is often called quasi-linear.† It will be discussed in § 18.

To conclude the present section we would point out that the solution of the equation with a self-consistent field described here is also valid, of course, when the initial momentum distribution $f_a^0(\boldsymbol{p})$ is not isotropic. The corresponding expression for the dielectric constant tensor is given in § 14.

† Vedenov, Velikhov and Sagdeyev (1961); Vedenov and Velikhov (1963); Vedenov (1962); Drummond and Pines (1961); Shapiro (1963); and Karpman (1964).

8. Propagation of Electromagnetic Waves in a Plasma when there are no External Fields

It has been shown in the previous section that in the linear approximation independent equations are obtained for the longitudinal (in relation to the vector $\boldsymbol{k}$) and transverse components of the electrical field strength vector. This means that when there are no external fields in the linear approximation the longitudinal and transverse waves are propagated independently.

Let us first examine the propagation of longitudinal waves in a plasma.

It follows from the formulae given in § 7 that the longitudinal component of the electrical field strength is determined by two factors. Firstly, by the form of the initial distribution function $f_a(\boldsymbol{q}, \boldsymbol{p}, 0)$ or the corresponding distribution of the external charge and current density. Secondly, by the dielectric constant $\varepsilon^{\parallel}(\omega, \boldsymbol{k})$ which is a characteristic of the plasma's properties in the linear approximation.

It follows from the expression (7.40) that to calculate the function $\boldsymbol{E}^{\parallel}(\boldsymbol{q}, t)$ we must find the zeros of the numerator, i.e. solve the equation

$$\varepsilon^{\parallel}(\omega, \boldsymbol{k}) = 0 \tag{8.1}$$

or in the expanded form

$$1+\sum_a \frac{4\pi e_a^2 n_a}{k^2} \int \frac{\left(\boldsymbol{k}\cdot\dfrac{\partial f_a^0}{\partial \boldsymbol{p}}\right)}{\omega-(\boldsymbol{k}\cdot\boldsymbol{v})}\, d^3\boldsymbol{p} = 0, \qquad \omega = \omega' + i\omega''. \tag{8.2}$$

Equation (8.2) defines the complex frequency ω as a function of the wave vector, i.e. defines the nature of the longitudinal waves which can be propagated in a plasma.

Let us examine the solution of the dispersion relation for different forms of the functions $f_a^0(\boldsymbol{p})$.

Let us start with the simplest case when we can neglect the motion of the ions and consider that they are evenly distributed throughout the plasma.

We shall assume that the plasma consists of two components: electrons and ions. Then the suffix a in the expression (8.2) takes the two values $a = \mathrm{e}$, i.

In order to satisfy the condition of immobility of the ions we make their mass in expression (8.2) approach infinity.

As a result we obtain the following dispersion relation:

$$1+\frac{4\pi e^2 n_e}{k^2}\int \frac{\left(\boldsymbol{k}\cdot\frac{\partial f_e^0}{\partial \boldsymbol{p}}\right)}{\omega-(\boldsymbol{k}\cdot\boldsymbol{v})}\,d^3\boldsymbol{p} = 0, \qquad \omega = \omega'+i\omega''. \tag{8.3}$$

Let us examine some examples of the solution of this equation.

1. Let the electron temperature $T_e = 0$ and their mean velocity be zero, i.e. $\boldsymbol{U}_e = 0$. Then the distribution function can be written in the form

$$f_e(\boldsymbol{p}) = \delta(\boldsymbol{p}), \tag{8.4}$$

where $\delta(\boldsymbol{p})$ is a δ-function.

We substitute this expression in eqn. (8.3) and integrate by parts with respect to the momenta. As a result we obtain the expression

$$1-\frac{4\pi e^2 n_\mathrm{e}}{m_\mathrm{e}}\int \frac{\delta(\boldsymbol{p})}{[\omega-(\boldsymbol{k}\cdot\boldsymbol{v})]^2}\,d^3\boldsymbol{p} = 0.$$

Integrating over $\boldsymbol{p}$ and using the properties of the δ-function we obtain

$$1-\frac{4\pi e^2 n_\mathrm{e}}{m_\mathrm{e}\omega^2} = 0, \qquad \omega^2 = \frac{4\pi e^2 n_\mathrm{e}}{m_\mathrm{e}}. \tag{8.5}$$

Therefore when the temperature is zero the only oscillations possible in an electron plasma are those with a frequency

$$\omega_\mathrm{e} = \sqrt{\left(\frac{4\pi e^2 n_\mathrm{e}}{m_\mathrm{e}}\right)}, \tag{8.6}$$

which is called the electron Langmuir or plasma frequency.

It is important that the frequency does not depend on the wave vector, i.e. the oscillations occur at the same frequency for any wavelength or, to put it better, for any size of non-uniformity.

2. We shall now assume that there are two groups of electrons, 1 and 2 in the plasma. For group 1 the mean velocity is $\boldsymbol{U}_1 \neq 0$, whilst $\boldsymbol{U}_2 = 0$. As before the temperature of all the electrons is zero.

In this case the distribution function $f_e(\boldsymbol{p})$ becomes

$$n_e f_e(\boldsymbol{p}) = n_1\delta(\boldsymbol{p}-\boldsymbol{U}_1)+n_2\delta(\boldsymbol{p}), \quad n_e=n_1+n_2, \tag{8.7}$$

where n_1 and n_2 are the concentrations of the first and second groups of electrons.

Substituting this expression in equation (8.3) and integrating over $\boldsymbol{p}$ we obtain the following expression:

$$1 = \frac{\omega_1^2}{[\omega-(\boldsymbol{k}\cdot\boldsymbol{U}_1)]^2}+\frac{\omega_2^2}{\omega^2}, \tag{8.8}$$

where $\omega_1 = \sqrt{(4\pi e^2 n_1/m_e)}$, $\omega_2 = \sqrt{(4\pi e^2 n_2/m_e)}$ are the plasma frequencies of the corresponding groups of electrons.

Equation (8.8) of the fourth degree in ω has complex-conjugate roots. This means that the state of the system for a certain range of values of the wave numbers is not stable. We shall prove this.

If we assume that the increasing root of eqns. (8.8) is close to $(\boldsymbol{k}\cdot\boldsymbol{U}_1)$, we can find the solution in the form

$$\omega = (\boldsymbol{k}\cdot\boldsymbol{U}_1)+\varepsilon; \quad |\varepsilon| \ll (\boldsymbol{k}\cdot\boldsymbol{U}_1). \tag{8.9}$$

We substitute relations (8.9) in eqn. (8.8) and by using the smallness of ε we obtain

$$1 = \frac{\omega_1^2}{\varepsilon^2}+\frac{\omega_2^2}{(\boldsymbol{k}\cdot\boldsymbol{U}_1)^2}\cdot \tag{8.10}$$

From formulae (8.10, 9) we obtain

$$\omega = (\boldsymbol{k}\cdot\boldsymbol{U}_1)\left(1\pm\frac{\omega_1}{\sqrt{[(\boldsymbol{k}\cdot\boldsymbol{U}_1)^2-\omega_2^2]}}\right)\cdot \tag{8.11}$$

It follows from the solution obtained that for the wave number values that satisfy the condition

$$(\boldsymbol{k}\cdot\boldsymbol{U}_1)^2 < \omega_2^2, \tag{8.12}$$

there are two complex-conjugate frequencies, i.e. there is a wave with an amplitude rising in time and therefore the initial state is unstable.

The absence of a lower limit in the instability condition (8.12) can be explained by the fact that we are not allowing for thermal motion. For $T_e \neq 0$ the instability arises only when the velocity of the relative motion is greater than the mean thermal velocity.

In accordance with the condition (8.9) the formula (8.11) is valid if the second term in eqn. (8.11) is small when compared with the first. When $(\boldsymbol{k}\cdot\boldsymbol{U}_1) \ll \omega_2$ this condition means that

$$\omega_1 \ll \omega_2 \quad \text{or} \quad n_1 \ll n_2. \tag{8.13}$$

In order to obtain the solution in the region where $(\boldsymbol{k}\cdot\boldsymbol{U}) \sim \omega_2$ we put

$$(\boldsymbol{k}\cdot\boldsymbol{U}_1) = \omega_2, \quad \text{and} \quad \omega = \omega_2+\alpha. \tag{8.14}$$

Substituting these expressions in (8.8) we obtain the equation for α

$$\alpha^4+2\omega_2\alpha^3-\omega_1^2\alpha^2+2\omega_1^2\omega_2\alpha-\omega_1^2\omega_2^2 = 0.$$

From this, when the condition (8.13) is satisfied, we find

$$2\omega_2\alpha^3-\omega_1^2\omega_2^2 = 0; \qquad \alpha = -\frac{1\pm i\sqrt{3}}{2^{4/3}}\,\omega_2\left(\frac{\omega_1}{\omega_2}\right)^{2/3}. \tag{8.15}$$

Therefore for this region the complex-conjugate roots are defined by the formula

$$\omega = \omega_2-\frac{1\pm i\sqrt{3}}{2^{4/3}}\,\omega_2\left(\frac{\omega_1}{\omega_2}\right)^{2/3}. \tag{8.16}$$

Just as in the first case the increment when the condition (8.13) is satisfied is much less than the real part of the frequency.

If the concentrations n_1 and n_2 are the same then by the substitution $\omega-(\boldsymbol{k}\cdot\boldsymbol{U}_1)/2 = \Omega$, eqn. (8.8) is reduced to the biquadratic equation

$$\Omega^4-\left(\omega_1^2+2\left(\frac{(\boldsymbol{k}\cdot\boldsymbol{U}_1)}{2}\right)^2\right)\Omega^2+\left[\left(\frac{(\boldsymbol{k}\cdot\boldsymbol{U}_1)}{2}\right)^4 -\omega_1^2\left(\frac{(\boldsymbol{k}\cdot\boldsymbol{U}_1)}{2}\right)^2\right] = 0. \tag{8.17}$$

We can write the solution of eqn. (8.17) in the form

$$\Omega^2 = \frac{\omega_1^2}{2}\left\{1+\frac{1}{2}\left(\frac{(\boldsymbol{k}\cdot\boldsymbol{U}_1)}{\omega_1}\right)^2 \pm\sqrt{\left[1+2\left(\frac{(\boldsymbol{k}\cdot\boldsymbol{U}_1)}{\omega_1}\right)^2\right]}\right\}. \tag{8.18}$$

It follows from this that if

$$(\boldsymbol{k}\cdot\boldsymbol{U}_1)/2 \geqslant \omega_1 \tag{8.19}$$

all the roots are real, and when

$$0 < (\boldsymbol{k}\cdot\boldsymbol{U})/2 < \omega_1 \tag{8.20}$$

there are complex-conjugate roots for Ω, one of which corresponds to a negative imaginary part of the frequency and leads to the appearance of a solution that increases with time.

It follows from formula (8.20) that the state is unstable for all wavelengths whose wave numbers are within the range

$$0 < k < k_{\max} = 2\omega_1/U_1, \quad \boldsymbol{k}\,||\,\boldsymbol{U}_1. \tag{8.21}$$

The example of an unstable state in an electron plasma discussed here is given only by way of illustration. The question of describing unstable states in a plasma requires separate discussion (see Leontovich, 1963).

3. Now let $T_e \neq 0$ and the function f_e^0 be the Maxwell distribution, i.e.

$$f_e^0 = \frac{1}{(2\pi m_e \varkappa T)^{3/2}}\, e^{-\frac{p^2}{2m_e\varkappa T}}, \quad T_e \equiv T. \tag{8.22}$$

We substitute the expression (8.22) in the formula (8.3). In the integral over $\boldsymbol{p}$ we take the vector $\boldsymbol{k}$ along the x-axis. We can then immediately integrate over p_y, p_z. Remembering that

$$\int_{-\infty}^{\infty} e^{-\frac{p}{2m_e\varkappa T}}\, dp_i = \sqrt{(2\pi m_e \varkappa T)}, \quad i = x, y, z,$$

we obtain the following dispersion relation:

$$1 + \frac{4\pi e^2 n_e}{k^2}\cdot\frac{1}{\sqrt{(2\pi m_e\varkappa T)}}\int_{-\infty}^{\infty}\frac{k\dfrac{\partial}{\partial p_x}e^{-\frac{p_x^2}{2m_e\varkappa T}}}{\omega - k v_x}\, dp_x = 0. \tag{8.23}$$

If we introduce the integration variable $t = p_x/\sqrt{(2m_e\varkappa T)}$ and use $z = m_e\omega/k\sqrt{(2m_e\varkappa T)}$ to denote the ratio of the phase velocity to the thermal velocity, then the dispersion relation can be written in the form

$$1 + \frac{1}{r_d^2 k^2}\left(1 + \frac{z}{\sqrt{\pi}}\int_{-\infty}^{\infty}\frac{e^{-t^2}}{t - z}\, dt\right) = 0. \tag{8.24}$$

In the expression (8.24) the complex quantity z has a positive imaginary part since $\omega = \omega' + i\omega''$, $\omega'' > 0$.

Tables have been compiled for the integral

$$\int_{-\infty}^{\infty} \frac{e^{-t^2}}{t-z}\, dt$$

for complex values of z (see Faddeyeva and Terent'ev, 1954). By using these tables we can find the value of the frequency for any value of the wave number.

In the very interesting case of low values of k, when $r_d^2 k^2 \ll 1$ and the wavelength $\lambda \gg r_d$, the dispersion equation can be solved analytically. We see that as $k \to 0$, $\omega \to \omega_e$, i.e. ω approaches a finite value, so that small $k (r_d k \ll 1)$ correspond to phase velocities considerably greater than the thermal velocity of the electrons, i.e.

$$\frac{\omega}{k} \gg \sqrt{\left(\frac{\varkappa T}{m_e}\right)}. \tag{8.25}$$

In addition it is to be expected that for low k the imaginary part of the frequency ω'' is much less than the real part $\omega'' \ll \omega'$. This will be confirmed by a result obtained below.

Bearing these conditions in mind we can take the limiting value of the Cauchy-type integral in the dispersion equation (8.23).

Remembering that when $z = z' + iz''$ the integral

$$\lim_{z'' \to 0} \int_{-\infty}^{\infty} \frac{f(y)}{z-y}\, dy = P \int_{-\infty}^{\infty} \frac{f(y)}{z'-y}\, dy - i\pi f(z'), \tag{8.26}$$

where P denotes the principal value integral, the dispersion relation can be approximately written, taking the quantity ω'' to be small, in the form

$$1 + \frac{\omega_e^2 m_e}{k^2 \sqrt{(2\pi m_e \varkappa T)}} \int_{-\infty}^{\infty} \frac{k \dfrac{\partial}{\partial p_x} e^{-\frac{p_x^2}{2m_e \varkappa T}}}{\omega - k v_x}\, dp_x$$

$$- i\pi \frac{\omega_e^2 m_e^2}{k^2 \sqrt{(2\pi m_e \varkappa T)}} \left(\frac{\partial}{\partial p_x} e^{-\frac{p_x^2}{2m_e \varkappa T}} \right)_{p_x = m_e \frac{\omega}{k}} = 0. \tag{8.27}$$

When calculating the first integral we use the condition (8.25). Then under the integral sign we can make the expansion

$$\frac{1}{\omega-kv_x}=\frac{1}{\omega}\left(1+\frac{kv_x}{\omega}+\left(\frac{kv_x}{\omega}\right)^2+\left(\frac{kv_x}{\omega}\right)^3+\ldots\right) \quad (8.28)$$

Substituting the expansion (8.28) into eqn. (8.27) and when integrating over p_x leaving the first two non-vanishing terms, we obtain

$$1-\frac{\omega_e^2}{\omega^2}\left(1+3\frac{\varkappa T}{m_e\omega^2}k^2\right)+i\sqrt{\left(\frac{\pi}{2}\right)}\frac{\omega_e^2\omega}{k^3\left(\frac{\varkappa T}{m_e}\right)^{3/2}}e^{-\frac{m_e(\omega/k)^2}{2\varkappa T}}=0. \quad (8.29)$$

We substitute $\omega=\omega'+i\omega''$ in (8.29), remember that $\omega''\ll\omega'$, and make the real and imaginary parts vanish. In the zero approximation with respect to $r_d^2k^2$ we find

$$\omega'^2=\omega_e^2, \quad (8.30)$$

and the more precise value

$$\omega'^2=\omega_e^2+3\frac{\varkappa T}{m_e}k^2. \quad (8.31)$$

It can be seen from this that when $r_d^2k^2\ll 1$ the real part of the frequency differs but little from the plasma frequency ω_e.

Putting the imaginary part of eqn. (8.29) equal to zero and leaving the main terms we obtain the expression for $\gamma=-\omega''$

$$\gamma=\sqrt{\left(\frac{\pi}{8}\right)}\cdot\frac{\omega_e}{r_d^3k^3}e^{-1/2r_d^2k^2}. \quad (8.32)$$

The imaginary part of the frequency ω'' is found to be negative since the function $\varepsilon^{\|}(\omega, \boldsymbol{k})$ is an analytical function in the upper half-plane and therefore has singularities only in the lower half-plane.

The quantity γ is called the plasma wave damping decrement. The formula (8.32) was first derived by Landau.

It follows from the expression (8.32) that when $r_d^2k^2\ll 1$ the damping decrement is much less than ω' as was assumed above.

We can find from the formula (8.31) the magnitude of the phase velocity

$$\frac{\omega}{k} \approx \frac{\omega_e}{k} + \frac{3}{2} \cdot \frac{\varkappa T}{m_e \omega_e} k, \quad \text{when} \quad r_d^2 k^2 \ll 1$$

$$\frac{\omega}{k} \gg \sqrt{\left(\frac{\varkappa T}{m_e}\right)}. \tag{8.33}$$

Therefore for plasma electron waves the phase velocity is a function of k i.e. wave dispersion occurs.

We would also point out that the damping decrement γ is small only for long waves. Using the tables (see Faddeyeva and Teren-t'ev, 1954) compiled from eqn. (8.24) it can be found that when $kr_d \approx 1$ the damping decrement becomes comparable to the real part of the frequency.

Let us now turn to discussing the longitudinal waves in a plasma taking into account the motion of the ions.

We shall assume that the plasma is strongly non-isothermal. This means that the electron temperature is much higher than the ion temperature

$$T_e \gg T_i \tag{8.34}$$

In the first approximation we can neglect the thermal motion of the ions and assume that the distribution functions of the electrons and the ions f_e^0, f_i^0 are of the form

$$f_e^0 = \frac{1}{(2\pi m_e \varkappa T_e)^{3/2}} e^{-\frac{p^2}{2m_e \varkappa T_e}}, \quad f_i = \delta(\boldsymbol{p}). \tag{8.35}$$

We substitute the function (8.35) in the dispersion relation (8.2). We can at once integrate with respect to $\boldsymbol{p}_i$. By taking the vector $\boldsymbol{k}$ along the x-axis we can integrate with respect to p_{ey}, p_{ez}. After this we obtain the following equation:

$$1 + \frac{4\pi e^2 n_e}{k^2 \sqrt{(2\pi m_e \varkappa T_e)}} \int \frac{k \dfrac{\partial}{\partial p_x} e^{-\frac{p_x^2}{2m_e \varkappa T_e}}}{\omega - kv_x} dp_x - \frac{\omega_i^2}{\omega^2} = 0. \tag{8.36}$$

Here

$$\omega_i^2 = \frac{4\pi e_i^2 n_i}{m_i} \tag{8.37}$$

is the square of the plasma frequency for the ions.

We shall show that in an electron–ion non-isothermal plasma longitudinal waves are propagated with phase velocities much less than the thermal velocity of the electrons but much greater than the thermal velocity of the ions:

$$\sqrt{\left(\frac{\varkappa T_e}{m_e}\right)} \gg \frac{\omega}{k} \gg \sqrt{\left(\frac{\varkappa T_i}{m_i}\right)}. \tag{8.38}$$

Assuming once again that the damping decrement is small we calculate the integral in eqn. (8.36) in just the same way as in eqn. (8.27). By virtue of the condition (8.38), however, we can once again expand in powers of $\omega/k\sqrt{(\varkappa T_e/m_e)}$.

As a result we obtain the following dispersion relation

$$1+\frac{\omega_e^2 m_e}{k^2\varkappa T_e}+i\sqrt{\left(\frac{\pi}{2}\right)}\frac{\omega_e^2}{k^3}\left(\frac{m_e}{\varkappa T_e}\right)^{3/2}\omega-\frac{\omega_i^2}{\omega^2}=0. \tag{8.39}$$

Remembering that $\varkappa T_e/m_e\omega_e^2 = r_{de}^2$, we can rewrite this equation in the form

$$\omega^2 = \frac{\omega_i^2 r_{de}^2 k^2}{1+r_{de}^2 k^2} - i\sqrt{\left(\frac{\pi}{2}\right)}\frac{\omega^3}{\sqrt{\left(\frac{\varkappa T_e}{m_e}\right)}\,k(1+r_{de}^2 k^2)}. \tag{8.40}$$

From this, by putting $\omega = \omega' - i\gamma$ and remembering that $\gamma \ll \omega'$, we find

$$\omega'^2 = \frac{\omega_i^2 r_{de}^2 k^2}{1+r_{de}^2 k^2}; \quad \gamma = \sqrt{\left(\frac{\pi}{8}\right)}\frac{\omega_i^2 r_{de}^2 k^2}{\sqrt{\left(\frac{\varkappa T_e}{m_e}\right)}\,k(1+r_{de}^2 k^2)^2}. \tag{8.41}$$

For long waves when

$$r_{de}^2 k^2 \ll 1, \tag{8.42}$$

the expressions (8.41) become

$$\omega' = v_s k, \quad \gamma = v_s k\sqrt{\left(\frac{\pi}{8}\cdot\frac{m_e}{m_i}\right)} = \omega\sqrt{\left(\frac{\pi}{8}\cdot\frac{m_e}{m_i}\right)}, \tag{8.43}$$

where v_s is the velocity of sound waves in the plasma

$$v_s = \sqrt{\left(\frac{\varkappa T_e}{m_i}\right)}, \tag{8.44}$$

which is determined by the temperature of the electrons and the mass of the ions.

It can be seen from the formula (8.43) that $\gamma \ll \omega'$ since $m_e/m_i \ll 1$.

By virtue of the non-isothermal nature of the plasma the condition (8.38) for sound waves is in fact satisfied.

Let us look at another extreme case when

$$r_{de}^2 k^2 \gg 1, \tag{8.45}$$

where

$$\omega' = \omega_i, \quad \gamma = \sqrt{\left(\frac{\pi}{8}\right)} \frac{\omega_i^2}{\sqrt{\left(\frac{\varkappa T_e}{m_e}\right)} r_{de}^2 k^3}. \tag{8.46}$$

In this case the oscillations occur at the ion plasma frequency and are called ion oscillations. In the first approximation, just as for the electron oscillations, the frequency is independent of the magnitude of the wave vector $\boldsymbol{k}$.

Let us now examine the dispersion equation for transverse waves in a plasma.

The dispersion equation, which defines the frequency of the transverse waves as a function of the vector $\boldsymbol{k}$, is of the form

$$\omega^2 \varepsilon^{\perp}(\omega, \boldsymbol{k}) - c^2 k^2 = 0. \tag{8.47}$$

By substituting in this the expression (7.34) for $\varepsilon^{\perp}(\omega, \boldsymbol{k})$ we can write the dispersion relation for the transverse plasma waves in the form

$$\omega^2 = c^2 k^2 + \sum_a \frac{4\pi e_a^2 n_a \omega}{m_a} \int \frac{f_a^0}{\omega - (\boldsymbol{k} \cdot \boldsymbol{v})} d^3\boldsymbol{p}. \tag{8.48}$$

If the functions f_e^0 and f_i^0 are Maxwell distributions, then by using the tables (see Faddeyeva and Terent'ev, 1954), we can find from eqn. (8.48) the values of the frequency ω for any magnitude of the vector $\boldsymbol{k}$.

For long waves in the first approximation in the integrals we can put $1/[\omega-(\boldsymbol{k}\cdot\boldsymbol{v})] \approx 1/\omega$.

Then from the eqn. (8.48) we find

$$\omega^2 = \omega_{\mathrm{L}}^2+c^2k^2, \quad \omega_{\mathrm{L}}^2 = \sum_a \frac{4\pi e_a^2 n_a}{m_a}. \tag{8.49}$$

The frequency is a real quantity. The fact that the damping decrement vanishes is caused by the fact that

$$(f_a^0(\boldsymbol{p}))_{p=m_a\omega/k} = 0, \tag{8.50}$$

since it can be seen from the expression (8.49) that the phase velocity of the transverse waves in the plasma is greater than the velocity of light and for velocities of $v > c$ the distribution function should be equal to zero. This occurs in fact for the relativistic Maxwell distribution (see § 13).

We have discussed the question of the propagation of electromagnetic waves in a plasma using the self-consistent equations in the linear approximation. This is possible if the wave amplitudes are so small that the non-linear terms can be neglected.

For stable plasma states the amplitudes are small if the initial perturbation or the external cause of the wave propagation is small. If these conditions are not satisfied, the non-linear terms must be taken into consideration when solving the equations.

It is, of course, absolutely necessary to allow for the non-linear terms in those cases when the plasma is in a non-stable state. The question of the solution of the system of the self-consistent equations for a plasma with the non-linear terms taken into consideration is still far from being resolved. Only certain special problems have been examined.

We shall make one more point here. It follows from the solution obtained for the dispersion relation for the longitudinal waves in a plasma that the longitudinal waves in a plasma are damped if the temperature is not zero. This means that the solution of the equations for the first moments in the approximation discussed describes a dissipative process.

A question arises. How can this be made to agree with the statement in § 6 about the constant entropy in the first moments approximation?

The point is that the Maxwell distribution, for example, is only one of an infinite number of distributions of the form $f_a^0(|p|)$ which satisfy the system of equations for the first moments. Therefore the equations of the first moments are insufficient for selecting a definite solution of the form f_a^0.

The use of some definite solution indicates that we have gone outside the framework of the first moments equations, i.e. we are quietly making use of correlations or of the higher moments.

It will be shown in § 11 that the kinetic equations, which contain a contribution from the higher moments, describe the dissipative processes.

9. Propagation of Electromagnetic Waves in a Plasma Located in a Constant Magnetic Field

We proceed from the system of equations with a self-consistent field (6.8–12) for the functions f_a, $\boldsymbol{E}$, $\boldsymbol{B}$.

Just as in § 7 we assume that

$$f_a(\boldsymbol{q}, \boldsymbol{p}, t) = f_a^0(\boldsymbol{p}) + f_a^1(\boldsymbol{q}, \boldsymbol{p}, t), \quad \boldsymbol{B} = \boldsymbol{B}^0 + \boldsymbol{B}^1,$$
$$\boldsymbol{E} = \boldsymbol{E}^1. \tag{9.1}$$

Here $\boldsymbol{B}^0$ is a constant magnetic field.

We shall assume that the function f_a^0 is of the form

$$f_a^0(\boldsymbol{p}) = f_a^0(p_\perp^2, p_\parallel^2), \tag{9.2}$$

i.e. that it depends only upon the transverse ($p^\perp$) and longitudinal ($p^\parallel$) components of the vector $\boldsymbol{p}$ relative to the external magnetic field vector $\boldsymbol{B}^0$. The function $f_a^0(|p|)$ is a special case of (9.2). This being so

$$\frac{e_a}{c}\left([\boldsymbol{v} \wedge \boldsymbol{B}] \cdot \frac{\partial f_a^0}{\partial \boldsymbol{p}}\right) = 0 \tag{9.3}$$

and the equation for the function f_a^1 in the linear approximation can be written in the form

$$\frac{\partial f_a^1}{\partial t} + \left(\boldsymbol{v} \cdot \frac{\partial f_a^1}{\partial \boldsymbol{q}}\right) + \frac{e_a}{c}\left([\boldsymbol{v} \wedge \boldsymbol{B}^0] \cdot \frac{\partial f_a^1}{\partial \boldsymbol{p}}\right) = -e_a\left(\boldsymbol{E} \cdot \frac{\partial f_a^0}{\partial \boldsymbol{p}}\right). \tag{9.4}$$

Below we shall omit the superscript 0 of $\boldsymbol{B}$.

We can write eqn. (9.4) in a more convenient form.

Let us examine the solution of the equations

$$\frac{d\boldsymbol{p}}{dt} = \frac{e_a}{m_a c}[\boldsymbol{p}\wedge\boldsymbol{B}], \quad m_a\frac{d\boldsymbol{q}}{dt} = \boldsymbol{p}, \tag{9.5}$$

which are characteristics of the homogeneous equation (9.4).

The solution of eqns. (9.5) connects the values of $\boldsymbol{q}, \boldsymbol{p}$ at the time t with the values of the coordinates and momenta

$$\begin{aligned} &\boldsymbol{R}_a(t', t, \boldsymbol{p}, \boldsymbol{q}) \equiv \boldsymbol{R}_a(0, t-t', \boldsymbol{p}, \boldsymbol{q}); \\ &\boldsymbol{P}_a(t', t, \boldsymbol{p}) \equiv \boldsymbol{P}_a(0, t-t', \boldsymbol{p}) \end{aligned} \tag{9.6}$$

at the time t'.

The arguments of $\boldsymbol{R}_a, \boldsymbol{P}_a$ indicate that $\boldsymbol{R}_a, \boldsymbol{P}_a$ are the values of the momenta and coordinates at the time t', if at the time t these values are $\boldsymbol{p}, \boldsymbol{q}$.

From eqns. (9.5) we find the solution

$$\begin{aligned} \boldsymbol{p} = (\boldsymbol{P}_a\cdot\boldsymbol{b})\,\boldsymbol{b}+[[\boldsymbol{b}\wedge\boldsymbol{P}_a]\wedge\boldsymbol{b}]\cos\Omega_a(t-t') \\ +[\boldsymbol{P}_a\wedge\boldsymbol{b}]\sin\Omega_a(t-t'); \end{aligned} \tag{9.7}$$

$$\begin{aligned} \boldsymbol{q} = \boldsymbol{R}_a+\frac{(\boldsymbol{b}\cdot\boldsymbol{P}_a)\boldsymbol{b}}{m_a}(t-t')+\frac{[[\boldsymbol{b}\wedge\boldsymbol{P}_a]\wedge\boldsymbol{b}]}{m_a\Omega_a}\sin\Omega_a(t-t') \\ +\frac{[\boldsymbol{P}_a\wedge\boldsymbol{b}]}{m_a\Omega_a}(1-\cos\Omega_a(t-t')). \end{aligned} \tag{9.8}$$

Here $\boldsymbol{b} = \boldsymbol{B}/|B|$ and $\Omega_a = e_a B/m_a c$.

The inverse relations are of the form

$$\begin{aligned} \boldsymbol{P}_a(0, t-t', \boldsymbol{p}) = (\boldsymbol{b}\cdot\boldsymbol{p})\,\boldsymbol{b}+[[\boldsymbol{b}\wedge\boldsymbol{p}]\wedge\boldsymbol{b}]\cos\Omega_a(t'-t) \\ -[\boldsymbol{b}\wedge\boldsymbol{p}]\sin\Omega_a(t'-t); \end{aligned} \tag{9.9}$$

$$\begin{aligned} \boldsymbol{R}_a(0, t-t', \boldsymbol{p}, \boldsymbol{q}) = \boldsymbol{q}+(\boldsymbol{b}\cdot\boldsymbol{v})\,\boldsymbol{b}(t'-t) \\ +\frac{[[\boldsymbol{b}\wedge\boldsymbol{v}]\wedge\boldsymbol{b}]}{\Omega_a}\sin\Omega_a(t'-t) \\ -\frac{[\boldsymbol{b}\wedge\boldsymbol{v}]}{\Omega_a}(1-\cos\Omega_a(t'-t)); \quad \boldsymbol{v} = \frac{\boldsymbol{p}}{m_a}. \end{aligned} \tag{9.10}$$

Below we need the expressions (9.7–10) for the individual components. When $\boldsymbol{B} \,\|\, z$ we have from (9.7)

$$p_x = P_{ax} \cos \Omega_a(t-t') + P_{ay} \sin \Omega_a(t-t');$$
$$p_y = P_{ay} \cos \Omega_a(t-t') - P_{ax} \sin \Omega_a(t-t'), \quad p_z = P_{az}. \tag{9.7a}$$

From (9.8)

$$q_x = R_{ax} + \frac{P_{ax}}{m_a \Omega_a} \sin \Omega_a(t-t') + \frac{P_{ay}}{m_a \Omega_a} (1 - \cos \Omega_a(t-t'));$$

$$q_y = R_{ay} + \frac{P_{ay}}{m_a \Omega_a} \sin \Omega_a(t-t') - \frac{P_{ax}}{\Omega_a m_a} (1 - \cos \Omega_a(t-t')). \tag{9.8a}$$

When $\boldsymbol{B} = 0$, $q_z = R_{az} + v_z(t-t')$ follows from (9.9, 10).

$$\boldsymbol{P} = \boldsymbol{p}, \quad \boldsymbol{R} = \boldsymbol{q} - \boldsymbol{v}(t-t'). \tag{9.11}$$

Using the formulae (9.9, 10), eqn. (9.4) can be put in the form

$$f_a^1(\boldsymbol{q}, \boldsymbol{p}, t) = f_a^1(\boldsymbol{R}_a(0, t-t_0, \boldsymbol{p}, \boldsymbol{q}), \boldsymbol{P}_a(0, t-t_0, \boldsymbol{p}), t_0)$$
$$- e_a \int_{t_0}^{t} \left(\boldsymbol{E}(\boldsymbol{R}_a(0, t-t', \boldsymbol{p}, \boldsymbol{q}), t') \cdot \left(\frac{\partial f_a^0}{\partial \boldsymbol{p}} \right)_{\boldsymbol{p} \to \boldsymbol{P}_a(0, t-t', \boldsymbol{p})} \right) dt'. \tag{9.12}$$

The first term on the right-hand side of (9.12) is determined by the initial value of the function f_a^1 and is the solution of the homogeneous equation (9.4), whilst the second term is the solution of a non-homogeneous equation (9.4). Below we shall take $t_0 = 0$.

We use eqn. (9.12) to connect the value of the current $\boldsymbol{j}$ with the value of the electrical field strength $\boldsymbol{E}$. To do this we multiply (9.12) by $e_a n_a \boldsymbol{v}$, sum over a and integrate over $\boldsymbol{p}$.

We can write the expression obtained in this way, just as we did above, in the form of two components

$$\boldsymbol{j}(\boldsymbol{q}, t) = \boldsymbol{j}^{\mathrm{e}} + \boldsymbol{j}^{\mathrm{i}}. \tag{9.13}$$

We obtain the following expression for the external current $\boldsymbol{j}^{\mathrm{e}}$:

$$\boldsymbol{j}^{\mathrm{e}}(\boldsymbol{q}, t) = \sum_a e_a n_a \int \boldsymbol{v} f_a^1(\boldsymbol{R}_a(0, t, \boldsymbol{p}, \boldsymbol{q}), \boldsymbol{P}_a(0, t, \boldsymbol{p}), 0)\, d^3\boldsymbol{p}. \tag{9.14}$$

The induced current $\boldsymbol{j}^{\mathrm{i}}$ is defined by the expression

$$\boldsymbol{j}^{\mathrm{i}}(\boldsymbol{q}, t) = -\sum_a e_a^2 n_a \int_0^t dt' \int d^3\boldsymbol{p}$$
$$\times \boldsymbol{v}\left(\left(\boldsymbol{E}(\boldsymbol{R}_a(0, t-t', \boldsymbol{p}, \boldsymbol{q},), t')\cdot\left(\frac{\partial f_a^0}{\partial \boldsymbol{p}}\right)_{\boldsymbol{p}\to \boldsymbol{P}_a(0, t-t', \boldsymbol{p})}\right)\right). \tag{9.15}$$

In (9.15) we carry out a two-variable Fourier transform with respect to $\boldsymbol{q}$ and a single-variable one with respect to t. Using the folding theorem we obtain

$$\boldsymbol{j}^{\mathrm{i}}(\omega, \boldsymbol{k}) = -\sum_a e_a^2 n_a \int_0^\infty dt \int d^3\boldsymbol{p} e^{-\Delta t + i[\omega t + (\boldsymbol{k}\cdot\boldsymbol{R}_a(0, t, \boldsymbol{p}, 0))]}\boldsymbol{v}$$
$$\times \left(\boldsymbol{E}(\omega, \boldsymbol{k})\cdot \frac{\partial f_a^0}{\partial \boldsymbol{p}}\right)_{\boldsymbol{p}\to \boldsymbol{P}_a(0, t, \boldsymbol{p})}. \tag{9.16}$$

By comparing (9.16) with (7.23) we obtain the expression for the conductivity tensor of a plasma located in a magnetic field.

$$\sigma_{ij}(\omega, \boldsymbol{k}) = -\sum_a e_a^2 n_a \int_0^\infty dt \int d^3\boldsymbol{p}$$
$$\times e^{-\Delta t + i[\omega t + (\boldsymbol{k}\cdot\boldsymbol{R}_a(0, t, \boldsymbol{p}, 0))]}\, v_i\left(\frac{\partial f_a^0}{\partial p_j}\right)_{\boldsymbol{p}\to \boldsymbol{P}_a(0, t, \boldsymbol{p})}. \tag{9.17}$$

When $\boldsymbol{B} = 0$ the expression (9.17) is the same as (7.24). In order to make this limiting transition we must use (9.11) and remember that

$$\int_0^\infty e^{-\Delta t + i[\omega - (\boldsymbol{k}\cdot\boldsymbol{v})]t}\, dt = \frac{i}{\omega - (\boldsymbol{k}\cdot\boldsymbol{v}) + i\Delta}. \tag{9.18}$$

We transform the expression (9.17). We make use of the equality

$$v_i\left(\frac{\partial f_a^0(\boldsymbol{p})}{\partial p_j}\right)_{\boldsymbol{p}\to \boldsymbol{P}_a} = v_i \frac{\partial f_a^0(\boldsymbol{P}_a)}{\partial p_k}\cdot\frac{dp_k}{dP_{aj}}. \tag{9.19}$$

For functions of the form of (9.2)

$$f_a^0(\boldsymbol{P}_a) = f_a^0(\boldsymbol{p}). \tag{9.20}$$

Using (9.20) and the formulae (9.7a) and (9.9) the expression (9.19) can be written in the form

$$\frac{1}{m_a}\frac{\partial f_a^0(\boldsymbol{p})}{\partial p_i} P_{aj}(0, t, \boldsymbol{p}). \tag{9.21}$$

The expression (9.17) may be expressed in the form

$$\sigma_{ij}(\omega, \boldsymbol{k}) = -\sum_a \frac{e_a^2 n_a}{m_a} \int_0^\infty dt$$

$$\times \int d^3\boldsymbol{p} e^{-\Delta t + i[\omega t + (\boldsymbol{k}\cdot\boldsymbol{R}_a(0,\, t,\, \boldsymbol{p},\, 0))]} P_{aj}(0, t, p) \frac{\partial f_a^0(\boldsymbol{p})}{\partial p_i}. \qquad (9.22)$$

The dielectric-constant tensor is connected with the conductivity tensor by the expression (7.26)

$$\varepsilon_{ij}^+ = \delta_{ij} + i\,\frac{4\pi}{\omega + i\Delta}\,\sigma_{ij}^+. \qquad (9.23)$$

The index "+" means that the appropriate functions are analytical in the upper half-plane.

In the expression (9.17) (or (9.22)) we can integrate over t. The corresponding calculations will be given in § 15 for the case of a Coulomb plasma.

Here we give only the final expression for the tensor ε_{ij}:

$$\varepsilon_{ij}^+ = \delta_{ij} + \sum_a \frac{4\pi e_a^2 n_a}{\omega + i\Delta} \sum_{n=-\infty}^{\infty} \int \frac{\Pi_{ij}^{n,a}}{\omega - n\Omega_a - k^{\parallel} v^{\parallel} + i\Delta} \cdot \frac{\partial f_a^0}{\partial \dfrac{p^2}{2m_a}}\, d^3\boldsymbol{p}.$$

In this expression

$$\Pi_{ij}^{n,a} = \begin{vmatrix} v_\perp^2 \left(n \dfrac{I_n}{\alpha_a}\right)^2 & i v_\perp^2 \left(n \dfrac{I_n}{\alpha_a}\right) I_n' & v^\perp v^\parallel \dfrac{n I_n^2}{\alpha_a} \\ -i v_\perp^2 \left(n \dfrac{I_n}{\alpha_a}\right) I_n' & v_\perp^2 (I_n')^2 & -i v^\perp v^\parallel I_n I_n' \\ v^\perp v^\parallel \dfrac{n I_n^2}{\alpha_a} & i v^\perp v^\parallel I_n I_n' & v_\parallel^2 I_n^2 \end{vmatrix}$$

Here we have used the notations: $v^\perp$, $v^\parallel$, $k^\perp$, $k^\parallel$ are the transverse and longitudinal components of the vectors $\boldsymbol{v}$, $\boldsymbol{k}$ in relation to the vector $\boldsymbol{B}$, $\alpha_a = k_\perp v_\perp / \Omega_a$, $I_n = I_n(\alpha_a)$ is a Bessel function of the nth order and I_n' is its derivative.

We can now find the dispersion relation for a plasma located in the magnetic field. We turn to eqns. (7.35, 36) to do this.

By using the expression $D_i = \varepsilon_{ij}E_j$ and remembering that $[\boldsymbol{k} \wedge [\boldsymbol{k} \wedge \boldsymbol{E}]] = \boldsymbol{k}(\boldsymbol{k}\cdot\boldsymbol{E}) - \boldsymbol{E}k^2$, we can write the homogeneous equation (7.35) in the form

$$\left(k_i k_j - \delta_{ij}k^2 + \frac{\omega^2}{c^2}\,\varepsilon_{ij}\right) E_j = 0. \tag{9.24a}$$

From the solubility condition for this system of equations we find the dispersion relation

$$\left| k^2\delta_{ij} - k_i k_j - \frac{\omega^2}{c^2}\,\varepsilon_{ij}(\omega, \boldsymbol{k}) \right| = 0. \tag{9.24}$$

When there is no magnetic field in the isotropic case the tensor ε_{ij} depends only upon the components of one vector and therefore can be represented in the form (7.29). In this case eqn. (9.24) degenerates into two equations: the dispersion relations for the longitudinal and transverse waves. This means that when there is no magnetic field the longitudinal and transverse waves are propagated independently in the linear approximation. When there is a magnetic field it is generally impossible to make this division of eqn. (9.24).

Let us examine some important special cases.

1. *Waves in a cold plasma.* We make the temperature T_a of all the plasma components equal to zero. In this approximation

$$f_a^0(\boldsymbol{p}) = \delta(\boldsymbol{p}).$$

We substitute this expression in the formula (9.22), integrate by parts and carry out the integration with respect to $\boldsymbol{p}$.

Using (9.23) we obtain the expression

$$\varepsilon_{ij}^{+} = \delta_{ij} + i\sum_a \frac{4\pi e_a^2 n_a}{m_a(\omega + i\Delta)} \int_0^\infty e^{-\Delta t + i\omega t}\, \frac{dP_{aj}(0, t, \boldsymbol{p})}{dp_i}\, dt. \tag{9.25}$$

By means of formula (9.9) we find

$$\frac{dP_{aj}}{dp_i} = \begin{vmatrix} \cos\Omega_a t & \sin\Omega_a t & 0 \\ -\sin\Omega_a t & \cos\Omega_a t & 0 \\ 0 & 0 & 1 \end{vmatrix} \tag{9.26}$$

We substitute (9.26) in (9.25), integrate over t and take the limit as $\Delta \to 0$. As a result we obtain the following expressions for the components of the tensor ε_{ij}:

$$\varepsilon_{11} = \varepsilon_{22} = 1 - \sum_a \frac{4\pi e_a^2 n_a}{m_a} \cdot \frac{1}{\omega^2 - \Omega_a^2};$$

$$\varepsilon_{33} = 1 - \sum_a \frac{4\pi e_a^2 n_a}{m_a \omega^2} = 1 - \frac{\omega_L^2}{\omega^2};$$

$$\varepsilon_{12} = \varepsilon_{21}^* = i \sum_a \frac{4\pi e_a^2 n_a}{m_a} \frac{\Omega_a}{\omega(\omega^2 - \Omega_a^2)}; \tag{9.27}$$

$$\varepsilon_{13} = \varepsilon_{23} = \varepsilon_{31} = \varepsilon_{32} = 0.$$

In this approximation the tensor ε_{ij} is Hermitean, i.e.

$$\varepsilon_{ij} = \varepsilon_{ij}^* \quad \text{or} \quad \varepsilon_{ij}(\boldsymbol{B}) = \varepsilon_{ji}(-\boldsymbol{B}). \tag{9.28}$$

This means that there is no absorption in this approximation, i.e. the dissipative processes are not taken into account.

Therefore when there is an external magnetic field the plasma's dielectric constant tensor is complex even if absorption is not taken into consideration.

A medium which is characterized by a complex dielectric constant tensor is called magneto-active or gyrotropic when there is no absorption.

In the case in question the tensor ε_{ij} can be given in the form

$$\varepsilon_{ij} = \begin{pmatrix} \varepsilon_1 & ig & 0 \\ -ig & \varepsilon_1 & 0 \\ 0 & 0 & \varepsilon_2 \end{pmatrix} \tag{9.29}$$

When thermal motion and absorption are taken into consideration the tensor ε_{ij} is not Hermitean. It can always be split into components, however: the Hermitean and the anti-Hermitean part.

Indeed, in an arbitrary case the tensor ε_{ij} can be written as the sum of two tensors

$$\varepsilon_{ij} = \frac{1}{2}(\varepsilon_{ij} + \varepsilon_{ji}^*) + \frac{1}{2}(\varepsilon_{ij} - \varepsilon_{ji}^*), \tag{9.30}$$

the first of which is Hermitean and the second anti-Hermitean. The second component of the tensor defines the absorption in the case of a weakly absorbing medium (see formula (2.84)).

In accordance with (2.87) the amount of heat evolved per unit time and unit volume at a frequency ω is defined by the expression

$$Q(\omega) = \frac{1}{2\pi}\,\omega\varepsilon''_{ij}(\omega)E_iE_j^* = -\frac{i\omega}{4\pi}\left(\varepsilon_{ij}(\omega)-\varepsilon_{ji}^*\right)E_iE_j^*. \quad (9.31)$$

It follows from formula (9.23) that

$$-i\omega(\varepsilon_{ij}-\varepsilon_{ji}^*) = \frac{\sigma_{ij}+\sigma_{ji}^*}{4\pi},$$

so that the expression (9.31) can be written in the form

$$Q(\omega) = \frac{\sigma_{ij}+\sigma_{ji}^*}{16\pi^2}E_iE_j^*, \quad (9.32)$$

i.e. the amount of heat evolved is defined by the Hermitean component of the conductivity tensor.

Let us now proceed to the solution of the dispersion relation (9.24). It is sufficient to discuss an electron plasma to explain the basic features of the waves in a cold magneto-active plasma. All the ions do really is to form a positively charged background.

We use $\omega_e = \sqrt{(4\pi e^2 n_e/m_e)}$ to denote the plasma frequency of the electrons. For an electron plasma the formulae (9.27) become:

$$\varepsilon_1 = \varepsilon_{11} = \varepsilon_{22} = 1-\frac{\omega_e^2}{\omega^2-\Omega_e^2}, \quad \varepsilon_2 = \varepsilon_{33} = 1-\frac{\omega_e^2}{\omega^2},$$

$$ig = \varepsilon_{12} = \varepsilon_{21}^* = i\frac{\omega_e^2\Omega_e}{\omega(\omega^2-\Omega_e^2)}, \quad (9.33)$$

$$\varepsilon_{13} = \varepsilon_{23} = \varepsilon_{31} = \varepsilon_{32} = 0.$$

Here we have used the notations of (9.29) for the components of the tensor ε_{ij}.

If the waves are propagated along the magnetic field we can assume that the vectors

$$\boldsymbol{k} \,||\, z, \quad \boldsymbol{B} \,||\, z \quad (9.34)$$

and the system of eqns. (9.24) becomes:

$$\left(\frac{\omega^2}{c^2}\varepsilon_1-k^2\right)E_x+i\frac{\omega^2}{c^2}gE_y=0,$$
$$-i\frac{\omega^2}{c^2}gE_x+\left(\frac{\omega^2}{c^2}\varepsilon_1-k^2\right)E_y=0, \tag{9.35}$$

$$\varepsilon_2E_z=0. \tag{9.36}$$

Here we have used the notations of (9.29) for the tensor components ε_{ij}.

It follows from these equations that when the waves are propagated along the magnetic field the dispersion equation degenerates into the two:

$$\varepsilon_2=0 \quad \text{or} \quad 1-\frac{\omega_e^2}{\omega^2}=0, \tag{9.37}$$

$$\left(\frac{\omega^2}{c^2}\varepsilon_1-k^2\right)^2-\left(\frac{\omega^2}{c^2}\right)^2g^2=0. \tag{9.38}$$

The first of these equations is the dispersion relation for longitudinal waves in a plasma. The second is the dispersion relation for transverse waves.

We shall first show that when $\boldsymbol{B}=0$ the second equation agrees with the dispersion relation obtained in § 8. In fact, when $\boldsymbol{B}=0$

$$g=0, \quad \varepsilon_2=\varepsilon_1=1-\frac{\omega_e^2}{\omega^2}\equiv\varepsilon. \tag{9.39}$$

Equation (9.38) in this case provides two identical solutions

$$\omega^2=\omega_e^2+c^2k^2,$$

agreeing with (8.49).

When $\boldsymbol{B}=0$ the tensor ε_{ij} for a cold plasma is of the form

$$\varepsilon_{ij}=\left(\delta_{ij}-\frac{k_ik_j}{k^2}\right)\varepsilon^{\perp}+\frac{k_ik_j}{k^2}\varepsilon^{||}=\varepsilon\delta_{ij}. \tag{9.40}$$

Here we have taken into consideration the fact that for a cold plasma when $\boldsymbol{B}=0$

$$\varepsilon^{||}=\varepsilon^{\perp}\equiv\varepsilon=1-\frac{\omega_e^2}{\omega^2}.$$

Let us examine eqn. (9.38) when $\boldsymbol{B} \neq 0$.

We can rewrite it in another form:

$$(n^2-\varepsilon_1)^2 = g^2, \tag{9.41}$$

where

$$n = \frac{ck}{\omega}. \tag{9.42}$$

Depending upon the problem under discussion we may be interested in the solution of eqn. (9.41) for ω for a fixed k, i.e. for a fixed wavelength, or in the solution of eqn. (9.41) for n with a fixed frequency. In the latter case we find from eqn. (9.41)

$$n_{1,2}^2 = \varepsilon_1 \pm g. \tag{9.43}$$

Therefore three waves are propagated along the magnetic field: one longitudinal and two transverse. The phase velocities of the transverse waves when $\boldsymbol{B} \neq 0$ are different.

Let us examine the question of the polarization of the transverse waves. To do this we turn to eqns. (9.35). Using the solution (9.43) we can find the ratio of the components E_x, E_y:

$$\left(\frac{E_x}{E_y}\right)_{1,2} = \pm i. \tag{9.44}$$

Since $\pm i = e^{\pm i\pi/2}$ it follows from (9.44) that the maximum values of the components E_x, E_y are shifted a quarter of a wavelength. Therefore the vector $\boldsymbol{E}$ describes a helix, i.e. circular polarization occurs. The wave with the refractive index n_2 is called the ordinary and the wave with an index n_1 the extraordinary wave.

It follows from (9.44) that the end of the vector of an ordinary wave turns clockwise and of an extraordinary wave anticlockwise.

If the vector $\boldsymbol{k}$ is directed at an angle θ to the vector $\boldsymbol{B}$, then instead of eqn. (9.38) we obtain the more complicated equation

$$(\varepsilon_1 \sin^2\theta+\varepsilon_2\cos^2\theta)n^4+[(g^2-\varepsilon_1^2+\varepsilon_1\varepsilon_2)\sin^2\theta-2\varepsilon_1\varepsilon_2]n^2 + \varepsilon_2(\varepsilon_1^2-g^2) = 0. \tag{9.45}$$

This equation degenerates into two equations for longitudinal and transverse waves only when $\theta = 0$.

From (9.45) we find two solutions for n^2

$$n_{1,2}^2 = \frac{1}{2(\varepsilon_1 \sin^2\theta + \varepsilon_2 \cos^2\theta)} \{(\varepsilon_1^2 - g^2 - \varepsilon_1\varepsilon_2)\sin^2\theta + 2\varepsilon_1\varepsilon_2 \pm \sqrt{[(\varepsilon_1^2 - g^2 - \varepsilon_1\varepsilon_2)^2 \sin^4\theta + 4\varepsilon_1^2 g^2 \cos^2\theta]}\}. \quad (9.46)$$

Thermal motion in many ways alters the nature of the propagation of waves whose phase velocities are comparable with their thermal velocities. In this case new effects, e.g. resonance at frequencies that are multiples of Ω_a, appear that cannot be obtained if we neglect the thermal motion. In addition, thermal motion determines the wave damping.

Here we shall take only one example which has received insufficient attention in published papers. Other cases of wave propagation in a magneto-active plasma are discussed in detail in other books (see Silin and Rukhadze, 1961; Ginzburg, 1964; and Leontovich, 1963).

2. *Propagation of magnetohydrodynamic and magnetosonic waves in a non-isothermal plasma.* Let us return to the expression (9.16) for $\boldsymbol{j}^{\mathrm{i}}(\omega, \boldsymbol{k})$. We shall discuss it for the case when the f_a^0 are Maxwell distributions with components at different temperatures, i.e.

$$f_a^0 = \frac{1}{(2\pi m_a \varkappa T_a)^{3/2}} e^{-\frac{p^2}{2m_a \varkappa T_a}}. \quad (9.47)$$

We substitute this expression in the formula (9.16) and replace the variable $\boldsymbol{p}$ by $\boldsymbol{P}_a$. The Jacobian of this transform is equal to unity. As a result we obtain the expression

$$\boldsymbol{j}^{\mathrm{i}}(\omega, \boldsymbol{k}) = -\sum_a \frac{e_a^2 n_a}{m_a} \int_0^\infty dt \int d^3\boldsymbol{P}_a\, e^{-\Delta t + i\left[\omega t + \left(\boldsymbol{k}\cdot\boldsymbol{R}_a(0,\, t,\, \boldsymbol{p}(\boldsymbol{P}_a), 0)\right)\right]} \times \boldsymbol{p}(\boldsymbol{P}_a) \left(\boldsymbol{E}(\omega, \boldsymbol{k}) \cdot \frac{\partial f_a^0(\boldsymbol{P}_a)}{\partial \boldsymbol{P}_a}\right). \quad (9.48)$$

The function $\boldsymbol{p}(\boldsymbol{P}_a)$ is defined by the expression (9.7).

We transform the expression $\left(\boldsymbol{k}\cdot\boldsymbol{R}_a(0, t, \boldsymbol{p}(\boldsymbol{P}_a), 0)\right)$. To do this we substitute the expression (9.7) in (9.10):

$$\boldsymbol{R}_a(0, t, \boldsymbol{p}(\boldsymbol{P}_a), 0) = -\left\{\frac{(\boldsymbol{b}\cdot\boldsymbol{P}_a)\boldsymbol{b}}{m_a} t + \frac{[[\boldsymbol{b}\wedge\boldsymbol{P}_a]\wedge\boldsymbol{b}]}{m_a\Omega_a} \sin\Omega_a t + \frac{[\boldsymbol{P}\wedge\boldsymbol{b}]}{m_a\Omega_a}(1-\cos\Omega_a t)\right\}. \quad (9.49)$$

Using this expression the scalar product $(\boldsymbol{k}\cdot\boldsymbol{R}_a(0,\,t,\,\boldsymbol{p}(\boldsymbol{P}_a,\,0)))$ can be written in the form

$$\big(\boldsymbol{k}\cdot\boldsymbol{R}_a(0,\,t,\,\boldsymbol{p}(\boldsymbol{P}_a),\,0)\big) = -\Bigg\{P_{ax}\left(\frac{k_x}{m_a\Omega_a}\sin\Omega_a t - \frac{k_y}{m_a\Omega_a}(1-\cos\Omega_a t)\right)+P_{ay}\left(\frac{k_y}{m_a\Omega_a}\sin\Omega_a t + \frac{k_x}{m_a\Omega_a}(1-\cos\Omega_a t)\right)+\frac{P_{az}}{m_a}k_z t\Bigg\} = (\boldsymbol{P}_a\cdot\boldsymbol{K}_a(0,t,\boldsymbol{k})). \tag{9.50}$$

The vector $\boldsymbol{K}_a$ is defined by the expression

$$\boldsymbol{K}_a(0,\,t,\,\boldsymbol{k}) = -\left\{\frac{(\boldsymbol{b}\cdot\boldsymbol{k})\boldsymbol{b}}{m_a}t+\frac{[[\boldsymbol{b}\wedge\boldsymbol{k}]\wedge\boldsymbol{b}]}{m_a\Omega_a}\sin\Omega_a t - \frac{[\boldsymbol{k}\wedge\boldsymbol{b}]}{m_a\Omega_a}(1-\cos\Omega_a t)\right\}. \tag{9.51}$$

Using (9.50) we can write the expression (9.48) in the form

$$\boldsymbol{j}^{\mathrm{i}}(\omega,\,\boldsymbol{k}) = -\sum_a\frac{e_a^2 n_a}{m_a}\int_0^\infty dt\int d^3\boldsymbol{P}_a e^{-\Delta t+i[\omega t+(\boldsymbol{K}_a\cdot\boldsymbol{P}_a)]} \times\boldsymbol{p}(\boldsymbol{P}_a)\left(\boldsymbol{E}(\omega,\,\boldsymbol{k})\cdot\frac{\partial f_a^0}{\partial\boldsymbol{P}_a}\right). \tag{9.52}$$

In (9.52) we integrate by parts with respect to $\boldsymbol{P}_a$

$$\boldsymbol{j}^{\mathrm{i}}(\omega,\,\boldsymbol{k}) = \sum_a\frac{e_a^2 n_a}{m_a}\int_0^\infty dt\int d^3\boldsymbol{P}_a e^{-\Delta t+i[\omega t+(\boldsymbol{K}_a\cdot\boldsymbol{P}_a)]} \times\big(\boldsymbol{p}(\boldsymbol{E})+i\boldsymbol{p}(\boldsymbol{P}_a)(\boldsymbol{E}\cdot\boldsymbol{K}_a)\big)f_a^0. \tag{9.52a}$$

The vector $\boldsymbol{p}(\boldsymbol{E})$ is defined by (9.7) in which $\boldsymbol{P}_a$ $\boldsymbol{E}$.

We substitute the Maxwell distributions (9.47) in this and integrate with respect to $\boldsymbol{P}_a$. For this we use the value of the integrals

$$I^a = \frac{1}{(2\pi m_a\varkappa T_a)^{3/2}}\int e^{i(\boldsymbol{K}_a\cdot\boldsymbol{P}_a)-\frac{P_a^2}{2m_a\varkappa T_a}}d^3\boldsymbol{P}_a = e^{-\frac{1}{2}m_a\varkappa T_a K_a^2}; \tag{9.53}$$

$$I_i^a = \frac{1}{(2\pi m_a\varkappa T_a)^{3/2}}\int P_{ai}e^{i(\boldsymbol{K}_a\cdot\boldsymbol{P}_a)-\frac{P_a^2}{2m_a\varkappa T_a}}d^3\boldsymbol{P}_a = -i\frac{\partial I^a}{\partial K_{ai}} = im_a\varkappa T_a K_{ai}I^a. \tag{9.54}$$

As a result we obtain the following expression for the current:

$$\boldsymbol{j}^{\mathrm{i}}(\omega, \boldsymbol{k}) = \sum_a \frac{e_a^2 n_a}{m_a} \int_0^\infty dt e^{-\Delta t + i\omega t - \frac{1}{2} m_a \varkappa T_a K_a^2}$$
$$\times [\boldsymbol{p}(\boldsymbol{E}) - m_a \varkappa T_a \boldsymbol{p}(\boldsymbol{K}_a)(\boldsymbol{E}\cdot\boldsymbol{K}_a)]. \tag{9.55}$$

In this formula the vectors $\boldsymbol{p}(\boldsymbol{E}), \boldsymbol{p}(\boldsymbol{K})$ are defined by the formula (9.7) in which we must take $t' = 0$ and replace the vector $\boldsymbol{P}_a$ by the vectors $\boldsymbol{E}$, $\boldsymbol{K}_a$ respectively. The vector $\boldsymbol{K}_a$ is defined by the expression (9.51).

Let us make use of the formula (9.55) to examine the expression for the current in a cold plasma. For this we take $T_a = 0$ in (9.55). Then we obtain

$$\boldsymbol{j}^{\mathrm{i}}(\omega, \boldsymbol{k}) = \sum_a \frac{e_a^2 n_a}{m_a} \int_0^\infty dt e^{-\Delta t + i\omega t} \boldsymbol{p}(\boldsymbol{E}). \tag{9.56}$$

In this we substitute the expression for $\boldsymbol{p}(\boldsymbol{E})$ and integrate over t. Using the values of the integrals

$$\int_0^\infty e^{-\Delta t - i\omega t} \cos \Omega_a t \, dt = \frac{i(\omega + i\Delta)}{(\omega + i\Delta)^2 - \Omega_a^2},$$
$$\int_0^\infty e^{-\Delta t + i\omega t} \sin \Omega_a t \, dt = -\frac{\Omega_a}{(\omega + i\Delta)^2 - \Omega_a^2}, \tag{9.57}$$

we obtain the following expression for the current:

$$\boldsymbol{j}^{\mathrm{i}}(\omega, \boldsymbol{k}) = \sum_a \frac{e_a^2 n_a}{m_a} \left\{ i \frac{(\boldsymbol{b}\cdot\boldsymbol{E})\boldsymbol{b}}{\omega + i\Delta} \right.$$
$$\left. + \frac{i(\omega + i\Delta)}{(\omega + i\Delta)^2 - \Omega_a^2} [[\boldsymbol{b}\wedge\boldsymbol{E}]\wedge\boldsymbol{b}] - \frac{\Omega_a}{(\omega + i\Delta)^2 - \Omega_a^2} [\boldsymbol{E}\wedge\boldsymbol{b}] \right\}. \tag{9.57a}$$

From this, by using the formula (9.23) when $\Delta \to 0$ we obtain the tensor with the components defined by the formula (9.27).

We can now proceed to the solution of the question of the propagation of magnetohydrodynamic and magnetosonic waves in a non-isothermal plasma.

In a non-isothermal plasma $T_{\mathrm{e}} \gg T_{\mathrm{i}}$. We denote the thermal velocities of the electrons and ions by

$$V_{T_{\mathrm{e}}} = \sqrt{\left(\frac{\varkappa T_{\mathrm{e}}}{m_{\mathrm{e}}}\right)}, \quad V_{T_{\mathrm{i}}} = \sqrt{\left(\frac{\varkappa T_{\mathrm{i}}}{m_{\mathrm{i}}}\right)}, \quad V_{T_{\mathrm{e}}} \gg V_{T_{\mathrm{i}}}. \tag{9.58}$$

Let us examine the waves, the phase velocities $\omega/k = V_{\text{ph}}$ of which satisfy the condition

$$V_{T_i} \ll \frac{\omega}{k} \ll V_{T_e}. \tag{9.59}$$

We shall find for them the expressions for the ion and electron currents.

When calculating the ion current we can, by virtue of the condition $T_e \gg T_i$, put $T_i = 0$. Allowing for the thermal motion of the ions leads only to small corrections.

In this approximation we can use the formula (9.57) to obtain the expression for the ion current.

Using the identity $[[\boldsymbol{b} \wedge \boldsymbol{E}] \wedge \boldsymbol{b}] = \boldsymbol{E} - \boldsymbol{b}(\boldsymbol{E} \cdot \boldsymbol{b})$ we can write the expression for the ion current in the form

$$\boldsymbol{j}_i^i = -\frac{e_i^2 n_i}{m_i[(\omega + i\Delta)^2 - \Omega_i^2]} \left\{ \Omega_i [\boldsymbol{E} \wedge \boldsymbol{b}] + \frac{i\Omega_i^2}{\omega + i\Delta} \boldsymbol{b}(\boldsymbol{E} \wedge \boldsymbol{b}) - i(\omega + i\Delta)\boldsymbol{E} \right\}. \tag{9.60}$$

Let us now examine the expression for the electron component of the current defined by the formula (9.55).

In the expression for the electron current there are three time parameters:

$$\tau_\omega = \frac{1}{\omega} = \frac{1}{V_{\text{ph}} k}, \quad \tau_{V_{T_e}} = \frac{1}{V_{T_e} k}, \quad \tau_{\Omega_e} = \frac{1}{\Omega_e}. \tag{9.61}$$

We shall omit the suffix e from T_e since $T_i = 0$.

For the case when the wavelength is much greater than the Larmor radius V_T/Ω_e for the electrons, i.e. when

$$\frac{k V_T}{\Omega_e} \ll 1 \tag{9.62}$$

and when the condition (9.59) is satisfied, the values of the parameters (9.61) satisfy the inequalities

$$\tau_\omega \gg \tau_{V_T} \gg \tau_{\Omega_e} \quad \text{or} \quad V_{\text{ph}} \ll V_T \ll \frac{\Omega_e}{k}. \tag{9.63}$$

In the expression for $\boldsymbol{j}_{\mathrm{e}}^{\mathrm{i}}(\omega, \boldsymbol{k})$, which follows from (9.55), there is the quantity K_a^2. Using (9.51) when $a = \mathrm{e}$ we obtain for K_{e}^2 the expression

$$K_{\mathrm{e}}^2 = \frac{(\boldsymbol{b}\cdot\boldsymbol{k})^2}{m_{\mathrm{e}}^2}t^2 + 2\frac{[\boldsymbol{k}\wedge\boldsymbol{b}]^2}{m_{\mathrm{e}}^2}\frac{(1-\cos\Omega_{\mathrm{e}}t)}{\Omega^2}. \tag{9.64}$$

The main contribution to the integral in t applies to the region $t \lesssim \tau_{V_T}$. Hence from (9.64), we have for the angles for which

$$\tan^2\theta \ll \frac{\Omega_{\mathrm{e}}^2}{V_T^2k^2} = \left(\frac{\tau_{V_T}}{\tau_{\Omega_{\mathrm{e}}}}\right)^2 \text{ that } K_{\mathrm{e}}^2 \approx \frac{(\boldsymbol{b}\cdot\boldsymbol{k})t^2}{m_{\mathrm{e}}^2}, \tag{9.65}$$

i.e. the second term in (9.64) is much less than the first. By virtue of (9.63) the condition (9.65) is satisfied for practically all angles θ.

Consider now the expression for $\boldsymbol{j}_{\mathrm{e}}^{\mathrm{i}}$ in the zero approximation in the parameter $\tau_{\Omega_{\mathrm{e}}}/\tau_{V_T}$. In this approximation in the formula for $\boldsymbol{j}_{\mathrm{e}}^{\mathrm{i}}$ all the terms which contain $\cos\Omega_{\mathrm{e}}t$, $\sin\Omega_{\mathrm{e}}t$ and $1/\Omega_{\mathrm{e}}$ can be omitted. We therefore obtain the expression:

$$\boldsymbol{j}_{\mathrm{e}}^{\mathrm{i}} = \frac{e_{\mathrm{e}}^2n_{\mathrm{e}}}{m_{\mathrm{e}}}\int_0^\infty \left\{\boldsymbol{b}(\boldsymbol{E}\cdot\boldsymbol{b}) - \frac{\varkappa T}{m_{\mathrm{e}}}\boldsymbol{b}(\boldsymbol{E}\cdot\boldsymbol{b})(\boldsymbol{b}\cdot\boldsymbol{k})t^2\right\} e^{-\Delta t + i\omega t - \frac{\varkappa T}{2m_{\mathrm{e}}}k^2\cos^2\theta\, t^2}\,dt. \tag{9.66}$$

Given the conditions (9.59, 62), $\omega \ll \tau_{V_T}$.

Since the main contribution to the integral applies to the region $t \lesssim \tau_{V_T}$, within the integral one may put

$$e^{-i\omega\tau} = 1 - i\omega\tau - \frac{(\omega\tau)^2}{2}.$$

Therefore, performing the integration in (9.66), we get

$$\boldsymbol{j}_{\mathrm{e}}^{\mathrm{i}}(\omega, \boldsymbol{k}) = \frac{e_{\mathrm{e}}^2n_{\mathrm{e}}}{m_{\mathrm{e}}}\left\{\frac{\sqrt{\pi}}{4a^3}\omega^2 + i\frac{\omega}{2a^2}\right\}\boldsymbol{b}(\boldsymbol{E}\cdot\boldsymbol{b});$$

$$a^2 = \frac{\varkappa T}{2m_{\mathrm{e}}}(\boldsymbol{k}\cdot\boldsymbol{b})^2. \tag{9.67}$$

Here and below we put $\Delta = 0$. Since Δ only enters the initial formulae in the combination $\omega = \omega + i\Delta$, in order to obtain formulae which hold for finite Δ, we must make the substitution $\omega \to \omega + i\Delta$.

Our expression implies that the real part of the current which determines the wave attenuation, is proportional to the second power of the small parameter $\omega\tau_{V_T}$, whilst the imaginary part is proportional to its first power.

The expression (9.67), is, of course, incomplete since all the terms containing the second small parameter $\tau_{\Omega_e}/\tau_{V_T} = V_T k/\Omega_e$ have been discarded.

We must thus obtain a more precise expression from (9.55), namely, one which is correct to order $(V_T k/\Omega_e)^2$ for the real part of the current, and to order $(V_T k/\Omega_e)$ for the imaginary part.

The corresponding expression for the electron current is

$$j_e^i(\omega, \boldsymbol{k}) = -i\frac{\omega_i^2}{4\pi}\frac{\omega}{v_s^2}\frac{\boldsymbol{b}(\boldsymbol{E}\cdot\boldsymbol{b})}{(\boldsymbol{b}\cdot\boldsymbol{k})^2} - \frac{\omega_i^2}{4\pi\Omega_i}\frac{[\boldsymbol{E}\wedge\boldsymbol{k}]}{(\boldsymbol{b}\cdot\boldsymbol{k})}$$

$$+\tau(\boldsymbol{k})\frac{\omega_i^2}{4\pi}\left\{\frac{\omega^2\boldsymbol{b}(\boldsymbol{E}\cdot\boldsymbol{b})}{v_s^2(\boldsymbol{b}\cdot\boldsymbol{k})^2} + i\omega\frac{\boldsymbol{b}(\boldsymbol{E}\cdot[\boldsymbol{b}\wedge\boldsymbol{k}])}{\Omega_i(\boldsymbol{k}\cdot\boldsymbol{b})} - i\omega\frac{[\boldsymbol{b}\wedge\boldsymbol{k}](\boldsymbol{b}\cdot\boldsymbol{E})}{\Omega_i(\boldsymbol{k}\cdot\boldsymbol{b})}\right.$$

$$\left.+2\frac{v_s^2}{\Omega_i^2}[\boldsymbol{k}\wedge\boldsymbol{b}](\boldsymbol{E}\cdot[\boldsymbol{k}\wedge\boldsymbol{b}])\right\}. \tag{9.68}$$

Here $\Omega_i = e_i B/m_i c$,

$$\tau(\boldsymbol{k}) = \frac{\sqrt{\pi}}{2a} = \sqrt{\left(\frac{\pi m_e}{2\varkappa T}\right)}\frac{1}{|(\boldsymbol{b}\cdot\boldsymbol{k})|}; \quad \omega_i = \sqrt{\left(\frac{4\pi e_i^2 n_i}{m_i}\right)};$$

$$v_s = \sqrt{\left(\frac{\varkappa T_e}{m_i}\right)}, \tag{9.69}$$

and v_s is the velocity of sound in a non-isothermal plasma.

To obtain the dispersion equation, one needs, using the formulae (9.60, 68), to determine the dielectric constant tensor, and then to substitute it into (9.24) and evaluate the determinant.

The dispersion equation simplifies further for waves associated with the motion of ions as well as electrons. For such waves, which are often called the low-frequency waves, it is also necessary to satisfy the condition

$$\omega \ll \Omega_i. \tag{9.70}$$

We shall see that magnetohydrodynamic waves in a plasma with phase velocity $v_A = B/\sqrt{(4\pi n_i m_i)}$ are also low-frequency waves. Substituting into (9.70) the phase velocity of magnetosonic waves instead of ω/k, the condition (9.70) becomes

$$v_A^2 \ll \frac{\Omega_i^2}{k^2} \quad \text{or} \quad c^2k^2 \ll \omega_i^2 = \frac{4\pi e_i^2 n_i}{m_i}. \tag{9.70a}$$

Using the condition (9.70), the dispersion equation obtained by the above method can be written as two independent equations, one of which is

$$\omega^2 = v_A^2(\boldsymbol{b}\cdot\boldsymbol{k})^2 \tag{9.71}$$

and it determines the transverse magnetohydrodynamic waves in a plasma. In the approximation under consideration the damping decrement of these waves is zero.

The other equation determines the frequency and damping decrement of the magnetosonic waves in a plasma in the approximation when the dissipation due to collisions between charged particles is negligible.

For the frequency, we have

$$\omega^4 - (v_A^2 + v_s^2)\,k^2\omega^2 + v_A^2 v_s^2 (\boldsymbol{b}\cdot\boldsymbol{k})^2 k^2 = 0. \tag{9.72}$$

This equation coincides exactly with (3.23) from the equations of magnetohydrodynamics.

The solution of eqn. (9.72) for the phase velocity of the accelerated and retarded waves is given by the formula (3.24).

For the damping decrement, we have

$$\gamma_\pm = \frac{1}{2}\gamma_0 \left\{ 1 \pm \frac{(\cos 2\theta - x)\cos 2\theta}{\sqrt{(1+x^2-2x\cos 2\theta)}} \right\} \frac{1}{|\cos\theta|}. \tag{9.73}$$

Here $\gamma_\pm$ is the damping decrement of the accelerated and retarded magnetosonic waves respectively;

$$x = \left(\frac{v_A}{v_s}\right)^2, \quad \gamma_0 = v_s k \sqrt{\left(\frac{\pi}{8} \left| \frac{e_i}{e_e} \right| \frac{m_e}{m_i}\right)}. \tag{9.74}$$

Thus, if the conditions (9.59, 63, 70) are satisfied, magnetohydrodynamic and also magnetosonic waves can be propagated in a plasma.

However, this does not imply that the hydrodynamic equation (3.7–11) can be used under these conditions.

In § 3 it was pointed out that to use the hydrodynamic equations it is necessary to satisfy the conditions (3.3), i.e. the hydrodynamic functions must vary little during the attainment of local equilibrium over the corresponding path length.

In § 21 we shall see that if these conditions are fulfilled, the usual hydrodynamic equations (and, in particular, the magnetohydrodynamic equations) can be used for describing processes in a plasma. In this case the dissipative terms in the hydrodynamic equations are determined by the correlation functions or, using our terminology, by the "collisions" between the charged particles of the plasma.

But right now we are considering the propagation of waves in a plasma on the basis of the self-consistent field equations which are only applicable in the other limiting case when the characteristic time is much less than the relaxation time (the "collision time"). The usual hydrodynamic equations in which the dissipative terms are determined by the collisions, are not therefore applicable here.

The damping decrement, as defined by (9.73), is of a different nature from the damping in ordinary magnetohydrodynamics. Here the attenuation is due to the absorption of magnetosonic waves by the electrons of the plasma.

Recapitulating, in a "plasma without collisions", i.e. in the domain where the self-consistent field equations are applicable, there is a range of parameter values for which the magnetohydrodynamic equations are applicable, but with different dissipative terms. This topic will be discussed in more detail in § 21.

If $\boldsymbol{B} \to 0$ and $\theta \to 0$ in (9.72, 73), these formulae coincide with the formulae (8.43) for the frequency and decrement of attenuation of sonic waves in a plasma.

Note finally that, as in § 8, the influence of the collisions can be taken into account approximately by substituting $\omega \to \omega + i\Delta$, where Δ is the effective collision frequency.

A more systematic way of taking the "collisions" between charged particles into account is treated in the following sections.

CHAPTER IV

Correlation Functions and Spectral Functions. Kinetic Equations for a Plasma. Landau Equations

10. Simultaneous Correlation Functions for a Non-relativistic Plasma †

A set of equations for the first moments $\overline{N}_a = n_a f_a$, $\boldsymbol{E} = \overline{\boldsymbol{E}}^{\text{M}}$, $\boldsymbol{B} = \overline{\boldsymbol{H}}^{\text{M}}$ was considered in §§ 6–9. This set of equations (equations with self-consistent field) is obtained from the chain of equations for the moments or the functions f_a, q_{ab}, g_{abc}, . . ., by neglecting the higher moments or correlation functions q_{ab}, g_{abc}, ...

In § 6 it was shown in the self-consistent field approximation that the entropy of the charged particles of the system is constant, i.e. dissipative processes in a plasma cannot be taken into account.

To obtain approximate equations which describe irreversible processes in a plasma, it is thus necessary to have regard to the correlation between the charged particles. This is the topic treated in §§ 10–11.

To elucidate the main features of the problem, consider the case of a spatially homogeneous plasma.

In the absence of external fields the average electric and magnetic field strengths are zero, i.e. the first moments of the microscopic strengths $\boldsymbol{E}^{\text{M}}$, $\boldsymbol{H}^{\text{M}}$ are zero. Only the first moments $\overline{N}_a = n_a f_a$ are non-zero. In this case

$$f_a = f_a(\boldsymbol{p}, t), \tag{10.1}$$

† Bogolyubov (1962); Balescu (1946); Balescu and Taylor (1961); Lenard (1960); Silin (1961, 1962a); Klimontovich (1961).

i.e. the first distribution functions depend only on momentum and time.

Equations (5.21) in this approximation become

$$\frac{\partial f_a}{\partial t} = -\frac{e_a}{n_a}\left(\frac{\partial}{\partial \boldsymbol{p}}\cdot\overline{(\delta N_a\,\delta \boldsymbol{E})}\right) \equiv S_a(\boldsymbol{p}, t). \tag{10.2}$$

The case under consideration is the opposite of the self-consistent field approximation. In fact, in the self-consistent field approximation, of the second moment

$$\overline{N_a \boldsymbol{E}^{\mathrm{M}}} = \overline{N_a}\boldsymbol{E} + \overline{\delta N_a\,\delta \boldsymbol{E}} \tag{10.3}$$

only the first term is retained, and the second term which takes into account the correlation of the field and the particle distribution is discarded.

In the approximation of a spatially homogeneous plasma the first term in (10.3) vanishes since $\boldsymbol{E} = 0$. Only the second term taking into account the correlation remains.

In the spatially homogeneous case the simultaneous second moments depend only on the coordinate difference $\boldsymbol{q}-\boldsymbol{q}'$. We expand the second moments as a Fourier integral in $\boldsymbol{q}-\boldsymbol{q}'$. For example,

$$\overline{\delta N_a(\boldsymbol{q}, \boldsymbol{p}, t)\,\delta N_b(\boldsymbol{q}', \boldsymbol{p}', t)} = \frac{1}{(2\pi)^3}\int (\delta N_a(\boldsymbol{p})\,\delta N_b(\boldsymbol{p}'))_{\boldsymbol{k}, t}\, e^{i(\boldsymbol{k}\cdot\boldsymbol{q}-\boldsymbol{q}')}\, d^3\boldsymbol{k}, \tag{10.4}$$

$$\overline{\delta N_a(\boldsymbol{q}, \boldsymbol{p}, t)\,\delta \boldsymbol{E}(\boldsymbol{q}', t)} = \frac{1}{(2\pi)^3}\int (\delta N_a(\boldsymbol{p})\,\delta \boldsymbol{E})_{\boldsymbol{k}, t}\, e^{i(\boldsymbol{k}\cdot\boldsymbol{q}-\boldsymbol{q}')}\, d^3\boldsymbol{k}. \tag{10.5}$$

We shall call the Fourier components the spatial spectral functions. From (10.5) it follows that

$$(\delta N_a(\boldsymbol{p})\,\delta \boldsymbol{E})_{\boldsymbol{k}, t} = (\delta \boldsymbol{E}\delta N_a(\boldsymbol{p}))^{*}_{\boldsymbol{k}, t}. \tag{10.6}$$

We write the equation for the spatial spectral function $(\delta N_a \delta N_b)_{\boldsymbol{k}, t}$ using equation (5.34). If $\boldsymbol{E} = 0$, from (10.6), we obtain:

$$\frac{\partial}{\partial t}(\delta N_a\,\delta N_b)_{k,t}+i[(\boldsymbol{k}\cdot\boldsymbol{v})-(\boldsymbol{k}\cdot\boldsymbol{v}')](\delta N_a\,\delta N_b)_{k,t}$$

$$+e_a n_a\left((\delta N_b(\boldsymbol{p}')\,\delta\boldsymbol{E})^*_{k,t}\cdot\frac{\partial f_a}{\partial \boldsymbol{p}}\right)+e_b n_b\left((\delta N_a(\boldsymbol{p})\,\delta\boldsymbol{E})_{k,t}\cdot\frac{\partial f_b}{\partial \boldsymbol{p}'}\right)$$

$$=0. \tag{10.7}$$

From (10.5) for $\boldsymbol{q}=\boldsymbol{q}'$ we find

$$\overline{\delta N_a(\boldsymbol{q},\boldsymbol{p},t)\,\delta\boldsymbol{E}(\boldsymbol{q}',t)}=\frac{1}{(2\pi)^3}\int \mathrm{Re}\,(\delta N_a(\boldsymbol{p})\,\delta\boldsymbol{E})_{k,t}\,d^3\boldsymbol{k}. \tag{10.8}$$

Using this formula, eqn. (10.2) can be written as

$$\frac{\partial f_a}{\partial t}=-\frac{e_a}{(2\pi)^3 n_a}\left(\frac{\partial}{\partial \boldsymbol{p}}\cdot\int \mathrm{Re}\,(\delta N_a\,\delta\boldsymbol{E})_{k,t}\right)d^3\boldsymbol{k}\equiv S_a(\boldsymbol{p},t). \tag{10.9}$$

Since all the second moments can be found if the moments $\overline{\delta N_a \delta N_b}$ are known, eqns. (10.9,7) form a closed set of equations for the first distribution functions and the spatial spectral functions $(\delta N_a \delta N_b)_{k,t}$.

This set is still too complicated, though for the solution of many problems these equations simplify further for the following reasons.

The solution of the set (10.7,9) in the general case depends on the initial values of the functions f_a as well as of the spatial spectral functions $(\delta N_a \delta N_b)_{k,t}$.

We denote the relaxation time for the distribution functions f_a by τ_r. It represents the time taken to establish a state which is independent of the initial distribution $f_a(\boldsymbol{p},0)$.

The relaxation time for the spectral functions depends on the wave number k. We denote it by $\tau(k)$. For small $k(k \ll 1/r_d)$ it is determined more particularly by the damping increment $\gamma(k)$ of the plasma waves.

The time $\tau(k)$ usually decreases with increasing k, i.e. the stationary state is established more rapidly for large k than for small.

In statistical equilibrium the spatial spectral function in effect changes only if $k > 1/r_d$, i.e. $k_{\text{min}} \sim 1/r_d$.

It is therefore assumed that the plasma state differs little from the equilibrium state in the sense that the spatial spectral function is small if $k < k_{\text{min}}$.

In this case a maximum relaxation time exists for the spatial spectral functions:

$$\tau_{\text{max}} = \tau(k_{\text{min}}). \tag{10.10}$$

For states close to equilibrium

$$\tau_{\text{max}} \sim \frac{r_d}{V_T} = \frac{1}{\omega_{\text{L}}}, \tag{10.11}$$

which is of the order of the natural oscillation period of a plasma.

In the following we shall see that the relaxation time of the distribution functions f_a is

$$\tau_{\text{r}} \sim \frac{1}{\omega_{\text{L}}\varepsilon} \gg \tau_{\text{max}}, \quad \text{since} \quad \varepsilon = \left(\frac{r_{\text{av}}}{r_d}\right)^3 \ll 1. \tag{10.12}$$

Here we avail ourselves of the fact that the parameter (5.26) for a rarefied plasma is much less than unity.

The condition (10.12) implies that the stationary state is established much more rapidly for spectral functions than for functions f_a.

We introduce an auxiliary time parameter $1/\Delta$ such that

$$\tau_{\text{r}} \gg \frac{1}{\Delta} \gg \tau_{\text{max}}. \tag{10.13}$$

Let us consider the asymptotic solution of (10.7) which holds good for times t such that

$$\tau_{\text{max}} \ll t - t_0 \sim \frac{1}{\Delta} \ll \tau_{\text{r}}, \tag{10.14}$$

where t_0 is the initial time.

Owing to (10.14) one can only seek the solution of (10.7) which depends on time, not explicitly, but through the first distribution functions. In this case the first term in (10.7) is small compared with the others and so it can be discarded.

Considering that the function $(\delta N_a \delta N_b)_{\boldsymbol{k},t}$ is associated with the Fourier component of the correlation function g_{ab} by the relation

$$(\delta N_a \delta N_b)_{\boldsymbol{k},t} = n_a n_b g_{ab}(\boldsymbol{k}, \boldsymbol{p}, \boldsymbol{p}', t) + \delta_{ab} n_a \delta(\boldsymbol{p}-\boldsymbol{p}') f_a, \tag{10.15}$$

from eqns. (10.7) and (10.14) we get

$$\begin{aligned}(\delta N_a \delta N_b)_{\boldsymbol{k}} &= \frac{i}{(\boldsymbol{k}\cdot\boldsymbol{v})-(\boldsymbol{k}\cdot\boldsymbol{v}')-i\Delta}\left\{\frac{e_a n_a}{k^2}(\delta N_b(\boldsymbol{k}\cdot\delta\boldsymbol{E}))^*_{\boldsymbol{k}}\left(\boldsymbol{k}\cdot\frac{\partial f_a}{\partial \boldsymbol{p}}\right)\right. \\ &\left.+\frac{e_b n_b}{k^2}(\delta N_a(\boldsymbol{k}\cdot\delta\boldsymbol{E}))_{\boldsymbol{k}}\left(\boldsymbol{k}\cdot\frac{\partial f_b}{\partial \boldsymbol{p}'}\right)\right\} + \delta_{ab}\delta(\boldsymbol{p}-\boldsymbol{p}') n_a f_a .\end{aligned} \tag{10.16}$$

Here we use the fact that $[\boldsymbol{k} \wedge \delta\boldsymbol{E}] = 0$, i.e. that the vector $\delta\boldsymbol{E}$ is parallel to the vector $\boldsymbol{k}$. We take the quantity Δ to be zero at the end of the calculations. According to (10.13) this implies that $\Delta \ll 1/\tau_{\max}$, but $\Delta \gg 1/\tau_r$.

From eqn. (10.16) we can obtain a closed equation for the simpler function $(\delta N_a \delta \boldsymbol{E})_{\boldsymbol{k}}$ which also occurs on the right-hand side of (10.9).

For this we multiply (10.16) by $4\pi e_b$, sum over b and then integrate over $\boldsymbol{p}'$. From the last two equations of (5.31) it follows that

$$\delta\boldsymbol{E}(\boldsymbol{k}) = -i\frac{\boldsymbol{k}}{k^2}4\pi\sum_b e_b\int \delta N_b(\boldsymbol{k}\cdot\boldsymbol{p}')\, d^3\boldsymbol{p}'. \tag{10.17}$$

Using this expression, the equation for the function $(\delta N_a(\boldsymbol{k}\cdot\delta\boldsymbol{E}))_{\boldsymbol{k}}$ is

$$\begin{aligned}&\left(1+\sum_b\frac{4\pi e_b^2 n_b}{k^2}\int\frac{\left(\boldsymbol{k}\cdot\dfrac{\partial f_b}{\partial \boldsymbol{p}'}\right)}{(\boldsymbol{k}\cdot\boldsymbol{v})-(\boldsymbol{k}\cdot\boldsymbol{v}')-i\Delta}d^3\boldsymbol{p}'\right)(\delta N_a(\boldsymbol{k}\cdot\delta\boldsymbol{E}))_{\boldsymbol{k}} \\ &= -\frac{4\pi e_a n_a}{k^2}\left(\boldsymbol{k}\cdot\frac{\partial f_a}{\partial \boldsymbol{p}}\right)\sum_b e_b\int\frac{(\delta N_b(\boldsymbol{p}')(\boldsymbol{k}\cdot\delta\boldsymbol{E}))^*_{\boldsymbol{k}}}{(\boldsymbol{k}\cdot\boldsymbol{v})-(\boldsymbol{k}\cdot\boldsymbol{v}')-i\Delta}d^3\boldsymbol{p}' \\ &\quad + i4\pi e_a n_a f_a .\end{aligned} \tag{10.18}$$

An integral equation with a Cauchy-type kernel is thus obtained for the spatial spectral function $(\delta N_a(\boldsymbol{k}\cdot\delta\boldsymbol{E}))_{\boldsymbol{k}}$.

The expression in brackets on the left-hand side of (10.18) coincides with that for the longitudinal dielectric constant of a plasma at the frequency $\omega = (\boldsymbol{k}\cdot\boldsymbol{v})$:

$$\varepsilon^{\pm}(\omega, \boldsymbol{k}) = 1+\sum_a \frac{4\pi e_a^2 n_a}{k^2}\int \frac{\left(\boldsymbol{k}\cdot\dfrac{\partial f_a(\boldsymbol{p}, t)}{\partial \boldsymbol{p}}\right)}{\omega-(\boldsymbol{k}\cdot\boldsymbol{v})\pm i\Delta}\, d^3\boldsymbol{p}. \quad (10.19)$$

This formula only differs from (7.33) in that the function $f_a(\boldsymbol{p}, t)$ is still unknown; its kinetic equation is found in § 11.

The formula (10.19) determines two functions: (1) ε^+ analytic in the upper half-plane, and (2) ε^- in the lower half-plane of the variable $\omega \pm i\Delta$.

For a convenient solution of (10.18) we introduce functions $H_1^{\pm}$ and $H_2^{\pm}$, defined as:

$$iH_1^{\pm}(\omega, \boldsymbol{k}) = \frac{1}{2\pi i}\sum_b e_b \int \frac{(\delta N_b(\boldsymbol{k}\cdot\delta\boldsymbol{E}))_{\boldsymbol{k}}}{\omega-(\boldsymbol{k}\cdot\boldsymbol{v})\pm i\Delta}\, d^3\boldsymbol{p}. \quad (10.20)$$

$$-iH_2^{\pm}(\omega, \boldsymbol{k}) = \frac{1}{2\pi i}\sum_b e_b \int \frac{(\delta N_b(\boldsymbol{k}\cdot\delta\boldsymbol{E}))^*_{\boldsymbol{k}}}{\omega-(\boldsymbol{k}\cdot\boldsymbol{v})\pm i\Delta}\, d^3\boldsymbol{p} = i(H_1^{\mp})^*. \quad (10.21)$$

From (10.19–21) it follows that as $\Delta \to 0$

$$2\pi i \sum_b \frac{4\pi e_e^2 n_b}{k^2}\int \delta(\omega-(\boldsymbol{k}\cdot\boldsymbol{v}))\left(\boldsymbol{k}\cdot\frac{\partial f_b}{\partial \boldsymbol{p}}\right) d^3\boldsymbol{p} = \varepsilon^-(\omega, \boldsymbol{k})-\varepsilon^+(\omega, \boldsymbol{k}), \quad (10.22)$$

$$\sum_b e_b \int \delta(\omega-(\boldsymbol{k}\cdot\boldsymbol{v}))\,(\delta N_b(\boldsymbol{p})\,(\boldsymbol{k}\cdot\delta\boldsymbol{E}))_{\boldsymbol{k}}\, d^3\boldsymbol{p} = i\big(H_1^-(\omega, \boldsymbol{k})-H_1^+(\omega, \boldsymbol{k})\big). \quad (10.23)$$

Using (10.19, 20), the equation (10.18) can be written as

$$(\delta N_a(\boldsymbol{k}\cdot\delta\boldsymbol{E}))_{\boldsymbol{k}}\, \varepsilon^-((\boldsymbol{k}\cdot\boldsymbol{v})\cdot\boldsymbol{k}) = i2\pi i\, \frac{4\pi e_a n_a}{k^2}\left(\boldsymbol{k}\cdot\frac{\partial f_a}{\partial \boldsymbol{p}}\right) H_2^-((\boldsymbol{k}\cdot\boldsymbol{v})\cdot\boldsymbol{k})+i4\pi e_a n_a f_a. \quad (10.24)$$

From (10.24) we first obtain the equation for the functions H. We multiply this equation by $e_a\delta(\omega-(\boldsymbol{kv}))$, sum over a and then integrate over $\boldsymbol{p}$. Using the formulae (10.22, 23) we get the following equation

$$\begin{aligned}(H_1^-(\omega, \boldsymbol{k}) - H_1^+(\omega, \boldsymbol{k}))\, \varepsilon^-(\omega, \boldsymbol{k}) \\ = (\varepsilon^-(\omega, \boldsymbol{k}) - \varepsilon^+(\omega, \boldsymbol{k}))\, H_2^-(\omega, \boldsymbol{k}) \\ + \sum_a 4\pi e_a^2 n_a \int \delta(\omega - (\boldsymbol{k}\cdot\boldsymbol{v}))\, f\, d^3\boldsymbol{p}.\end{aligned} \quad (10.25)$$

Since the last term is real, putting the imaginary part of the other terms equal to zero, we obtain the relation

$$(H_1^- - H_2^-)\, \varepsilon^- = (H_1^+ - H_2^+)\, \varepsilon^+. \quad (10.26)$$

This implies that the discontinuity of the piecewise-analytic function $(H_1 - H_2)\, \varepsilon$ on the real axis is zero. Since this function tends to zero as $\omega \to \infty$, the vanishing of the discontinuity implies the vanishing of the function itself, i.e.

$$(H_1 - H_2)\, \varepsilon(\omega, \boldsymbol{k}) = 0. \quad (10.27)$$

Hence

$$H_1(\omega, \boldsymbol{k}) = H_2(\omega, \boldsymbol{k}) \quad \text{if} \quad \varepsilon(\omega, \boldsymbol{k}) \neq 0. \quad (10.28)$$

The condition $\varepsilon(\omega, \boldsymbol{k}) \neq 0$ is satisfied for the region under consideration.

Using this condition, eqn. (10.25) simplifies to

$$\begin{aligned}H^-(\omega, \boldsymbol{k})\, \varepsilon^+(\omega, \boldsymbol{k}) - H^+(\omega, \boldsymbol{k})\, \varepsilon^-(\omega, \boldsymbol{k}) \\ = \sum_a 4\pi e_a^2 n_a \int \delta(\omega - (\boldsymbol{k}\cdot\boldsymbol{v}))\, f_a\, d^3\boldsymbol{p}.\end{aligned} \quad (10.29)$$

So, dividing by $|\varepsilon(\omega, \boldsymbol{k})|^2$, the expression for the discontinuity of the piecewise-analytic function $H(\omega, \boldsymbol{k})/\varepsilon(\omega, \boldsymbol{k})$ is

$$\frac{H_1^-}{\varepsilon^-} - \frac{H_1^+}{\varepsilon^+} = \frac{\sum_a 4\pi e_a^2 n_a \int \delta(\omega - (\boldsymbol{k}\cdot\boldsymbol{v}))\, f_a\, d^3\boldsymbol{p}}{|\varepsilon(\omega, \boldsymbol{k})|^2}. \quad (10.30)$$

Knowing the discontinuity, the formula for the functions $H^\pm/\varepsilon^\pm$ is

$$\left(\frac{H^\pm}{\varepsilon^\pm}\right)_{\omega, \boldsymbol{k}} = -\frac{1}{2\pi i} \int \left(\frac{H^+}{\varepsilon^+} - \frac{H^-}{\varepsilon^-}\right)_{\omega', \boldsymbol{k}} \frac{d\omega'}{\omega - \omega' \pm i\Delta}, \quad (10.31)$$

As a result

$$\left(\frac{H^{\pm}}{\varepsilon^{\pm}}\right)_{\omega,\,\boldsymbol{k}} = \frac{1}{2\pi i}\sum_b 4\pi e_b^2 n_b \int \frac{f_b}{(\omega-(\boldsymbol{k}\cdot\boldsymbol{v})\pm i\Delta)\,|\,\varepsilon((\boldsymbol{k}\cdot\boldsymbol{v})\cdot\boldsymbol{k})\,|^2}\,d^3\boldsymbol{p}. \tag{10.32}$$

By using (10.32), eqn. (10.24) yields an expression for the required function $(\delta N_a(\boldsymbol{k}\cdot\delta\boldsymbol{E}))_{\boldsymbol{k}}$

$$(\delta N_a(\boldsymbol{k}\cdot\delta\boldsymbol{E}))_{\boldsymbol{k}} = i\sum_b \frac{4\pi e_a n_a}{k^2}\left(\boldsymbol{k}\cdot\frac{\partial f_a}{\partial\boldsymbol{p}}\right) 4\pi e_b^2 n_b \int \frac{f_b(\boldsymbol{p}', t)}{((\boldsymbol{k}\cdot\boldsymbol{v})-(\boldsymbol{k}\cdot\boldsymbol{v}')-i\Delta)} \times\frac{d^3\boldsymbol{p}'}{|\,\varepsilon(\boldsymbol{k}\cdot\boldsymbol{v}')\,|^2}+i\frac{4\pi e_a n_a}{\varepsilon^{-}((\boldsymbol{k}\cdot\boldsymbol{v})\cdot\boldsymbol{k})}f_a. \tag{10.33}$$

To form an expression for the most general spectral function $(\delta N_a\,\delta N_b)_{\boldsymbol{k}}$, the solution of (10.33) has to be substituted in (10.16). Corresponding expressions for the correlation functions $g_{ab}(\boldsymbol{k}, \boldsymbol{p}, \boldsymbol{p}')$ are obtained by formula (10.15).

From (10.33) we find an expression for the real part of the function $(\delta N_a(\boldsymbol{k}\cdot\delta\boldsymbol{E}))_{\boldsymbol{k}}$ occurring on the right-hand side of (10.9).

Using the expression for the imaginary part of the dielectric constant

$$\varepsilon''(\omega, \boldsymbol{k}) = -\pi\sum_a \frac{4\pi e_a^2 n_a}{k^2}\int \delta(\omega-(\boldsymbol{k}\cdot\boldsymbol{v}))\left(\boldsymbol{k}\cdot\frac{\partial f_b}{\partial\boldsymbol{p}}\right)d^3\boldsymbol{p}, \tag{10.34}$$

which follows from (10.19), we get

$$\mathrm{Re}\,(\delta N_a\,\delta\boldsymbol{E})_{\boldsymbol{k}} = -\frac{16\pi^3 e_a n_a}{k^4}\boldsymbol{k}\sum_b e_b^2 n_b \int \frac{\delta((\boldsymbol{k}\cdot\boldsymbol{v})-(\boldsymbol{k}\cdot\boldsymbol{v}'))}{|\,\varepsilon((\boldsymbol{k}\cdot\boldsymbol{v})\cdot\boldsymbol{k})\,|^2} \times\left\{\left(\boldsymbol{k}\cdot\frac{\partial f_a}{\partial\boldsymbol{p}}\right)f_b-\left(\boldsymbol{k}\cdot\frac{\partial f_b}{\partial\boldsymbol{p}'}\right)f_a\right\}d^3\boldsymbol{p}'. \tag{10.35}$$

By using the expression for the function $(\delta N_a\,\delta N_b)_{\boldsymbol{k}}$ an expression can be found for the spatial spectral functions of any characteristics of a plasma.

We form the expression for the spatial spectral function of the electric field strength $(\delta\boldsymbol{E}\cdot\delta\boldsymbol{E})_{\boldsymbol{k}}$ by means of formula (10.33). We multiply (10.33) by $-4\pi i e_a \boldsymbol{k}/k^2$, sum over a and then integrate over $\boldsymbol{p}$.

Using the expressions (10.17, 19),

$$(\delta\boldsymbol{E}\cdot\delta\boldsymbol{E})_{\boldsymbol{k}} = \sum_a \frac{(4\pi)^2 e_a^2 n_a}{k^2} \int \frac{f_a}{|\varepsilon((\boldsymbol{k}\cdot\boldsymbol{v})\cdot\boldsymbol{k})|^2}\, d^3\boldsymbol{p}. \quad (10.36)$$

The spectral function for arbitrary components $(\delta E_i\, \delta E_j)_{\boldsymbol{k}}$ is given by (10.36) if we bear in mind that

$$(\delta E_i\, \delta E_j)_{\boldsymbol{k}} = \frac{k_i k_j}{k^2}(\delta\boldsymbol{E}\cdot\delta\boldsymbol{E})_{\boldsymbol{k}}. \quad (10.37)$$

In the equilibrium case the expression for the function $(\delta N_a\, \delta N_b)_{\boldsymbol{k}}$ becomes

$$(\delta N_a\, \delta N_b)_{\boldsymbol{k}} = \delta_{ab} n_a\, \delta(\boldsymbol{p}-\boldsymbol{p}') f_a(\boldsymbol{p}') - \frac{e_a e_b n_a n_b}{\sum_c e_c^2 n_c (1+r_d^2 k^2)} f_a(\boldsymbol{p}) f_b(\boldsymbol{p}'). \quad (10.38)$$

By using (10.15) we obtain an expression for the function $g_{ab}(\boldsymbol{k}, \boldsymbol{p}, \boldsymbol{p}')$ in the equilibrium case.

The expression for the spectral function $(\delta\boldsymbol{E}\cdot\delta\boldsymbol{E})_{\boldsymbol{k}}$ in the equilibrium case is

$$(\delta\boldsymbol{E}\cdot\delta\boldsymbol{E})_{\boldsymbol{k}} = 4\pi \frac{\varkappa T}{1+r_d^2 k^2}. \quad (10.39)$$

To obtain (10.39) directly from (10.36), one uses the identity

$$\sum_a e_a^2 n_a \int \frac{f_a}{|\varepsilon((\boldsymbol{k}\cdot\boldsymbol{v})\cdot\boldsymbol{k})|^2}\, d^3\boldsymbol{p} = \sum_a e_a^2 n_a \frac{r_d^2 k^2}{1+r_d^2 k^2}, \quad (10.40)$$

which is satisfied in the equilibrium case.

If $k^2 r_d^2 \ll 1$, it follows from (10.39) that

$$(\delta\boldsymbol{E}\cdot\delta\boldsymbol{E})_{\boldsymbol{k}} = 4\pi\varkappa T. \quad (10.41)$$

Consider another expression for $g_{ab}(\boldsymbol{k}, \boldsymbol{p}, \boldsymbol{p}')$. From (10.15, 38) we find that

$$g_{ab}(\boldsymbol{k}, \boldsymbol{p}, \boldsymbol{p}') = -\frac{e_a e_b}{\sum_c e_c^2 n_c} \frac{f_a(\boldsymbol{p}) f_b(\boldsymbol{p}')}{1+r_d^2 k^2}. \quad (10.42)$$

We find the function $g_{ab}(\boldsymbol{q}-\boldsymbol{q}',\boldsymbol{p},\boldsymbol{p}')$ itself. For this, using the value of the integral

$$\frac{1}{(2\pi)^3}\int\frac{1}{1+r_d^2k^2}\,e^{i(\boldsymbol{k}\cdot\boldsymbol{q}-\boldsymbol{q}')}\,d^3\boldsymbol{k}=\frac{1}{4\pi r_d^2}\,\frac{e^{-\frac{|\boldsymbol{q}-\boldsymbol{q}'|}{r_d}}}{|\boldsymbol{q}-\boldsymbol{q}'|}\,,\qquad(10.43)$$

we get

$$g_{ab}(\boldsymbol{q}-\boldsymbol{q}',\boldsymbol{p},\boldsymbol{p}')=-\frac{e_ae_b}{\varkappa T}\,\frac{e^{-\frac{|\boldsymbol{q}-\boldsymbol{q}'|}{r_d}}}{|\boldsymbol{q}-\boldsymbol{q}'|}\,f_a(\boldsymbol{p})f_b(\boldsymbol{p}').\qquad(10.44)$$

Here the expression for the Debye radius is used

$$r_d^2=\frac{\varkappa T}{4\pi\sum\limits_c e_c^2n_c}\,,\qquad(10.45)$$

Substituting (10.44) into the expression (5.11) for the distribution function of the coordinates and momenta of two particles, we get

$$f_{ab}(\boldsymbol{q},\boldsymbol{q}',\boldsymbol{p},\boldsymbol{p}')=f_a(\boldsymbol{p})f_a(\boldsymbol{p})\left(1-\frac{e_ae_b}{\varkappa T}\,\frac{e^{-|\boldsymbol{q}-\boldsymbol{q}'|/r_d}}{|\boldsymbol{q}-\boldsymbol{q}'|}\right).\qquad(10.46)$$

From the formulae (10.44, 46) it follows that

$$g_{ab}=0;\qquad f_{ab}(\boldsymbol{q},\boldsymbol{q}',\boldsymbol{p},\boldsymbol{p}')=f_a(\boldsymbol{p})f_b(\boldsymbol{p}')\quad\text{if}\quad |\boldsymbol{q}-\boldsymbol{q}'|\gg r_d,\qquad(10.47)$$

i.e. if $|\boldsymbol{q}-\boldsymbol{q}'|\gg r_d$ the motion of charged particles is statistically independent.

One may therefore say that r_d is the radius of correlation since it defines the distance $|\boldsymbol{q}-\boldsymbol{q}'|$ over which the correlation function is non-zero.

From (10.44) it follows that the correlation function is negative for charged particles of the same sign, but positive for particles of different sign.

For short distances $|\boldsymbol{q}-\boldsymbol{q}'|$ the use of (10.44) is restricted by the proviso that the second term in (10.46) is small compared with the first. Consequently, formula (10.44) applies to the following distances

$$\boldsymbol{q}-\boldsymbol{q}'|\gg\frac{|e_ae_b|}{\varkappa T}\quad\text{or}\quad\frac{|e_ae_b|}{|\boldsymbol{q}-\boldsymbol{q}'|}\ll\varkappa T,\qquad(10.48)$$

i.e. to distances over which the particle potential energy is much less than the average kinetic energy.

For the Fourier spatial component this condition implies that (10.42) holds for wave numbers

$$k^{-1} \ll \frac{\varkappa T}{|e_a e_b|}. \tag{10.49}$$

This result justifies the assumption that the effective radius of action between charged particles in a plasma is of the order r_d.

It must be stressed that there is an important difference between the effective radius of action or range in a gas and that in a plasma.

In a gas the effective range r_0 is the distance at which two molecules interact effectively. In simple models this is the radius of the spheres representing the molecules.

In a plasma the effective range r_d depends on the thermodynammic parameters of the plasma, i.e. the temperature and density of the charged particles. The lack of mutual influence between particles at distances greater than r_d results from the interaction of many charged particles.

11. Set of Kinetic Equations for the Functions f_a neglecting Plasma Wave Radiation. Landau Equations

In § 6 the set of kinetic equations for an electron–ion plasma was treated in the self-consistent field approximation. The equations referred to rapid processes with characteristic times much less than the relaxation time τ_r, i.e.

$$T \ll \tau_r \sim 1/\omega_L \varepsilon. \tag{11.1}$$

We shall now form kinetic equations for f_a which are equally descriptive of the transient process of establishing equilibrium, in other words, equations which apply to time intervals greater or less than the relaxation time τ_r [see Landau, 1937; Bogolyubov 1962; Balescu, 1946; Balescu and Taylor, 1961; Lenard, 1960; Silin, 1961, 1962a; and Klimontovich, 1961].

As previously, it is assumed that the following condition is fulfilled

$$\varepsilon = (r_{\text{av}}^3/r_d^3) \ll 1. \tag{11.2}$$

Consider, firstly, the case when the plasma is spatially homogeneous. For the functions f_a we can then use eqn. (10.9)

$$\frac{\partial f_a}{\partial t} = -\frac{e_a}{(2\pi)^3 n_a}\left(\frac{\partial}{\partial \boldsymbol{p}} \cdot \int \mathrm{Re}\,(\delta N_a\,\delta \boldsymbol{E})_{\boldsymbol{k},\,t}\right) d^3\boldsymbol{k} \equiv S_a(\boldsymbol{p}, t). \tag{11.3}$$

If conditions (10.12–14) are fulfilled, the function Re $(\delta N_a\,\delta \boldsymbol{E})_{\boldsymbol{k}}$ in conformity with (10.35) is expressible in terms of f_a.

Substituting the expression (10.35) into eqn. (11.3), we get a closed set of equations for the first distribution functions—the set of kinetic equations.

It is convenient to write the set as

$$\frac{\partial f_a}{\partial t} = \sum_b n_b \frac{\partial}{\partial p_i} \int Q_{ij}^{ab}(\boldsymbol{v}-\boldsymbol{v}')\left\{\frac{\partial f_a}{\partial p_j} f_b - \frac{\partial f_b}{\partial p_j'} f_a\right\} d^3\boldsymbol{p}'.$$

$$i, j = 1, 2, 3. \tag{11.4}$$

Here we have put

$$Q_{ij}^{ab}(\boldsymbol{v}-\boldsymbol{v}') = 2e_a^2 e_b^2 \int \frac{k_i k_j}{k^4\,|\varepsilon((\boldsymbol{k}\cdot\boldsymbol{v})\cdot\boldsymbol{k})|^2}\,\delta((\boldsymbol{k}\cdot\boldsymbol{v})-(\boldsymbol{k}\cdot\boldsymbol{v}'))\,d^3\boldsymbol{k}. \tag{11.5}$$

As before, we assume summation over repeated subscripts i, j.

Sometimes convenient expressions for the right-hand sides of (11.4) are

$$S_a = \frac{\partial}{\partial p_i} D_{ij}^a \frac{\partial f_a}{\partial p_j} + \frac{\partial}{\partial p_i} A_i^a f_a. \tag{11.6}$$

Expressions for the coefficients D_{ij}^a and A_i^a are

$$D_{ij}^a(\boldsymbol{p}) = \sum_b 2e_a^2 e_b^2 n_b \int \frac{k_i k_j}{k^4\,|\varepsilon((\boldsymbol{k}\cdot\boldsymbol{v})\cdot\boldsymbol{k})|^2}\,\delta((\boldsymbol{k}\cdot\boldsymbol{v})-(\boldsymbol{k}\cdot\boldsymbol{v}'))\,f_b\,d^3\boldsymbol{k}\,d^3\boldsymbol{p}', \tag{11.7}$$

$$A_i^a(\boldsymbol{p}) = -\sum_b 2e_a^2 e_b^2 n_b \int \frac{k_i k_j}{k^4\,|\varepsilon((\boldsymbol{k}\cdot\boldsymbol{v})\cdot\boldsymbol{k})|^2}\,\delta((\boldsymbol{k}\cdot\boldsymbol{v})-(\boldsymbol{k}\cdot\boldsymbol{v}'))\,\frac{\partial f_b}{\partial p_j'}\,d^3\boldsymbol{k}\,d^3\boldsymbol{p}'. \tag{11.8}$$

Here D_{ij}^a, A_i^a are the diffusion and the systematic friction coefficients in momentum space respectively.

An expression for the friction coefficient $\boldsymbol{A}_a$ is

$$A_i^a = \frac{e_a^2}{2\pi^2} \int \frac{k_i}{k^2} \frac{\varepsilon''((\boldsymbol{k}\cdot\boldsymbol{v})\cdot\boldsymbol{k})}{|\varepsilon((\boldsymbol{k}\cdot\boldsymbol{v})\cdot\boldsymbol{k})|^2} d^3\boldsymbol{k}, \tag{11.9}$$

i.e. the systematic friction coefficient is proportional to the imaginary part of the dielectric constant at the frequency $(\boldsymbol{k}\cdot\boldsymbol{v})$.

Consider now some general properties of the set of kinetic equations (11.4, 5).

Firstly, we show that the set (11.4) is satisfied when Maxwell distributions with identical temperatures are taken as the functions f_a, i.e.

$$f_a = \frac{1}{(2n m_a \varkappa T)^{3/2}} e^{-\frac{p^2}{2m_a \varkappa T}}. \tag{11.10}$$

Substituting expressions (11.10) into (11.4), the left-hand side vanishes. Consider the right-hand sides of these equations, which we again denote by S_a. Performing differentiation, we obtain the expression

$$S_a = -\frac{1}{\varkappa T} \sum_b n_b \frac{\partial}{\partial p_i} \int Q_{ij}^{ab}(v_j - v_j') f_a f_b \, d^3\boldsymbol{p}'. \tag{11.11}$$

By using the formula (11.5) we see that (11.11) vanishes since (11.5) contains the factor $\delta((\boldsymbol{k}\cdot\boldsymbol{v})-(\boldsymbol{k}\cdot\boldsymbol{v}'))$.

So the right-hand sides of (11.4) vanish on substituting the Maxwell distributions.

We thus come to the conclusion that the Maxwell distributions for electrons and ions are solutions of the set (11.4).

We establish some general properties of the right-hand sides of these equations.

We multiply the right-hand sides of (11.4) by an arbitrary momentum function $\varphi_a(\boldsymbol{p})$ and by n_a, and then sum over a and integrate over $\boldsymbol{p}$. We use the notation

$$I(\boldsymbol{q}, t) = \sum_{ab} n_a n_b \int \varphi_a(\boldsymbol{p}) \frac{\partial}{\partial p_i} Q_{ij}^{ab} \left\{ \frac{\partial f_a}{\partial p_j} f_b - \frac{\partial f_b}{\partial p_j'} f_a \right\} d^3\boldsymbol{p}\, d^3\boldsymbol{p}', \tag{11.12}$$

and summation is carried out over the subscripts i, j.

By analogy with the corresponding expression in the investigation of Boltzmann's equation, the function $I(\boldsymbol{q}, t)$ may be called the "collision integral".

Integrating by parts over the momentum $\boldsymbol{p}$ in (11.12) and then interchanging the variables $\boldsymbol{p} \rightleftarrows \boldsymbol{p}'$ and $a \rightleftarrows b$ in the expression for I, considering that according to (11.5) the tensor Q_{ij}^{ab} remains unchanged on the substitutions $\boldsymbol{p} \rightleftarrows \boldsymbol{p}'$ and $a \rightleftarrows b$, the expression for $I(\boldsymbol{q}, t)$ can be written as

$$I = \frac{1}{2}\sum_{ab} n_a n_b \int\int \left(\frac{\partial \varphi_b(\boldsymbol{p}')}{\partial p_i'} - \frac{\partial \varphi_a(\boldsymbol{p})}{\partial p_i}\right) \times Q_{ij}^{ab} \left(\frac{\partial f_a}{\partial p_j} f_b - \frac{\partial f_b}{\partial p_j'} f_a\right) d^3\boldsymbol{p}\, d^3\boldsymbol{p}'. \quad (11.13)$$

It follows from (11.13) that, as for a gas, the "collision integral" for arbitrary functions f_a vanishes for three choices of function $\varphi_a(\boldsymbol{p})$:

$$\varphi_a(\boldsymbol{p}) = 1; \quad \boldsymbol{p}; \quad p^2/2m_a. \quad (11.14)$$

The function I clearly vanishes for the first two cases. When $\varphi_a(p) = p^2/2m_a$, it must be borne in mind that the function Q_{ij}^{ab} contains the factor $\delta((\boldsymbol{k}\cdot\boldsymbol{v})-(\boldsymbol{k}\cdot\boldsymbol{v}'))$.

As in the case of Boltzmann's gas equation, it is therefore to be inferred that the relations (11.4) for f_a yield equations for the conservation laws of the total density of all the charged particles, the total momentum and the total energy density, i.e. for the functions

$$\varrho = \sum_a n_a \int f_a\, d^3\boldsymbol{p}, \quad \sum_a n_a \int \boldsymbol{p} f_a\, d^3\boldsymbol{p}, \quad \sum_a n_a \int \frac{p^2}{2m_a} f_a\, d^3\boldsymbol{p}. \quad (11.15)$$

This property of the kinetic equations (11.4) will be used later in deriving the hydrodynamic equations of a plasma.

We now show that the entropy of a plasma, given as

$$S(t) = -\varkappa \sum_a n_a \int f_a(\boldsymbol{q}, \boldsymbol{p}, t) \ln f_a(\boldsymbol{q}, \boldsymbol{p}, t)\, d^3\boldsymbol{q}\, d^3\boldsymbol{p}, \quad (11.16)$$

can either increase or remain constant. The latter applies only in statistical equilibrium when the f_a are Maxwell distributions.

Multiplying (11.4) by $-\varkappa n_a \ln f_a$, summing over a and integrating over $\boldsymbol{q}$, $\boldsymbol{p}$, we get

$$\frac{dS(t)}{dt} = \int I(\boldsymbol{q}, t)\, d^3\boldsymbol{q}. \tag{11.17}$$

The right-hand side of this equation is determined by (11.13) where one should put $\varphi_a = -\varkappa \ln f_a$. Expression (11.13) may in this case be written as

$$I = \frac{\varkappa}{2}\sum_{ab} n_a n_b \int \left\{\frac{\partial \ln f_a}{\partial p_i} - \frac{\partial \ln f_b}{\partial p'_i}\right\}\left\{\frac{\partial \ln f_a}{\partial p_j} - \frac{\partial \ln f_b}{\partial p'_j}\right\} \times Q^{ab}_{ij} f_a f_b\, d^3\boldsymbol{p}\, d^3\boldsymbol{p}'. \tag{11.18}$$

We show that the integrand in (11.18) is always positive.

Substituting into (11.18) the expression (11.5) for the tensor Q^{ab}_{ij}, we get

$$I = \varkappa \sum_{aa} e_a^2 e_b^2 n_a n_b \int \frac{(\boldsymbol{k}\cdot\boldsymbol{A})^2}{k^4\,|\,\varepsilon((\boldsymbol{k}\cdot\boldsymbol{v})\cdot\boldsymbol{k})\,|^2} \times \delta((\boldsymbol{k}\cdot\boldsymbol{v}) - (\boldsymbol{k}\cdot\boldsymbol{v}'))\, f_a f_b\, d^3\boldsymbol{k}\, d^3\boldsymbol{p}\, d^3\boldsymbol{p}'. \tag{11.19}$$

Here $\boldsymbol{A}$ is a vector with the components

$$A_i = \left(\frac{\partial \ln f_a}{\partial p_i} - \frac{\partial \ln f_b}{\partial p'_i}\right). \tag{11.19a}$$

From (11.19) it follows that the "collision integral" I is zero or greater than zero if $\varphi_a = -\varkappa \ln f_a$, i.e.

$$I \geqslant 0. \tag{11.20}$$

Hence

$$\frac{dS}{dt} \geqslant 0. \tag{11.21}$$

The equality sign in this formula applies when the collision integral vanishes, which is possible provided that

$$\frac{\partial}{\partial \boldsymbol{p}} \ln f_a - \frac{\partial}{\partial \boldsymbol{p}'} \ln f_b = \alpha(\boldsymbol{p} - \boldsymbol{p}'), \tag{11.22}$$

where α is a constant which is independent of the subscripts a and b. Equation (11.22) for arbitrary a and b has the solution

$$\ln f_a(\boldsymbol{p}) = \frac{\alpha}{2} p^2 + (\boldsymbol{\beta} \cdot \boldsymbol{p}) + \gamma. \tag{11.23}$$

As in solving Boltzmann's gas equation, the constants α, $\boldsymbol{\beta}$, γ are given by the conditions

$$n_a \int f_a \, d^3\boldsymbol{p} = \varrho_a, \quad n_a \int \frac{\boldsymbol{p}}{m_a} f_a \, d^3\boldsymbol{p} = \varrho_a \boldsymbol{U}_a; \tag{11.24}$$

$$n_a \int \frac{(\boldsymbol{p} - m_a \boldsymbol{U}_a)^2}{2m_a} f_a \, d^3\boldsymbol{p} = \frac{3}{2} \varrho_a \varkappa T_a.$$

Hence we obtain the following expressions for the functions:

$$f_a = \frac{1}{(2\pi m_a \varkappa T)^{3/2}} e^{-\frac{(\boldsymbol{p} - m_a \boldsymbol{U}_a)^2}{2m_a \varkappa T_a}}. \tag{11.25}$$

As expected, in the equilibrium state the functions f_a are Maxwell distributions. It is important to stress that the temperature and average velocities of all the components of a plasma in the state of equilibrium are identical in this case.

If the plasma is not in the equilibrium state, the entropy rises until the plasma reaches equilibrium and then remains constant thereafter.

The kinetic equations (11.4) are a very complicated set of integro-differential equations. The kernels of eqns. (11.4), given by (11.5), depend also on the required f_a since these are contained in the expression for the dielectric constant.

However, there are a few cases when the set (11.4) becomes much simpler. We consider one of the most important of such cases.

Suppose that the initial non-equilibrium state, the dynamics of which we are describing by (11.4), is such that the number of fast charged particles with a velocity greater than the corresponding average thermal velocity is small. It is assumed that the average kinetic energy of electrons and ions is of the same order.

For this case consider the second term in the expression for the dielectric constant of an electron–ion plasma:

$$\varepsilon(\omega, \boldsymbol{k}) = 1+\sum_a \frac{4\pi e_a^2 n_a}{k^2} \int \frac{\left(\boldsymbol{k}\cdot\dfrac{\partial f_a}{\partial \boldsymbol{p}}\right)}{\omega-(\boldsymbol{k}\cdot\boldsymbol{v})} d^3\boldsymbol{p}. \tag{11.26}$$

By making the foregoing assumption the distribution functions f_a have maxima at $v \sim \sqrt{(\varkappa T/m_a)}$. Therefore the second term in (11.26) is of the order $1/r_d^2 k^2$ or less.

Since the dielectric constant occurs in the denominator of (11.5), if

$$1/r_d^2 k^2 \gg 1 \tag{11.27}$$

the denominator is large and the integrand is small.

Therefore in evaluating the integral over $\boldsymbol{k}$ in (11.5) one may approximately put $\varepsilon = 1$, i.e. we can neglect the medium's polarization, while restricting the range of integration over $\boldsymbol{k}$ by the requirement $|\boldsymbol{k}| > 1/r_d$.

In this approximation (11.5) becomes

$$Q_{ij}^{ab}(\boldsymbol{v}-\boldsymbol{v}') = 2e_a^2 e_b^2 \int_{|k|>1/r_d} \frac{k_i k_j}{k^4} \delta((\boldsymbol{k}\cdot\boldsymbol{v})-(\boldsymbol{k}\cdot\boldsymbol{v}'))\, d^3\boldsymbol{k}. \tag{11.28}$$

To simplify the integration over $\boldsymbol{k}$ in this expression, note that the tensor Q_{ij}^{ab} depends only on the components of the one vector $\boldsymbol{v}-\boldsymbol{v}'$. In its most general form this tensor is

$$Q_{ij}^{ab} = A^{ab}(v-v')_i (v-v')_j + B^{ab}\delta_{ij}. \tag{11.29}$$

Here A and B are functions of the vector $\boldsymbol{v}-\boldsymbol{v}'$.

From (11.28) it follows that these functions are not independent. In fact by multiplying the tensor Q_{ij}^{ab} with $(v-v')_i$ and then summing over i, and also having regard to the function $\delta((\boldsymbol{k}\cdot\boldsymbol{v})-$ $-(\boldsymbol{k}\cdot\boldsymbol{v}'))$ in (11.28), we find that

$$(v-v')_i Q_{ij}^{ab} = 0. \tag{11.30}$$

Using this condition, from (11.29) we find the relationship between the functions A^{ab} and B^{ab}

$$A^{ab}(\boldsymbol{v}-\boldsymbol{v}')^2 + B^{ab} = 0. \tag{11.31}$$

Using this condition the expression (11.29) becomes

$$Q_{ij}^{ab} = A^{ab}\{(v-v')_i(v-v')_j-(\boldsymbol{v}-\boldsymbol{v}')^2\,\delta_{ij}\}. \tag{11.32}$$

Thus, to determine the tensor Q_{ij}^{ab}, it is sufficient to determine just one function A^{ab}, which is expressible without difficulty in terms of the sum of the diagonal elements of the tensor Q_{ij}^{ab}

$$\begin{aligned} A^{ab} &= -\frac{Q_{ij}^{ab}}{2(\boldsymbol{v}-\boldsymbol{v}')^2} \\ &= -\frac{e_a^2 e_b^2}{|\boldsymbol{v}-\boldsymbol{v}'|^2}\int\frac{\delta((\boldsymbol{k}\cdot\boldsymbol{v})-(\boldsymbol{k}\cdot\boldsymbol{v}'))}{k^2}\,d^3\boldsymbol{k}. \end{aligned} \tag{11.33}$$

Thus it only remains to evaluate the integral in (11.33). We take the z-axis in the direction of the vector $\boldsymbol{v}-\boldsymbol{v}'$ and also introduce spherical coordinates. Then

$$\begin{aligned} &\int\frac{\delta((\boldsymbol{k}\cdot\boldsymbol{v})-(\boldsymbol{k}\cdot\boldsymbol{v}'))}{k^2}\,d^3\boldsymbol{k} \\ &= 2\pi\int_0^\pi\int\delta(k|\boldsymbol{v}-\boldsymbol{v}'|\cos\theta)\,\sin\theta\,d\theta\,dk = \frac{2\pi}{|\boldsymbol{v}-\boldsymbol{v}'|}\int\frac{dk}{k}. \end{aligned} \tag{11.34}$$

We have to consider the limits of integration in the integral $\int dk/k$. It has been seen that in changing over from (11.5) to (11.28) for Q_{ij}^{ab}, the range of integration over k is bounded at the lower limit by the condition $k > 1/r_d$.

The restriction of the integration range at the other end of large k (short distances between particles) is due to assuming the correlation function to be small. According to (10.48) our formulae therefore hold good in the ranges

$$|\boldsymbol{q}-\boldsymbol{q}'| \gg \frac{|e_a e_b|}{\varkappa T}; \qquad \frac{|e_a e_b|}{|\boldsymbol{q}-\boldsymbol{q}'|} \ll \varkappa T. \tag{11.35}$$

Since the limits of the integration range in (11.34) are those on the integration sign, the minimal distance over which the results are valid, is given by the condition

$$r_{\min} \sim \frac{\varkappa T}{|e_a e_b|}. \tag{11.36}$$

Consequently, the maximum value of k is

$$k_{\max} \sim \frac{1}{r_{\min}} \sim \frac{\varkappa T}{|e_a e_b|}. \tag{11.37}$$

On these conditions

$$\int_{k_{\min}}^{k_{\max}} \frac{dk}{k} = \ln \frac{r_d}{r_{\min}}. \tag{11.38}$$

Using the formulae (11.34, 38), the expression for A^{ab} is

$$A^{ab} = -\frac{2\pi e_a^2 e_b^2}{|\boldsymbol{v}-\boldsymbol{v}'|^3} \ln \frac{r_d}{r_{\min}}. \tag{11.39}$$

Substituting this formula into (11.32), the required formula for the tensor is

$$Q_{ij}^{ab} = \frac{2\pi e_a^2 e_b^2}{|\boldsymbol{v}-\boldsymbol{v}'|^3} \{(\boldsymbol{v}-\boldsymbol{v}')^2 \delta_{ij} - (v-v')_i (v-v')_j\} \ln \frac{r_d}{r_{\min}}. \tag{11.40}$$

The kinetic equations (11.4) for the functions f_a with the kernel (11.40) were first treated in Landau's paper of 1937. They were derived from the set of Boltzmann's equations for the distribution functions of charged particles.

But Boltzmann's equations only have regard to binary collisions between charged particles. However, in conformity with (11.2) many particles are present simultaneously in a charged particle's sphere of action. It is therefore inconsistent to use Boltzmann's equations for deriving kinetic equations in a plasma on the condition (11.2). This is evident, more particularly, in that in forming the kinetic equations for a plasma from Boltzmann's equations, a logarithmically divergent integral $\int dk/k$ appears in the expression for the kernel and further assumptions have to be made regarding the limitation of the integration range for small k.

In using (11.5) for Q_{ij}^{ab} the integral is convergent at low values of k, if the medium's polarization is taken into account.

Note, however, that it is far from always possible to replace (11.5) by the simpler expression (11.40). It is the polarization of the plasma which is the real consideration for plasma states close to the boundary of the region of stability, and also for unstable states.

These kinetic equations will be later used for calculating kinetic coefficients for a plasma.

Here we only estimate the relaxation time, i.e. the time taken to establish statistical equilibrium. Hence, we must evaluate the right-hand sides of eqn. (11.4). We do this for a purely electron plasma.

For the tensor Q_{ij}^{ab} we use the expression (11.40).

On our assumption $vp \sim \varkappa T$, and so the right-hand side of the equation for the function f_a is of the order

$$\frac{f}{\tau_r}, \quad \text{where} \quad \tau_r \sim \frac{(\varkappa T)^{3/2} m^{1/2}}{e^4 n \ln \dfrac{r_d}{r_{\min}}}. \tag{11.41}$$

Considering that $r_d = \sqrt{(\varkappa T/4\pi e^2 n)}$; $\omega_L = \sqrt{(4\pi e^2 n/m)}$, $n \sim 1/r_{av}^3$, we get

$$\tau_r \sim \frac{1}{\omega_L \ln (r_d/r_{\min})} \frac{r_d^3}{r_{av}^3}. \tag{11.42}$$

But since $\ln (r_d/r_{\min})$ is usually of the order of several units, having regard to the definition of ε, the expression (11.42) can be rewritten as

$$\tau_r \sim \frac{1}{\omega_L \varepsilon} \gg \frac{1}{\omega_L}, \quad \text{since} \quad \varepsilon = \frac{r_{av}^3}{r_d^3} \ll 1. \tag{11.43}$$

Similarly for the relaxation path λ_r we have

$$\lambda_r \sim r_d/\varepsilon \gg r_d. \tag{11.44}$$

Since the kinetic equations for a plasma were originally formed from a consideration of Boltzmann's kinetic equations, the same terminology is often used. Thus the quantities τ_r and λ_r are called the free-path time and the mean free path. But this terminology, though it is apt, does not go to the heart of the matter since, if the condition (11.2) is satisfied, each charged particle is interacting with many other particles simultaneously.

Equations (11.4) are written for the case when the distribution functions f_a depend only on $\boldsymbol{p}$ and t, i.e. for the spatially homogeneous case.

However, they can be generalized without difficulty for a slightly inhomogeneous plasma. Slight inhomogeneity implies that the functions f_a, $\boldsymbol{E}$, $(\delta N_a\, \delta \boldsymbol{E})$ vary little over distances of the order of the correlation radius.

The correlation radius, as the correlation time $\tau(k)$, depends on the value of k. In § 10 an expression for the spatial correlation function was obtained on condition that the spatial spectrum is bounded on the side of low values of k, i.e. some value $k_{\min}$ exists. For states close to equilibrium (and only in this case does $k_{\min}$ exist)

$$k_{\min} \sim 1/r_d, \tag{11.45}$$

where r_d is the Debye radius.

Thus one may formulate the condition for slight inhomogeneity as follows: the functions f_a and $\boldsymbol{E}$, and therefore also $\overline{\delta N_a\, \delta \boldsymbol{E}}$, vary little over distances of the order of the Debye radius.

On this condition eqn. (11.4) can be written as

$$\frac{\partial f_a}{\partial t} + \left(\boldsymbol{v} \cdot \frac{\partial f_a}{\partial \boldsymbol{q}}\right) + e_a \left(\boldsymbol{E} \cdot \frac{\partial f_a}{\partial \boldsymbol{p}}\right) = S_a^{\text{inh}}(\boldsymbol{q}, \boldsymbol{p}, t), \tag{11.46}$$

where S_a^{inh} is the collision integral for an inhomogeneous plasma.

The right-hand side of the kinetic equation is defined by the function $\overline{\delta N_a\, \delta \boldsymbol{E}}$. From (5.21) it follows that

$$S_a(\boldsymbol{q}, \boldsymbol{q}, t) = -\frac{e_a}{n_a}\left(\frac{\partial}{\partial \boldsymbol{p}} \cdot \overline{\delta N_a(\boldsymbol{q}, \boldsymbol{p}, t)\, \delta \boldsymbol{E}(\boldsymbol{q}, t)}\right). \tag{11.47}$$

For a spatially homogeneous plasma this expression can be represented as (11.3). Using solutions of (10.35), we represent the collision integral S_a in the form of (11.5) or (11.6).

To obtain an expression for a slightly inhomogeneous plasma, we proceed as follows.

The formulae (10.4, 5) determine the spatial spectral functions for a homogeneous plasma when the correlations at the points $\boldsymbol{q}$, $\boldsymbol{q}'$ depend only on $\boldsymbol{q}-\boldsymbol{q}'$.

In the slightly inhomogeneous case the correlations at the two points depend not only on $\boldsymbol{q}-\boldsymbol{q}'$, but also on $(\boldsymbol{q}+\boldsymbol{q}')/2$. Using the condition for slight inhomogeneity, we write

$$\overline{(\delta N_a\,\delta N_b)}_{\boldsymbol{q}-\boldsymbol{q}',\,(\boldsymbol{q}+\boldsymbol{q}')/2} = \overline{(\delta N_a\,\delta N_b)}_{\boldsymbol{q}-\boldsymbol{q}',\,\boldsymbol{q}-(\boldsymbol{q}-\boldsymbol{q}')/2}$$
$$\approx \overline{(\delta N_a\,\delta N_b)}_{\boldsymbol{r},\,\boldsymbol{q}} - \left(\frac{\boldsymbol{r}}{2}\cdot\frac{\partial}{\partial \boldsymbol{q}}\overline{(\delta N_a\,\delta N_b)}_{\boldsymbol{r},\,\boldsymbol{q}}\right); \quad \boldsymbol{r}=\boldsymbol{q}-\boldsymbol{q}'. \tag{11.48}$$

We shall show that this expression can be used for determining the collision integral in the case of an inhomogeneous plasma.

Using the solution of Poisson's equation for $\delta \boldsymbol{E}$ (see formula (5.32)), we write the right-hand side of expression (11.47) so that it contains the function $\overline{\delta N_a\,\delta N_b}$

$$S_a^{\text{inh}}(\boldsymbol{q},\boldsymbol{p},t) = \frac{e_a}{n_a}\sum_b e_b\left(\frac{\partial}{\partial \boldsymbol{p}}\cdot\int\frac{\partial}{\partial \boldsymbol{q}}\right.$$
$$\left.\times\frac{1}{|\boldsymbol{q}-\boldsymbol{q}'|}\,\overline{\delta N_a(\boldsymbol{q},\boldsymbol{p},t)\,\delta N_b(\boldsymbol{q}',\boldsymbol{p}',t)}\right)d^3\boldsymbol{q}'\,d^3\boldsymbol{p}'. \tag{11.49}$$

Substituting into (11.49) the approximate expression (11.48) for $\overline{\delta N_a\,\delta N_b}$, we have

$$S_a^{\text{inh}}(\boldsymbol{q},\boldsymbol{p},t) = -\frac{e_a}{n_a}\sum_b e_b\left(\frac{\partial}{\partial \boldsymbol{p}}\cdot\int\frac{\partial}{\partial \boldsymbol{r}}\right.$$
$$\left.\times\frac{1}{|\boldsymbol{r}|}\left\{\overline{(\delta N_a\,\delta N_b)}_{\boldsymbol{r},\,\boldsymbol{q}} - \left(\frac{\boldsymbol{r}}{2}\cdot\frac{\partial}{\partial \boldsymbol{q}}\overline{(\delta N_a\,\delta N_b)}_{\boldsymbol{r},\,\boldsymbol{q}}\right)\right\}\right)d^3\boldsymbol{r}. \tag{11.50}$$

Here in the integral we substitute $\boldsymbol{q}-\boldsymbol{q}'=\boldsymbol{r}$, $d^3\boldsymbol{q}'=-d^3\boldsymbol{r}$.

We expand the integrand as a Fourier integral in $\boldsymbol{r}$. Using the formulae

$$\overline{(\delta N_a\,\delta N_b)}_{\boldsymbol{r},\,\boldsymbol{q}} = \frac{1}{(2\pi)^3}\int(\delta N_a\,\delta N_b)_{\boldsymbol{k},\,\boldsymbol{q}}e^{i(\boldsymbol{k}\cdot\boldsymbol{r})}\,d^3\boldsymbol{k}, \tag{11.51}$$

$$\frac{1}{|\boldsymbol{r}|} = \frac{1}{(2\pi)^3}\int\frac{4\pi}{k^2}e^{i(\boldsymbol{k}\cdot\boldsymbol{r})}\,d^3\boldsymbol{k}, \tag{11.52}$$

$$\frac{r_i}{2}\cdot\frac{\partial}{\partial r_j}\cdot\frac{1}{|\boldsymbol{r}|} = -\frac{1}{(2\pi)^3}\int\frac{4\pi}{k^2}\left(\frac{\delta_{ij}}{2}-\frac{k_ik_j}{k^2}\right)e^{i(\boldsymbol{k}\cdot\boldsymbol{r})}\,d^3\boldsymbol{k}, \tag{11.53}$$

the expression for the collision integral [Klimontovich, 1961; and Klimontovich and Ebeling, 1962] is

$$S_a^{\text{inh}}(\boldsymbol{q}, \boldsymbol{p}, t) = -\frac{e_a}{(2\pi)^3 n_a} \sum_b 4\pi e_b \frac{\partial}{\partial p_i} \int \left\{ \frac{ik_i}{k^2} (\delta N_a \, \delta N_b)_{\boldsymbol{k}, \boldsymbol{q}} - \frac{1}{k^2} \left(\frac{\delta_{ij}}{2} - \frac{k_i k_j}{k^2} \right) \frac{\partial}{\partial q_j} (\delta N_a \, \delta N_b)_{\boldsymbol{k}, \boldsymbol{q}} \right\} d^3\boldsymbol{p}' \, d^3\boldsymbol{k}. \tag{11.54}$$

The right-hand side is expressible in terms of the simpler function $(\delta N_a \, \delta \boldsymbol{E})_{\boldsymbol{k}, \boldsymbol{q}}$, availing ourselves of the formula

$$(\delta N_a \, \delta \boldsymbol{E})_{\boldsymbol{k}} = i4\pi \sum_b e_b \frac{\boldsymbol{k}}{k^2} \int (\delta N_a \, \delta N_b)_{\boldsymbol{k}} \, d^3\boldsymbol{p}', \tag{11.55}$$

which follows directly from Poisson's equation for $\delta \boldsymbol{E}$.

Bearing in mind that the collision integral is a real function, we get [Klimontovich, 1961; and Klimontovich and Ebeling, 1962]:

$$S_a^{\text{inh}}(\boldsymbol{q}, \boldsymbol{p}, t) = -\frac{e_a}{(2\pi)^3 n_a} \left(\frac{\partial}{\partial \boldsymbol{p}} \cdot \int \operatorname{Re} \, (\delta N_a \, \delta \boldsymbol{E})_{\boldsymbol{k}} \right) d^3\boldsymbol{k} + \frac{e_a}{(2\pi)^3 n_a} \cdot \frac{\partial}{\partial p_i} \int \left(\frac{\delta_{ij}}{2} - \frac{k_i k_j}{k^2} \right) \frac{1}{k^2} \frac{\partial}{\partial q_j} \operatorname{Im} \left(\delta N_a (\boldsymbol{k} \cdot \delta \boldsymbol{E}) \right)_{\boldsymbol{k}} d^3\boldsymbol{k}. \tag{11.56}$$

Comparing this expression with (11.3) for the collision integral of a homogeneous plasma, it is seen that the collision integral for an inhomogeneous plasma contains an additional term determined by the imaginary part of the function $(\delta N_a (\boldsymbol{k} \cdot \delta \boldsymbol{E}))_{\boldsymbol{k}}$ i.e. by the imaginary part of the formula (10.33). In § 18 we shall elucidate this additional term's rôle in the collision integral.

12. Conservation Laws taking Higher Moments into Account

In § 6 the laws of conservation were considered for a plasma in the self-consistent field approximation when a closed set of equations for the first moments served as the initial equations, i.e. when correlations were completely neglected.

The total energy and total momentum of a plasma were determined by the average phase densities $N_a(\boldsymbol{q}, \boldsymbol{p}, t)$ and average electric and magnetic field strengths. For a Coulomb plasma $\boldsymbol{B}=0$, whilst the average electric field can be expressed in terms of $\overline{N_a}$. Thus only average phase densities entered into the conservation laws.

In § 11 the conservation laws deriving from the kinetic equations of a spatially homogeneous plasma were treated. In these equations the contribution of the spatial spectral function $(\delta N_a \delta \boldsymbol{E})_{\boldsymbol{k}}$ is taken into account only for large values of k when it is expressible in terms of the first distribution functions f_a.

In this approximation the conservation laws again contain the first distribution functions f_a (or the average phase densities $\overline{N_a}$).

In §§ 16–17 the contribution to the equations for f_a from the spectral function $(\delta N_a \delta \boldsymbol{E})$ will be taken into account for domains of low values of k—the radiation region. If one takes radiation into account, a closed set of equations—a set of kinetic equations—cannot be obtained for the functions f_a.

Instead, we have a more complicated set of equations for functions f_a and also for the spectral function $(\delta \boldsymbol{E} \cdot \delta \boldsymbol{E})_{\omega, \boldsymbol{k}}$.

Thus, by taking radiation into account, not only do the first distribution functions f_a enter into the laws of conservation, but also the correlation functions.

In this connexion it is useful to present the conservation laws which follow from the set of exact microscopic equations (4.10) and (4.14–17) for the functions N_a, $\boldsymbol{E}^{\mathrm{M}}$ and $\boldsymbol{H}^{\mathrm{M}}$.

The set of microscopic equations coincides in form with set (6.8–12) for the first moments. To change over from eqns. (4.10, 14–17) to the set (6.8–12), it is necessary to perform the substitution:

$$N_a \to n_a f_a; \qquad \boldsymbol{E}^{\mathrm{M}} \to \boldsymbol{E}, \quad \boldsymbol{H}^{\mathrm{M}} \to \boldsymbol{B}. \tag{12.1}$$

To obtain the conservation laws, taking higher moments into account in the formulae of § 6, derived from the self-consistent field equations, we replace the functions $n_a f_a$, $\boldsymbol{E}$, $\boldsymbol{B}$ by N_a, $\boldsymbol{E}^{\mathrm{M}}$, $\boldsymbol{H}^{\mathrm{M}}$, and then carry out averaging.

Equation (6.16) for the law of the conservation of the number of particles, still remains unchanged, but we rewrite it here as

$$\frac{\partial}{\partial t}\sum_a \int \overline{N}_a\, d^3\boldsymbol{p}+\left(\frac{\partial}{\partial \boldsymbol{q}}\cdot\sum_a \int \boldsymbol{v}\right)\overline{N}_a\, d^3\boldsymbol{p} = 0. \tag{12.2}$$

Since the initial equations do not have regard to the processes which lead to a variation in the number of charged particles (ionization and recombination processes), not only is the total number of particles conserved, but also the number of particles of the individual components, i.e. besides (12.2) the following laws of conservation follow also from (4.10)

$$\frac{\partial}{\partial t}\int \overline{N}_a\, d^3\boldsymbol{p}+\left(\frac{\partial}{\partial \boldsymbol{q}}\cdot\int \boldsymbol{v}\right)\overline{N}_a\, d^3\boldsymbol{p} = 0. \tag{12.3}$$

Using (4.10) we form an expression for the average momentum of the charged particles of the component a taking correlation into account. For this we multiply (4.10) by $m_a\boldsymbol{v}$, integrate over $\boldsymbol{p}$ and then average.

As a result we get

$$\begin{aligned}\frac{\partial}{\partial t} m_a \int v_i \overline{N}_a\, d^3\boldsymbol{p}+\frac{\partial}{\partial q_j} m_a \int v_i v_j \overline{N}_a\, d^3\boldsymbol{p}\\ = \overline{q_a^{\mathrm{M}} E_i^{\mathrm{M}}}+\frac{1}{c}\,\overline{[\boldsymbol{j}_a^{\mathrm{M}}\wedge \boldsymbol{H}^{\mathrm{M}}]_i}\\ = q_a E_i+\frac{1}{c}\,[\boldsymbol{j}_a\wedge\boldsymbol{B}]_i+\overline{\delta q_a\,\delta E_i}+\frac{1}{c}\,\overline{[\delta\boldsymbol{j}_a\wedge\delta\boldsymbol{B}]_i},\end{aligned} \tag{12.4}$$

where q_a^{M}, $\boldsymbol{j}_a^{\mathrm{M}}$ represent the microdensity of the charge and current of the component a, whilst $\boldsymbol{E}^{\mathrm{M}}$ and $\boldsymbol{H}^{\mathrm{M}}$ are the microfield strengths.

In forming eqns. (12.2–4) we used the condition $N_a(\boldsymbol{q}, \boldsymbol{p}, t) = 0$ for $p_i = \pm\infty$ $(i = 1, 2, 3)$, and also the fact that

$$\left([\boldsymbol{v}\wedge\boldsymbol{H}^{\mathrm{M}}]\cdot\frac{\partial N_a}{\partial \boldsymbol{p}}\right) = \left(\frac{\partial}{\partial \boldsymbol{p}}\cdot[\boldsymbol{v}\wedge\boldsymbol{H}^{\mathrm{M}}]N_a\right),$$

since

$$\left(\frac{\partial}{\partial \boldsymbol{p}}\cdot[\boldsymbol{v}\wedge\boldsymbol{H}^{\mathrm{M}}]\right) = 0$$

(compare these expressions with (6.14), (6.15)).

We thus assume that if $p_i = \pm\infty$, any moments vanish which contain the functions $N_a(\boldsymbol{q}, \boldsymbol{p}, t)$.

To find the total change of momentum of all the components of a plasma, we sum (12.4) over a:

$$\frac{\partial}{\partial t}\sum_a m_a \int v_i \overline{N}_a \, d^3\boldsymbol{p} + \frac{\partial}{\partial q_j}\sum_a m_a \int v_i v_j \overline{N}_a \, d^3\boldsymbol{p}$$
$$= qE_i + \frac{1}{c}[\boldsymbol{j}\wedge\boldsymbol{B}]_i + \overline{\delta q\, \delta E_i} + \frac{1}{c}\overline{[\delta\boldsymbol{j}\wedge\delta\boldsymbol{B}]_i}. \qquad (12.5)$$

This equation differs from the corresponding (6.23) of the self-consistent field approximation, through the two last terms:

$$\overline{\delta q\, \delta\boldsymbol{E}}; \qquad \frac{1}{c}\overline{[\delta\boldsymbol{j}\wedge\delta\boldsymbol{B}]}. \qquad (12.6)$$

The first of these terms refers to the correlation of the charge density and electric field strength, and the other to the correlation of the current density and magnetic field.

Both these terms determine an additional change in momentum, as compared with that in the approximation of the first moments.

The right-hand side of (12.5) can be expressed in terms of the first and second moments of the microscopic field strengths $\boldsymbol{E}^{\mathrm{M}}$, $\boldsymbol{H}^{\mathrm{M}}$, if (4.14–17) are used for the microfields.

To obtain the corresponding expression, we replace in formula (6.25) all the average quantities by the microscopic quantities, and then carry out averaging. We then have

$$\frac{1}{4\pi c}\cdot\frac{\partial}{\partial t}\{[\boldsymbol{E}\wedge\boldsymbol{B}]_i + \overline{[\delta\boldsymbol{E}\wedge\delta\boldsymbol{B}]_i}\} = -\Big\{qE_i + \frac{1}{c}[\boldsymbol{j}\wedge\boldsymbol{B}]_i$$
$$+\overline{\delta q\, \delta E_i} + \frac{1}{c}\overline{[\delta\boldsymbol{j}\wedge\delta\boldsymbol{B}]_i}\Big\} - \frac{\partial}{\partial q_j}(T_{ij}+K_{ij}). \qquad (12.7)$$

Here T_{ij} is the electromagnetic stress tensor, defined as previously by (6.23), whilst the tensor

$$K_{ij} = -\frac{1}{4\pi}\left(\overline{\delta E_i\, \delta E_j} + \overline{\delta B_i\, \delta B_j} - \delta_{ij}\frac{\overline{(\delta\boldsymbol{E})^2 + (\delta\boldsymbol{B})^2}}{2}\right). \qquad (12.8)$$

Thus K_{ij} determines the additional electromagnetic stresses due to considering the correlation of the microfields.

We sum eqns. (12.5, 7) and so obtain the law of the conservation of momentum of a plasma taking correlation into account

$$\frac{\partial}{\partial t}\left\{\sum_a m_a \int v_i \overline{N}_a \, d^3\boldsymbol{p} + \frac{1}{4\pi c}\left([\boldsymbol{E}\wedge\boldsymbol{B}]_i + \overline{[\delta\boldsymbol{E}\wedge\delta\boldsymbol{B}]_i}\right)\right\}$$

$$= -\frac{\partial}{\partial q_j}\left\{\sum_a n_a \int v_i v_j \overline{N}_a \, d^3\boldsymbol{p} + T_{ij} + K_{ij}\right\}. \qquad (12.9)$$

This equation differs from (6.27) in the additional terms for the correlation of the microfields.

Integrating (12.9) over the whole plasma, its right-hand side contains the surface integral

$$\oint \{\Pi_{ij} + T_{ij} + K_{ij}\}\, d^2 s_j; \qquad \Pi_{ij} = \sum_a n_a \int v_i v_j \overline{N}_a \, d^3\boldsymbol{p}. \qquad (12.10)$$

In considering correlation the idea of a set being a closed one alters in that, from (12.10), it is deemed closed if the components of Π_{ij}, T_{ij} vanish on the boundary, and also those of K_{ij} which is determined by the electromagnetic stresses due to microfield correlation.

Taking the microscopic equations for the functions N_a and the microscopic strength of the longitudinal electric field as the initial equations, the terms containing the magnetic field in eqns. (12.5, 7, 9) drop out. Equation (12.9) then becomes

$$\frac{\partial}{\partial t}\sum_a m_a \int v_i \overline{N}_a \, d^3\boldsymbol{p} = -\frac{\partial}{\partial q_j}(\Pi_{ij} + T^{\mathrm{e}}_{ij} + K^{\mathrm{e}}_{ij}). \qquad (12.11)$$

The tensor T^{e}_{ij} in this equation is given by the formula (6.33), whilst for K^{e}_{ij} we have

$$K^{\mathrm{e}}_{ij} = \frac{-1}{4\pi}\left(\overline{\delta E_i \, \delta E_j} - \delta_{ij}\frac{\overline{(\delta\boldsymbol{E}\cdot\delta\boldsymbol{E})}}{2}\right). \qquad (12.12)$$

Consider, finally, the energy-balance equation taking correlation into account.

The equation for a change of the average kinetic energy taking correlation into account is

$$\frac{\partial}{\partial t}\sum_a \int \frac{p^2}{2m_a}\overline{N}_a\, d^3\boldsymbol{p} = -\frac{\partial}{\partial q_i}\sum_a \int v_i \frac{p^2}{2m}\overline{N}_a\, d^3\boldsymbol{p} + (\boldsymbol{j}\cdot\boldsymbol{E}) + (\overline{\delta\boldsymbol{j}\cdot\delta\boldsymbol{E}}). \tag{12.13}$$

It differs from (6.39) in the last term. From eqns. (4.14–17) for the microfields, in place of (6.41), we get the equation of the energy balance of the electromagnetic field

$$\frac{1}{8\pi}\cdot\frac{\partial}{\partial t}\{(\boldsymbol{E}^2+\boldsymbol{B}^2)+(\overline{(\delta\boldsymbol{E})^2}+\overline{(\delta\boldsymbol{B})^2})\} = -\frac{c}{4\pi}\operatorname{div}\{[\boldsymbol{E}\wedge\boldsymbol{B}]+\overline{[\delta\boldsymbol{E}\wedge\delta\boldsymbol{B}]}\}-(\boldsymbol{j}\cdot\boldsymbol{E})-(\overline{\delta\boldsymbol{j}\cdot\delta\boldsymbol{E}}). \tag{12.14}$$

Adding eqns. (12.13, 14) we get the equation of the total energy balance of a plasma. It differs to (6.44) by taking correlation into account.

For a Coulomb plasma, eqn. (12.13) still holds, but in (12.14) terms containing the magnetic field drop out.

Hence the conservation laws as derived from the self-consistent field equations, are only valid as an approximation when the state of the plasma is described just by the first moments.

The other extreme case when the plasma is spatially homogeneous and isotropic, is also of interest. In this case the average fields $\boldsymbol{E}$, $\boldsymbol{B}$ are zero and, therefore, the electromagnetic energy is entirely determined by the correlation terms.

The corresponding conservation laws follow from the foregoing equations if we put $\boldsymbol{E} = \boldsymbol{B} = 0$ and bear in mind that $\overline{N}_a$ in the isotropic case depends only on the absolute magnitude of the momentum.

For example, for a Coulomb plasma, eqns. (12.13, 14) in this approximation become

$$\frac{\partial}{\partial t}\sum_a \int \frac{p^2}{2m_a}\overline{N}_a\, d^3\boldsymbol{p} = (\overline{\delta\boldsymbol{j}\cdot\delta\boldsymbol{E}}), \tag{12.15}$$

$$\frac{\partial}{\partial t}\cdot\frac{(\overline{\delta\boldsymbol{E}\cdot\delta\boldsymbol{E}})}{8\pi} = -(\overline{\delta\boldsymbol{j}\cdot\delta\boldsymbol{E}}). \tag{12.16}$$

These equations imply that the total energy of a homogeneous and isotropic Coulomb plasma,

$$\sum_a \int \frac{p^2}{2m_a} \overline{N_a}\, d^3\boldsymbol{p} + \frac{1}{8\pi} \overline{(\delta \boldsymbol{E} \cdot \delta \boldsymbol{E})}, \tag{12.17}$$

is constant.

The conservation laws for a homogeneous and isotropic plasma will be used later in §§ 17, 21.

13. Kinetic Equations for a Relativistic Plasma†

Consider first the case when the plasma is homogeneous and isotropic and when no external fields are present. Under these conditions the functions f_a are

$$f_a = f_a(|\boldsymbol{p}|, t). \tag{13.1}$$

A more general case is considered in § 14.

Equations (5.21) for the functions f_a in this approximation become

$$\begin{aligned} \frac{\partial f_a}{\partial t} &= -\frac{e_a}{n_a} \left(\frac{\partial}{\partial \boldsymbol{p}} \cdot \overline{\delta N_a\, \delta \boldsymbol{E}} \right) \\ &= -\frac{e_a}{8\pi^3 n_a} \left(\frac{\partial}{\partial \boldsymbol{p}} \cdot \int \mathrm{Re}\, (\delta N_a\, \delta \boldsymbol{E})_{\boldsymbol{k}} \right) d^3\boldsymbol{k} \equiv S_a \end{aligned} \tag{13.2}$$

and they coincide in form with the corresponding equations (10.2, 9) for a non-relativistic plasma. The difference is that the function $(\delta N_a\, \delta \boldsymbol{E})_{\boldsymbol{k}}$ for a relativistic plasma does not coincide with the function defined by (10.33).

To find the spatial spectral function $(\delta N_a\, \delta \boldsymbol{E})_{\boldsymbol{k}}$ in the relativistic case, we use the set (5.41–43) for the functions δN_a, $\delta \boldsymbol{E}$, $\delta \boldsymbol{B}$. In the isotropic case the term $([\boldsymbol{v} \wedge \delta \boldsymbol{B}] \cdot \partial f_a / \partial \boldsymbol{p})$ in eqn. (5.41) drops out.

By virtue of its linearity, this set can be split into two sets which describe the transverse and longitudinal excitations in the plasma respectively.

† Belyayev and Budker (1957); Klimontovich (1960a, 1960b); Silin (1961, 1962a) and Klimontovich (1961).

Putting

$$\begin{aligned} \delta \boldsymbol{E} &= \delta \boldsymbol{E}^{\|} + \delta \boldsymbol{E}^{\perp}, \quad \operatorname{curl} \delta \boldsymbol{E}^{\|} = 0, \quad \operatorname{div} \delta \boldsymbol{E}^{\perp} = 0; \\ \delta \boldsymbol{j} &= \delta \boldsymbol{j}^{\|} + \delta \boldsymbol{j}^{\perp}, \quad \operatorname{curl} \delta \boldsymbol{j}^{\|} = 0, \quad \operatorname{div} \delta \boldsymbol{j}^{\perp} = 0, \end{aligned} \tag{13.3}$$

the first set of equations is

$$\frac{\partial \delta N_a^{\|}}{\partial t} + \left(\boldsymbol{v} \cdot \frac{\partial \delta N_a^{\|}}{\partial \boldsymbol{q}}\right) + e_a n_a \left(\delta \boldsymbol{E}^{\|} \cdot \frac{\partial f_a}{\partial \boldsymbol{p}}\right) = 0, \tag{13.4}$$

$$\frac{\partial \delta \boldsymbol{E}^{\|}}{\partial t} + 4\pi \delta \boldsymbol{j}^{\|} = 0, \quad \operatorname{curl} \delta \boldsymbol{E}^{\|} = 0, \tag{13.5}$$

$$\operatorname{div} \delta \boldsymbol{E}^{\|} = 4\pi \sum e_a \int \delta N_a^{\|} \, d^3\boldsymbol{p}. \tag{13.6}$$

Here the superscript $\|$ of the function δN_a indicates that the equations refer to longitudinal motions in the plasma.

The other set is

$$\frac{\partial \delta N_a^{\perp}}{\partial t} + \left(\boldsymbol{v} \cdot \frac{\partial \delta N_a^{\perp}}{\partial \boldsymbol{q}}\right) + e_a n_a \left(\delta \boldsymbol{E}^{\perp} \cdot \frac{\partial f_a}{\partial \boldsymbol{p}}\right) = 0, \tag{13.7}$$

$$\operatorname{curl} \delta \boldsymbol{B} = \frac{1}{c} \cdot \frac{\partial \delta \boldsymbol{E}^{\perp}}{\partial t} + \frac{4\pi}{c} \delta \boldsymbol{j}^{\perp}, \tag{13.8}$$

$$\operatorname{curl} \delta \boldsymbol{E}^{\perp} = -\frac{1}{c} \cdot \frac{\partial \delta \boldsymbol{B}}{\partial t}, \tag{13.9}$$

$$\operatorname{div} \delta \boldsymbol{B} = 0, \quad \operatorname{div} \delta \boldsymbol{E}^{\perp} = 0. \tag{13.10}$$

Such a division is justified in that the second moments of the current densities and of the fields, as calculated by means of the random functions $\delta N_a^{\|}$, $\delta N_a^{\perp}$, break down in the isotropic case into the sum of a potential component and a rotational component which are uncorrelated. This has been shown elsewhere [Klimontovich, 1958b].

More complicated correlations, e.g. $\overline{\delta N_a(\boldsymbol{q}, \boldsymbol{p}, t)\, \delta N_b(\boldsymbol{q}', \boldsymbol{p}', t)}$, contain common terms for the potential part and the transverse part, the form of which requires no explanation.

Of course, one does not have to make such a division, but it does usually reduce the calculations considerably.

Equations (13.4–6) coincide with (5.31) which are the initial equations for forming (10.7) for the spatial spectral function $(\delta N_a\,\delta N_b)_{\boldsymbol{k},\,t}$ of a non-relativistic plasma.

On this basis rather than solve eqns. (13.4–6) we can immediately use the expression (10.33) for the function $\big(\delta N_a(\boldsymbol{k}\cdot\delta\boldsymbol{E})\big)_{\boldsymbol{k}}$. It thus determines the longitudinal part of the collision integral in (13.2).

Naturally, the functions f_a in (10.33) satisfy other equations besides the kinetic equations (11.4) for a non-relativistic plasma.

We now pass on to the corresponding expressions for the transverse part, taking the set (13.7–10) as the initial equations.

From (13.7) we form an equation, analogous to (10.16), for the transverse spatial spectral function $(\delta N_a\,\delta N_b)_{\boldsymbol{k}}$,

$$
\begin{aligned}
&(\delta N_a\,\delta N_b)_{\boldsymbol{k}}\\
&\quad= \frac{i}{(\boldsymbol{k}\cdot\boldsymbol{v})-(\boldsymbol{k}\cdot\boldsymbol{v}')-i\Delta}\left\{e_a n_a\big(\delta N_b(\boldsymbol{p}')\,\delta E_j^{\perp}\big)_{\boldsymbol{k}}^{*}\frac{\partial f_a}{\partial p_j}\right.\\
&\qquad\left.+e_b n_b(\delta N_a\,\delta E_j^{\perp})_{\boldsymbol{k}}\frac{\partial f_b}{\partial p_j'}\right\}+\delta_{ab}\,\delta(\boldsymbol{p}-\boldsymbol{p}')n_a f_a, \qquad (13.11)
\end{aligned}
$$

omitting the $\perp$ sign on δN_a.

Multiplying (13.11) by $e_b[[\boldsymbol{k}\wedge\boldsymbol{v}']\wedge\boldsymbol{k}]/k^2$, summing over b and then integrating over $\boldsymbol{p}'$, the equation which relates the functions $(\delta N_a\,\delta\boldsymbol{j}^{\perp})_{\boldsymbol{k}}$, $(\delta N_b\,\delta\boldsymbol{E}^{\perp})_{\boldsymbol{k}}$ is:

$$
\begin{aligned}
&(\delta N_a\,\delta j_i^{\perp})_{\boldsymbol{k}}\\
&\quad= i\,\frac{e_a n_a}{k^2}\sum_b e_b\int\frac{[[\boldsymbol{k}\wedge\boldsymbol{v}']\wedge\boldsymbol{k}]_i\,(\delta N_b\,\delta E_j^{\perp})_{\boldsymbol{k}}^{*}}{(\boldsymbol{k}\cdot\boldsymbol{v})-(\boldsymbol{k}\cdot\boldsymbol{v}')-i\Delta}\,d^3\boldsymbol{p}'\,\frac{\partial f_a}{\partial p_j}\\
&\qquad+i(\delta N_a\,\delta E_j^{\perp})_{\boldsymbol{k}}\sum_b\frac{e_b^2 n_b}{k^2}\int\frac{[[\boldsymbol{k}\wedge\boldsymbol{v}']\wedge\boldsymbol{k}]_i\,\dfrac{\partial f_a}{\partial p_j'}}{(\boldsymbol{k}\cdot\boldsymbol{v})-(\boldsymbol{k}\cdot\boldsymbol{v}')-i\Delta}\,d^3\boldsymbol{p}'\\
&\qquad+e_a n_a\frac{[[\boldsymbol{k}\wedge\boldsymbol{v}]\wedge\boldsymbol{k}]_i}{k^2}f_a. \qquad (13.12)
\end{aligned}
$$

By using the Maxwell equations (13.8–10) we form two more equations for the spatial spectral functions $(\delta N_a\,\delta\boldsymbol{E}^{\perp})_{\boldsymbol{k}}$ and

$(\delta N_a \delta \boldsymbol{j}^{\perp})_{\boldsymbol{k}}$

$$i(\boldsymbol{k}\cdot\boldsymbol{v})(\delta N_a\,\delta E_i^{\perp})_{\boldsymbol{k}}+e_a n_a(\delta E_j^{\perp}\,\delta E_i^{\perp})\frac{\partial f_a}{\partial p_j}$$

$$+ic(\delta N_a[\boldsymbol{k}\wedge\delta\boldsymbol{B}]_i)_{\boldsymbol{k}}+4\pi(\delta N_a\,\delta j_i^{\perp})_{\boldsymbol{k}}=0, \tag{13.13}$$

$$(\boldsymbol{k}\cdot\boldsymbol{v})(\delta N_a\,\delta\boldsymbol{B})_{\boldsymbol{k}}-c(\delta N_a[\boldsymbol{k}\wedge\delta\boldsymbol{E}^{\perp}])_{\boldsymbol{k}}=0. \tag{13.14}$$

In the last equation we take into account the fact that in a homogeneous isotropic plasma the electric and magnetic fields are weakly correlated. The term with $\overline{\delta E_i\,\delta B_j}$ is discarded for this reason.

From eqns. (13.13, 14) we must eliminate the terms which contain the magnetic field. We multiply (13.14) vectorially with $\boldsymbol{k}$ and then use this equation to eliminate the term $(\delta N_a[\boldsymbol{k}\wedge\delta\boldsymbol{B}])_i$ from (13.13). We then get the equation

$$i((\boldsymbol{k}\cdot\boldsymbol{v})^2-c^2k^2)(\delta N_a\,\delta E_i^{\perp})_{\boldsymbol{k}}+e_a n_a(\boldsymbol{k}\cdot\boldsymbol{v})(\delta E_j^{\perp}\,\delta E_i^{\perp})_{\boldsymbol{k}}\frac{\partial f_a}{\partial p_j}$$

$$+4\pi(\boldsymbol{k}\cdot\boldsymbol{v})(\delta N_a\,\delta j_i^{\perp})_{\boldsymbol{k}}=0. \tag{13.15}$$

From eqns. (13.12, 15) we eliminate the function $(\delta N_a \delta j_i^{\perp})_{\boldsymbol{k}}$. We then arrive at the equation

$$((\boldsymbol{k}\cdot\boldsymbol{v})^2\,\varepsilon^{(-)\perp}((\boldsymbol{k}\cdot\boldsymbol{v})\cdot\boldsymbol{k})-c^2k^2)(\delta N_a\,\delta E_i^{\perp})_{\boldsymbol{k}}$$

$$=-\frac{4\pi e_a n_a}{k^2}(\boldsymbol{k}\cdot\boldsymbol{v})\frac{\partial f_a}{\partial p_j}\sum_b e_b\int\frac{[[\boldsymbol{k}\wedge\boldsymbol{v}']\wedge\boldsymbol{k}]_i(\delta N_b\,\delta E_j^{\perp})_{\boldsymbol{k}}}{(\boldsymbol{k}\cdot\boldsymbol{v})-(\boldsymbol{k}\cdot\boldsymbol{v}')-i\Delta}d^3\boldsymbol{p}'$$

$$+ie_a n_a(\boldsymbol{k}\cdot\boldsymbol{v})(\delta E_j^{\perp}\,\delta E_i^{\perp})_{\boldsymbol{k}}\frac{\partial f_a}{\partial p_j}$$

$$+i4\pi(\boldsymbol{k}\cdot\boldsymbol{v})e_a n_a\frac{[[\boldsymbol{k}\wedge\boldsymbol{v}]\wedge\boldsymbol{k}]_i}{k^2}f_a. \tag{13.16}$$

Here we denote the transverse dielectric constant by $\varepsilon^{\perp}(\omega,\,\boldsymbol{k})$.

$$\varepsilon^{(\pm)\perp}(\omega,\,\boldsymbol{k})$$

$$=1+\sum_b\frac{2\pi e_b^2 n_b}{k^2(\omega\pm i\Delta)}\int\frac{\left([[\boldsymbol{k}\wedge\boldsymbol{v}']\wedge\boldsymbol{k}]\cdot\dfrac{\partial f_b}{\partial\boldsymbol{p}'}\right)}{\omega-(\boldsymbol{k}\cdot\boldsymbol{v}')\pm i\Delta}\,d^3\boldsymbol{p}'. \tag{13.17}$$

The functions analogous to $H^{\pm}(\omega, \boldsymbol{k})$ in § 10 are

$$iH^{\pm}_{(1)ij} = \frac{1}{2\pi i}\sum_b e_b \int \frac{[[\boldsymbol{k}\wedge\boldsymbol{v}]\wedge\boldsymbol{k}]_i\,(\delta N_b\,\delta E^{\perp}_j)_{\boldsymbol{k}}}{\omega-(\boldsymbol{k}\cdot\boldsymbol{v})\pm i\Delta}\,d^3\boldsymbol{p}, \tag{13.18}$$

$$-iH^{\pm}_{(2)ij} = \frac{1}{2\pi i}\sum_b e_b \int \frac{[[\boldsymbol{k}\wedge\boldsymbol{v}]\wedge\boldsymbol{k}]_i\,(\delta N_a\,\delta E^{\perp}_j)^*_{\boldsymbol{k}}}{\omega-(\boldsymbol{k}\cdot\boldsymbol{v})\pm i\Delta}\,d^3\boldsymbol{p}. \tag{13.19}$$

The formula (13.18) implies that

$$\sum_a e_a \int \delta(\omega-(\boldsymbol{k}\cdot\boldsymbol{v}))\,[[\boldsymbol{k}\wedge\boldsymbol{v}]\wedge\boldsymbol{k}]_i\,(\delta N_a\,\delta E^{\perp}_j)_{\boldsymbol{k}}\,d^3\boldsymbol{p}$$
$$= i(H^{-}_{(1)ij}-H^{+}_{(1)ij}). \tag{13.20}$$

In a homogeneous isotropic plasma

$$H^{\pm}_{(\alpha)ij} = H^{\pm}_{(\alpha)ji}, \qquad \alpha = 1, 2. \tag{13.21}$$

Using formula (13.19), we write eqn. (13.16) as

$$\big((\boldsymbol{k}\cdot\boldsymbol{v})^2\,\varepsilon^{(-)\perp}((\boldsymbol{k}\cdot\boldsymbol{v})\cdot\boldsymbol{k})-c^2k^2\big)\,(\delta N_a\,\delta E^{\perp}_i)_{\boldsymbol{k}}$$
$$= i2\pi i\,\frac{4\pi e_a n_a}{k^2}\,(\boldsymbol{k}\cdot\boldsymbol{v})\,\frac{\partial f_a}{\partial p_j}\,H^{-}_{(2)ij}((\boldsymbol{k}\cdot\boldsymbol{v})\cdot\boldsymbol{k})$$
$$+ie_a n_a(\boldsymbol{k}\cdot\boldsymbol{v})\,(\delta E^{\perp}_j\,\delta E^{\perp}_i)_{\boldsymbol{k}}\,\frac{\partial f_a}{\partial p_j}$$
$$+i4\pi(\boldsymbol{k}\cdot\boldsymbol{v})e_a n_a\,\frac{[[\boldsymbol{k}\wedge\boldsymbol{v}]\wedge\boldsymbol{k}]_i}{k^2}\,f_a. \tag{13.22}$$

We then form the equation for the function H_{ij} $(\omega, \boldsymbol{k})$ by multiplying (13.22) with $\delta(\omega-(\boldsymbol{k}\cdot\boldsymbol{v}))\,e_a[[\boldsymbol{k}\wedge\boldsymbol{v}]\wedge\boldsymbol{k}]_l$, and then summing it over a and integrating over $\boldsymbol{p}$. By using the formula

$$2\pi i\sum_a \frac{2\pi e_a^2 n_a}{k^2\omega}\int \delta(\omega-(\boldsymbol{k}\cdot\boldsymbol{v}))\left([[\boldsymbol{k}\wedge\boldsymbol{v}]\wedge\boldsymbol{k}]\cdot\frac{\partial f_a}{\partial \boldsymbol{p}}\right)d^3\boldsymbol{p}$$
$$= \varepsilon^{(-)\perp}(\omega, \boldsymbol{k})-\varepsilon^{(+)\perp}(\omega, \boldsymbol{k}) \tag{13.23}$$

and also the formula (13.20), the equation for the functions H_{lj} is

$$(\omega^2\varepsilon^{(-)\perp}-c^2k^2)\,(H^{-}_{(1)lj}-H^{+}_{(1)lj}) = \omega^2(\varepsilon^{(-)\perp}-\varepsilon^{(+)\perp})H^{-}_{(2)lj}$$
$$+\frac{k^2}{8\pi^2 i}\,\omega^2(\varepsilon^{(-)\perp}-\varepsilon^{(+)\perp})\,(\delta E^{\perp}_l\,\delta E^{\perp}_j)_{\boldsymbol{k}}$$
$$+4\pi\omega\sum_a \frac{e_a^2 n_a}{k^2}\int [[\boldsymbol{k}\wedge\boldsymbol{v}]\wedge\boldsymbol{k}]_l\,[[\boldsymbol{k}\wedge\boldsymbol{v}]\wedge\boldsymbol{k}]_j$$
$$\times\,\delta(\omega-(\boldsymbol{k}\cdot\boldsymbol{v}))\,f_a\,d^3\boldsymbol{p}. \tag{13.24}$$

Bearing in mind that the last two terms in this expression are real, we can equate to zero the imaginary part of the other terms:

$$(\omega^2\varepsilon^- - c^2k^2)(H^-_{(1)ij} - H^-_{(2)ij}) = (\omega^2\varepsilon^+ - c^2k^2)(H^+_{(1)ij} - H^+_{(2)ij}). \tag{13.25}$$

Hence

$$H_{(1)ij}(\omega, \boldsymbol{k}) = H_{(2)ij}(\omega, \boldsymbol{k}), \quad \text{if} \quad \omega^2\varepsilon^\perp(\omega, \boldsymbol{k}) - c^2k^2 \neq 0, \tag{13.26}$$

i.e. the dispersion relation has no real roots.

This condition is equivalent to (10.28). By using it, eqn. (13.24) becomes

$$\frac{H^-_{ij}(\omega, \boldsymbol{k})}{\omega^2\varepsilon^{(-)\perp} - c^2k^2} - \frac{H^+_{ij}(\omega, \boldsymbol{k})}{\omega^2\varepsilon^{(+)\perp} - c^2k^2}$$

$$= \frac{\omega \sum_a \frac{4\pi e_a^2 n_a}{k^2} \int [[\boldsymbol{k}\wedge\boldsymbol{v}]\wedge\boldsymbol{k}]_i [[\boldsymbol{k}\wedge\boldsymbol{v}]\wedge\boldsymbol{k}]_j \,\delta(\omega - (\boldsymbol{k}\cdot\boldsymbol{v})) f_a \, d^3\boldsymbol{p}}{|\omega^2\varepsilon^\perp(\omega, \boldsymbol{k}) - c^2k^2|^2}$$

$$+ \frac{k^2}{8\pi^2 i}\left(\frac{1}{\omega^2\varepsilon^{(+)\perp} - c^2k^2} - \frac{1}{\omega^2\varepsilon^{(-)\perp} - c^2k^2}\right)(\delta E_i^\perp \, \delta E_j^\perp)_{\boldsymbol{k}}. \tag{13.27}$$

This formula determines the discontinuity of the piecewise analytic function $H_{ij}/(\omega^2\varepsilon - c^2k^2)$.

Knowing the discontinuity we find the expression for the functions $H^\pm_{ij}(\omega, \boldsymbol{k})/(\omega^2\varepsilon^\pm - c^2k^2)$:

$$\frac{H^\pm_{ij}(\omega, \boldsymbol{k})}{\omega^2\varepsilon^\pm(\omega, \boldsymbol{k}) - c^2k^2} = \frac{1}{2\pi i}$$

$$\times \int \frac{\omega' \sum_a \frac{4\pi e_a^2 n_a}{k^2} \int \delta(\omega' - (\boldsymbol{k}\cdot\boldsymbol{v}))[[\boldsymbol{k}\wedge\boldsymbol{v}]\wedge\boldsymbol{k}]_i [[\boldsymbol{k}\wedge\boldsymbol{v}]\wedge\boldsymbol{k}]_j f_a \, d^3\boldsymbol{p}}{(\omega - \omega' \pm i\Delta)\,|\omega'^2\varepsilon^\perp(\omega', \boldsymbol{k}) - c^2k^2|^2} \, d\omega'$$

$$- \frac{k^2}{8\pi^2 i} \cdot \frac{1}{\omega^2\varepsilon^\pm(\omega, \boldsymbol{k}) - c^2k^2}(\delta E_i^\perp \, \delta E_j^\perp)_{\boldsymbol{k}}. \tag{13.28}$$

We now return to (13.22), and having substituted into it (13.28), bearing in mind the isotropy and homogeneity conditions, we get

$$e_a(\delta N_a\,\delta E_i^{\perp})_{\boldsymbol{k}} = i\,\frac{4\pi e_a^2 n_a}{k^2}\cdot\frac{\partial f_a}{\partial p_j}$$

$$\times\int\frac{(\boldsymbol{k}\cdot\boldsymbol{v}')^2\sum_b\frac{4\pi e_b^2 n_b}{k^2}[[\boldsymbol{k}\wedge\boldsymbol{v}']\wedge\boldsymbol{k}]_i[[\boldsymbol{k}\wedge\boldsymbol{v}']\wedge\boldsymbol{k}]_j f_b}{((\boldsymbol{k}\cdot\boldsymbol{v})-(\boldsymbol{k}\cdot\boldsymbol{v}')-i\Delta)\,|(\boldsymbol{k}\cdot\boldsymbol{v}')^2\varepsilon^{\perp}((\boldsymbol{k}\cdot\boldsymbol{v}')\cdot\boldsymbol{k})-c^2k^2|^2}\,d^3\boldsymbol{p}'$$

$$+i\frac{4\pi(\boldsymbol{k}\cdot\boldsymbol{v})e_a^2 n_a}{(\boldsymbol{k}\cdot\boldsymbol{v})^2\varepsilon^{(-)\perp}((\boldsymbol{k}\cdot\boldsymbol{v})\cdot\boldsymbol{k})-c^2k^2}\cdot\frac{[[\boldsymbol{k}\wedge\boldsymbol{v}]\wedge\boldsymbol{k}]_i}{k^2}f_a. \qquad (13.29)$$

Formula (13.29) is analogous to the corresponding formula (10.33).

The total spatial spectral function of a relativistic plasma

$$(\delta N_a\,\delta\boldsymbol{E})_{\boldsymbol{k}} = (\delta N_a^{\parallel}\,\delta\boldsymbol{E}^{\parallel})_{\boldsymbol{k}}+(\delta N_a^{\perp}\,\delta\boldsymbol{E}^{\perp})_{\boldsymbol{k}} \qquad (13.30)$$

is given by the sum of the expressions (13.29) and (10.33).

To form the kinetic equation, we require an expression for the real part of the function $(\delta N_a\delta\boldsymbol{E})_{\boldsymbol{k}}$: from the formulae (10.35) and (13.29) we find

$$\mathrm{Re}\,(\delta N_a\delta E_i) = -\frac{4\pi^2 e_a n_a}{k^2}\sum_b\frac{4\pi e_b^2 n_b}{k^2}$$

$$\times\Bigg\{\int\!\!\int\Bigg[\frac{k_i k_j}{|\varepsilon^{\parallel}((\boldsymbol{k}\cdot\boldsymbol{v})\cdot\boldsymbol{k})|^2}$$

$$+\frac{(\boldsymbol{k}\cdot\boldsymbol{v})^2[[\boldsymbol{k}\wedge\boldsymbol{v}']\wedge\boldsymbol{k}]_j[[\boldsymbol{k}\wedge\boldsymbol{v}']\wedge\boldsymbol{k}]_i}{|(\boldsymbol{k}\cdot\boldsymbol{v})^2\varepsilon^{\perp}((\boldsymbol{k}\cdot\boldsymbol{v})\cdot\boldsymbol{k})-c^2k^2|^2}\Bigg]\delta((\boldsymbol{k}\cdot\boldsymbol{v})-(\boldsymbol{k}\cdot\boldsymbol{v}'))$$

$$\times f_b(\boldsymbol{p}')\frac{\partial f_a(\boldsymbol{p})}{\partial p_j}\,d^3\boldsymbol{p}'-\int\Bigg[\frac{k_i k_j}{|\varepsilon^{\parallel}((\boldsymbol{k}\cdot\boldsymbol{v})\cdot\boldsymbol{k})|^2}$$

$$+\frac{(\boldsymbol{k}\cdot\boldsymbol{v})^2[[\boldsymbol{k}\wedge\boldsymbol{v}]\wedge\boldsymbol{k}]_i[[\boldsymbol{k}\wedge\boldsymbol{v}']\wedge\boldsymbol{k}]_j}{2\,|(\boldsymbol{k}\cdot\boldsymbol{v})^2\,\varepsilon^{\perp}((\boldsymbol{k}\cdot\boldsymbol{v})\cdot\boldsymbol{k})-c^2k^2|^2}\Bigg]$$

$$\times\delta((\boldsymbol{k}\cdot\boldsymbol{v})-(\boldsymbol{k}\cdot\boldsymbol{v}'))\frac{\partial f_b}{\partial p_j'}f_a(\boldsymbol{p})\,d^3\boldsymbol{p}'\Bigg\}. \qquad (13.31)$$

It is necessary to transform this expression.

We change from differentiation with respect to the momenta to differentiation with respect to the energy $\varepsilon = \sqrt{(m^2c^4+p^2c^2)}$, bearing in mind that

$$\frac{\partial}{\partial \boldsymbol{p}} = \frac{d\varepsilon}{d\boldsymbol{p}} \cdot \frac{\partial}{\partial \varepsilon} = \frac{\boldsymbol{p}c^2}{\varepsilon} \cdot \frac{\partial}{\partial \varepsilon} = \boldsymbol{v}\frac{\partial}{\partial \varepsilon}, \quad \text{since} \quad \boldsymbol{p} = \frac{\varepsilon \boldsymbol{v}}{c^2}. \tag{13.32}$$

In the isotropic case the relevant formulae are

$$(\boldsymbol{k}\cdot\boldsymbol{v})[[\boldsymbol{k}\wedge\boldsymbol{v}]\wedge\boldsymbol{k}]_j \frac{\partial f_b}{\partial p_j} = (\boldsymbol{k}\cdot\boldsymbol{v})\,[\boldsymbol{k}\wedge\boldsymbol{v}]^2 \frac{\partial f_b}{\partial \varepsilon}$$

$$= k_j \frac{\partial f_b}{\partial p_j}[\boldsymbol{k}\wedge\boldsymbol{v}]^2, \tag{13.33}$$

$$\int [[\boldsymbol{k}\wedge\boldsymbol{v}]\wedge\boldsymbol{k}]_i [[\boldsymbol{k}\wedge\boldsymbol{v}]\wedge\boldsymbol{k}]_j\, \delta(\omega-(\boldsymbol{k}\cdot\boldsymbol{v}))f_a(\boldsymbol{p})\, d^3\boldsymbol{p}$$

$$= \frac{1}{2}(\delta_{ij}k^2 - k_i k_j)\int [\boldsymbol{k}\wedge\boldsymbol{v}]^2\, \delta(\omega-(\boldsymbol{k}\cdot\boldsymbol{v}))f_a(\boldsymbol{p})\, d^3\boldsymbol{p}. \tag{13.34}$$

Using (13.33, 34), in the last term of (13.31) we carry out the transformation

$$\frac{1}{2}[[\boldsymbol{k}\wedge\boldsymbol{v}]\wedge\boldsymbol{k}]_i [[\boldsymbol{k}\wedge\boldsymbol{v}']\wedge\boldsymbol{k}]_j \frac{\partial f_b}{\partial p'_j}(\boldsymbol{k}\cdot\boldsymbol{v}')$$

$$= \frac{1}{2}v_l\left(\delta_{il} - \frac{k_i k_l}{k^2}\right)[\boldsymbol{k}\wedge\boldsymbol{v}']^2 k_j \frac{\partial f_b}{\partial p'_j}$$

$$= v_l[[\boldsymbol{k}\wedge\boldsymbol{v}']\wedge\boldsymbol{k}]_l [[\boldsymbol{k}\wedge\boldsymbol{v}']\wedge\boldsymbol{k}]_i k_j \frac{\partial f_b}{\partial p'_j}$$

$$= ([\boldsymbol{k}\wedge\boldsymbol{v}]\cdot[\boldsymbol{k}\wedge\boldsymbol{v}'])\,[[\boldsymbol{k}\wedge\boldsymbol{v}']\wedge\boldsymbol{k}]_i k_j \frac{\partial f_b}{\partial p'_j}. \tag{13.35}$$

We now substitute the expression (13.31) into (13.2). Using formula (13.35) and the relation

$$[[\boldsymbol{k}\wedge\boldsymbol{v}']\wedge\boldsymbol{k}]_i \frac{\partial f_a}{\partial p_i}(\boldsymbol{k}\cdot\boldsymbol{v}) = ([\boldsymbol{k}\wedge\boldsymbol{v}]\cdot[\boldsymbol{k}\wedge\boldsymbol{v}'])\left(\boldsymbol{k}\cdot\frac{\partial f_a}{\partial \boldsymbol{p}}\right),$$

the resulting equation becomes

$$\frac{\partial f_a}{\partial t} = \sum_b n_b \frac{\partial}{\partial p_i}\int Q_{ij}^{ab}\left\{\frac{\partial f_a}{\partial p_j}f_b(\boldsymbol{p}') - \frac{\partial f_b}{\partial p'_j}f_a(\boldsymbol{p})\right\}d^3\boldsymbol{p}' \equiv S_a, \tag{13.36}$$

where

$$Q_{ij}^{ab} = 2e_a^2 e_b^2 \int \left\{ \frac{k_i k_j}{k^4 \,|\, \varepsilon^{\parallel}((\boldsymbol{k}\cdot\boldsymbol{v})\cdot\boldsymbol{k})\,|^2} + \frac{k_i k_j ([\boldsymbol{k}\wedge\boldsymbol{v}]\cdot[\boldsymbol{k}\wedge\boldsymbol{v}'])^2}{k^4 \,|\, (\boldsymbol{k}\cdot\boldsymbol{v})^2 \varepsilon^{\perp}((\boldsymbol{k}\cdot\boldsymbol{v})\cdot\boldsymbol{k}) - c^2 k^2 \,|^2} \right\} \delta((\boldsymbol{k}\cdot\boldsymbol{v}) - (\boldsymbol{k}\cdot\boldsymbol{v}'))\, d^3\boldsymbol{k}. \tag{13.37}$$

It is eqns. (13.36) with the kernel (13.37) which are the required relativistic kinetic equations for the distribution functions f_a. They differ from the corresponding non-relativistic equations (11.4) only in the form of the tensor Q_{ij}^{ab}.

In the non-relativistic approximation ($c \to \infty$) the expression (13.37) coincides with the corresponding expression (11.5).

The kinetic equations are sometimes conveniently written as Fokker–Planck equations

$$\frac{\partial f_a}{\partial t} = \frac{\partial}{\partial p_i} D_{ij}^a \frac{\partial f_a}{\partial p_j} + \frac{\partial (A_i^a f_a)}{\partial p_i}, \quad (i, j = 1, 2, 3). \tag{13.38}$$

The coefficients D_{ij}^a, A_i^a are

$$D_{ij}^a = \sum_b 2e_a^2 e_b^2 n_b \int \left[\frac{k_i k_j}{k^4 \,|\, \varepsilon^{\parallel}((\boldsymbol{k}\cdot\boldsymbol{v})\cdot\boldsymbol{k})\,|^2} + \frac{(\boldsymbol{k}\cdot\boldsymbol{v})^2 [[\boldsymbol{k}\wedge\boldsymbol{v}']\wedge\boldsymbol{k}]_i [[\boldsymbol{k}\wedge\boldsymbol{v}']\wedge\boldsymbol{k}]_j}{k^4 \,|\, (\boldsymbol{k}\cdot\boldsymbol{v})^2 \varepsilon^{\perp}((\boldsymbol{k}\cdot\boldsymbol{v})\cdot\boldsymbol{k}) - c^2 k^2 \,|^2} \right] \delta((\boldsymbol{k}\cdot\boldsymbol{v}) - (\boldsymbol{k}\cdot\boldsymbol{v}')) \times f_b(\boldsymbol{p}')\, d^3\boldsymbol{p}'\, d^3\boldsymbol{k}. \tag{13.39}$$

$$A_i^a = -\sum_b 2e_a^2 e_b^2 n_b \int \left[\frac{k_i k_j}{k^4 \,|\, \varepsilon^{\parallel}((\boldsymbol{k}\cdot\boldsymbol{v})\cdot\boldsymbol{k})\,|^2} + \frac{(\boldsymbol{k}\cdot\boldsymbol{v})^2 [[\boldsymbol{k}\wedge\boldsymbol{v}]\wedge\boldsymbol{k}]_i [[\boldsymbol{k}\wedge\boldsymbol{v}']\wedge\boldsymbol{k}]_j}{2k^4 \,|\, (\boldsymbol{k}\cdot\boldsymbol{v})^2 \varepsilon^{\perp}((\boldsymbol{k}\cdot\boldsymbol{v})\cdot\boldsymbol{k}) - c^2 k^2 \,|^2} \right] \delta((\boldsymbol{k}\cdot\boldsymbol{v}) - (\boldsymbol{k}\cdot\boldsymbol{v}')) \times \frac{\partial f_b}{\partial p_j'}\, d^3\boldsymbol{p}'\, d^3\boldsymbol{k}. \tag{13.40}$$

Other forms of notation for (13.39) and (13.40) may be convenient.

In § 14 expressions will be formed for the space–time spectral functions of various characteristics of a plasma and, more particularly, for the electric field strength.

In the isotropic case

$$(\delta\boldsymbol{E}\cdot\delta\boldsymbol{E})_{\omega,\,\boldsymbol{k}} = (\delta\boldsymbol{E}^{\parallel}\cdot\delta\boldsymbol{E}^{\parallel})_{\omega,\,\boldsymbol{k}}+(\delta\boldsymbol{E}^{\perp}\cdot\delta\boldsymbol{E}^{\perp})_{\omega,\,\boldsymbol{k}}. \quad (13.41)$$

This implies that the spectral function for the electric field strength is composed of two parts, viz. the spectral function of the longitudinal field and the spectral function of the transverse field. These functions are determined by the formulae (14.29, 30). The spectral functions of the different components $\delta E_i\,\delta E_j$ are formed by formulae (14.31, 32).

Using these expressions, the diffusion constant D_{ij}^a can be represented as

$$D_{ij}^a(\boldsymbol{p}) = \frac{e_a^2}{16\pi^3}\int \delta(\omega-(\boldsymbol{k}\cdot\boldsymbol{v}))\{(\delta E_i^{\parallel}\,\delta E_j^{\parallel})_{\omega,\,\boldsymbol{k}} + (\delta E_i^{\perp}\delta E_j^{\perp})_{\omega,\,\boldsymbol{k}}\}\,d\omega\,d^3\boldsymbol{k}. \quad (13.42)$$

Thus the diffusion constant in momentum space is determined by the spectrum of the fluctuations of electric field strength at the frequency $\omega = (\boldsymbol{k}\cdot\boldsymbol{v})$.

Under the conditions formulated in § 10, the fluctuation spectrum is in turn determined by the distribution functions f_a (see (14.29, 30)).

A more general case is considered in § 16.

In the non-relativistic approximation the formula (13.42) becomes

$$D_{ij}^a(\boldsymbol{p}) = \frac{e_a^2}{16\pi^3}\int \delta(\omega-(\boldsymbol{k}\cdot\boldsymbol{v}))\,(\delta E_i^{\parallel}\,\delta E_j^{\parallel})_{\omega,\,\boldsymbol{k}}\,d\omega\,d^3\boldsymbol{k}, \quad (13.43)$$

i.e. the diffusion constant is in this case determined by the spectral function of the longitudinal field.

Consider another form of notation for the coefficient A_i^a.

The formulae (10.22) and (13.23) define the imaginary parts of the function $\varepsilon^{\parallel}(\omega, \boldsymbol{k})$, $\varepsilon^{\perp}(\omega, \boldsymbol{k})$:

$$\operatorname{Im}\varepsilon^{\parallel}(\omega, \boldsymbol{k}) = -\pi\sum_a \frac{4\pi e_a^2 n_a}{k^2}\int \delta(\omega-(\boldsymbol{k}\cdot\boldsymbol{v}))\left(\boldsymbol{k}\cdot\frac{\partial f_a}{\partial \boldsymbol{p}}\right)d^3\boldsymbol{p}, \quad (13.44)$$

$$\operatorname{Im}\varepsilon^{\perp}(\omega, \boldsymbol{k}) = -\pi \sum_a \frac{2\pi e_a^2 n_a}{k^2 \omega} \int \delta(\omega - (\boldsymbol{k}\cdot\boldsymbol{v})) \times \left([[\boldsymbol{k}\wedge\boldsymbol{v}]\wedge\boldsymbol{k}] \cdot \frac{\partial f_a}{\partial \boldsymbol{p}} \right) d^3\boldsymbol{p}. \tag{13.45}$$

Using these formulae, the expression (13.40) becomes

$$A_i^a = \frac{e^2}{2\pi^2} \int \left\{ \frac{k_i \operatorname{Im}\varepsilon^{\parallel}(\omega, \boldsymbol{k})}{k^2 |\varepsilon^{\parallel}(\omega, \boldsymbol{k})|^2} + \frac{(\boldsymbol{k}\cdot\boldsymbol{v})^3 [[\boldsymbol{k}\wedge\boldsymbol{v}]\wedge\boldsymbol{k}]_i \operatorname{Im}\varepsilon^{\perp}(\omega, \boldsymbol{k})}{k^2 |(\omega^2 \varepsilon^{\perp}(\omega, \boldsymbol{k}) - c^2 k^2|^2} \right\} \delta(\omega - (\boldsymbol{k}\cdot\boldsymbol{v})) d\omega d^3\boldsymbol{k}. \tag{13.46}$$

Thus the coefficient A_i^a is proportional to the imaginary part of the dielectric constant tensor.

In the non-relativistic approximation from (13.46) we find

$$A_i^a = \frac{e^2}{2\pi^2} \int \frac{k_i \operatorname{Im}\varepsilon^{\parallel}(\omega, \boldsymbol{k})}{k^2 |\varepsilon^{\parallel}(\omega, \boldsymbol{k})|^2} \delta(\omega - (\boldsymbol{k}\cdot\boldsymbol{v}))\, d\omega\, d^3\boldsymbol{k}. \tag{13.47}$$

In § 11 some general properties of the collision integral were considered. It is easily verifiable that they also hold good in the relativistic case.

In particular, a Maxwell distribution is also the equilibrium solution of eqns. (13.36). In the relativistic case the solution is

$$f_a(\boldsymbol{p}) = A_a \exp\left[-\frac{c\sqrt{(p^2 + m_a^2 c^2)}}{\varkappa T} \right]. \tag{13.48}$$

The quantities A_a are determined from the normalization condition.

We show that the Maxwell distribution (13.48) satisfies eqns. (13.36). We substitute this distribution into the right-hand side of (13.36). Performing differentiation with respect to p_j and p_j', using (13.32), we get

$$S_a = -\frac{1}{\varkappa T} \sum_b n_b \frac{\partial}{\partial p_i} \int Q_{ij}^{ab}(v - v')_j f_a(\boldsymbol{p}) f_b(\boldsymbol{p}')\, d^3\boldsymbol{p}'.$$

This expression vanishes since the formula (13.37) for Q_{ab} contains the function $\delta((\boldsymbol{k}\cdot\boldsymbol{v})-(\boldsymbol{k}\cdot\boldsymbol{v}'))$, and $((\boldsymbol{k}\cdot\boldsymbol{v})-(\boldsymbol{k}\cdot\boldsymbol{v}'))\times\delta((\boldsymbol{k}\cdot\boldsymbol{v})-(\boldsymbol{k}\cdot\boldsymbol{v}')) = 0$.

In § 11 it was shown that the kinetic equations (11.4, 5) for a non-relativistic plasma can be simplified if the state of the plasma differs little from the equilibrium state. In this case one can neglect polarization in (11.5), but integrate over $\boldsymbol{k}$ in the range $k > 1/r_d$. In this approximation the tensor Q_{ij}^{ab} is given by (11.28) or by (11.40). The kinetic equations (11.4) with this kernel are Landau's equations.

We show that analogous equations can also be formed in the relativistic case.

In § 14 we shall see that in the relativistic case the Fourier space component of the correlation function $g_{ab}(\boldsymbol{q}-\boldsymbol{q}', \boldsymbol{p}-\boldsymbol{p}')$ is given by the expression

$$g_{ab}(\boldsymbol{k}, \boldsymbol{p}, \boldsymbol{p}') = -\frac{e_a e_b}{\sum\limits_c e_c^2 n_c}\,\frac{f_a(\boldsymbol{p}) f_b(\boldsymbol{p}')}{1+r_d^2 k^2}. \tag{13.49}$$

It differs from the corresponding non-relativistic expressions (10.42) in that now the Maxwell distribution $f_a(\boldsymbol{p})$ is relativistic, i.e. it is defined by the formula (13.48).

By the use of (13.49) we find the expression for the correlation function which coincides with (10.44).

$$g_{ab}(\boldsymbol{q}-\boldsymbol{q}', \boldsymbol{p}, \boldsymbol{p}') = \frac{1}{(2\pi)^3}\int g_{ab}(\boldsymbol{k}, \boldsymbol{p}, \boldsymbol{p}')\, e^{-i(\boldsymbol{k}\cdot\boldsymbol{q}-\boldsymbol{q}')}, \tag{13.50}$$

So in the relativistic case the correlation radius for the equilibrium state is of the order of the Debye radius r_d. This implies that in the equilibrium case the spatial spectrum is bounded towards small k, since, as in the non-relativistic case, there exists a value

$$k_{\min} \sim \frac{1}{r_d}. \tag{13.51}$$

The condition (13.51) holds also for states close to equilibrium. If it is fulfilled, we can put $\varepsilon^{\parallel} = 1$ and $\varepsilon^{\perp} = 1$ in (13.37), but integrating over the range $k > 1/r_d$, i.e. using the following expression for the tensor:

$$Q_{ij}^{ab} = 2e_a^2e_b^2 \int_{|k|>\frac{1}{r_d}} \frac{k_ik_j}{k^4}\left\{1+\frac{([\boldsymbol{k}\wedge\boldsymbol{v}]\cdot[\boldsymbol{k}\wedge\boldsymbol{v}'])^2}{|(\boldsymbol{k}\cdot\boldsymbol{v})^2-c^2k^2|^2}\right\}$$

$$\times\,\delta((\boldsymbol{k}\cdot\boldsymbol{v})-(\boldsymbol{k}\cdot\boldsymbol{v}'))\,d^3\boldsymbol{k}. \tag{13.52}$$

This integral diverges logarithmically as $|k| \to \infty$, so towards large $|k|$ the integration must be restricted by another condition similar to (11.37) or (11.36).

Equations (13.36, 52) are the relativistic analogy of Landau's kinetic equations.

Using the isotropy condition of the functions $f_a(|\boldsymbol{p}|, t)$, the expression (13.52) can be rewritten as

$$Q_{ij}^{ab} = 2e_a^2e_b^2 \int \frac{k_ik_j}{k^4}\left[1+\frac{([\boldsymbol{k}\wedge\boldsymbol{v}]\cdot[\boldsymbol{k}\wedge\boldsymbol{v}'])}{(\boldsymbol{k}\cdot\boldsymbol{v})^2-c^2k^2}\right]^2$$

$$\times\,\delta((\boldsymbol{k}\cdot\boldsymbol{v})\ -(\boldsymbol{k}\cdot\boldsymbol{v}'))\,d^3\boldsymbol{k}. \tag{13.53}$$

Compared with (13.52) this expression contains the additional term

$$4e_a^2e_b^2 \int \frac{k_ik_j}{k^4}\cdot\frac{([\boldsymbol{k}\wedge\boldsymbol{v}]\cdot[\boldsymbol{k}\wedge\boldsymbol{v}'])}{(\boldsymbol{k}\cdot\boldsymbol{v})^2-c^2k^2}\,\delta((\boldsymbol{k}\cdot\boldsymbol{v})-(\boldsymbol{k}\cdot\boldsymbol{v}'))\,d^3\boldsymbol{k}.$$

This term, however, in no way contributes to the right-hand side of (13.36). This can easily be seen by substituting the expression (13.53) into equation (13.36) and replacing inside the integral the component of momentum $p'^{\perp}$ transverse to $\boldsymbol{k}$ by $-p'^{\perp}$.

The expression (13.53) simplifies to

$$Q_{ij}^{ab} = 2e_a^2e_b^2[(\boldsymbol{v}\cdot\boldsymbol{v}')-c^2]^2 \int \frac{k_ik_j}{(c^2k^2-(\boldsymbol{k}\cdot\boldsymbol{v})^2)^2}$$

$$\times\,\delta((\boldsymbol{k}\cdot\boldsymbol{v})-(\boldsymbol{k}\cdot\boldsymbol{v}'))\,d^3\boldsymbol{k}. \tag{13.54}$$

We can transform (13.37) in the same way.

The kinetic equations (13.36) and (13.38) are given for a spatially homogeneous plasma.

Their generalization to an inhomogeneous plasma is the same as in § 11.

To conclude this section, we introduce without derivation (the derivation is given by Klimontovich [1960a, 1960b]) the relativistic kinetic equations for distribution functions of eight variables $q_i(\boldsymbol{q}, ict)$, $p_i(\boldsymbol{p}, i\varepsilon/c)$

$$F_a(q_i, p_i) = \overline{N}_a(q_i, p_i). \tag{13.55}$$

The microscopic function $N_a(q_i, p_i)$ is defined by (4.27–29).

The distribution function of eight variables $F_a(q_i, p_i)$ is so defined that the expression

$$F_a(q_i p_i)\, \gamma\, d^3\boldsymbol{q}\, d^3\boldsymbol{p}\, d\varepsilon \tag{13.56}$$

is the mean number of particles of kind a having world lines which intersect some element of a hypersurface which is oriented along the time axis, and also momenta which lie within the limits $d^3\boldsymbol{p}\, d\varepsilon$ about p_i.

For states which differ little from the equilibrium state, the equations for the functions F_a are

$$U_i \frac{\partial F_a}{\partial q_i} = \sum_b \frac{\partial}{\partial p_i} \int \varepsilon_{ij}^{ab} \left\{ \frac{\partial F_a}{\partial p_j} F_b - \frac{\partial F_b}{\partial p'_j} F_a \right\} d^3\boldsymbol{p}'\, d\varepsilon', \tag{13.57}$$

$$\varepsilon_{ij}^{ab} = 2e_a^2 e_b^2 (U_n U'_n)^2 \int \frac{k_i k_j}{(c^2k^2 - \omega^2)^2}\, \delta(k_l U_l)\, \delta(k_m U'_m)\, d^3\boldsymbol{k}\, d\omega.$$

$$i, j, n, l, m = 1, 2, 3, 4 \tag{13.58}$$

Here $k_i\,(\boldsymbol{k}, i\omega/c)$ is a four-dimensional wave vector, $U_i(\gamma\boldsymbol{v}, ic\gamma)$ is the four-dimensional velocity, and $p_i = m_{ai} U_i$.

In (13.58) one can integrate over ω and $\boldsymbol{k}$. If we avail ourselves of the symmetry of the tensor ε_{ij}^{ab} about U_i and U'_i and also the fact that

$$U_i \varepsilon_{ij} = 0, \quad U'_i \varepsilon_{ij} = 0, \tag{13.59}$$

in order to determine the tensor ε_{ij}^{ab} it is then sufficient to find the sum of the diagonal elements. As a result we get the following expression (see Klimontovich, 1960a, 1960b; and Belyayev and Budker, 1957):

$$\varepsilon_{ij}^{ab} = \frac{2\pi e_a^2 e_b^2}{c^5}\left[\ln\frac{r_d}{r_{\min}}\right]\left\{\left[\frac{(U_n U_n')^2}{c^4}-1\right]\delta_{ij}\right.$$

$$\left. -(U_i U_j + U_i' U_j')\frac{1}{c^2} - \frac{(U_l U_l')}{c^4}(U_i U_j' + U_i' U_j)\right\}$$

$$\times\left[\frac{(U_m U_m')^2}{c^4}-1\right]^{-3/}.$$

(13.60)

The values $k_{\max} \sim 1/r_{\min}$ and $k_{\min} \sim 1/r_d$, as in the forego-ing, determine the range of wave numbers for which the solution holds good.

Equation (13.57) with kernel (13.60) corresponds to (13.36) with kernel (13.54). To change over from (13.57) to (13.36), it is necessary to use the relationship between f_a and F_a

$$F_a(q_i, p_i) = n_a f_a(\mathbf{q}, \mathbf{p}, t)\,\delta[\varepsilon - c\sqrt{(p^2+m_a^2c^2)}]\frac{m_a c^2}{\varepsilon}, \tag{13.61}$$

and then substitute this expression into (13.57) and integrate over ε.

The formula (13.61) follows from (13.56) considering that all possible states are on the surface

$$\sum_i p_i^2 = -m_a^2 c^2. \tag{13.62}$$

In the equilibrium case eqns. (13.57) are satisfied by a relati-vistic Maxwell distribution, which for constant particle-mass m_a can be written as

$$F_a(q_i, p_i) = C\delta(p_i^2 + m_a^2c^2)\exp\left(\frac{p_i \overline{U}_i}{\varkappa T}\right), \tag{13.63}$$

where C is a normalization constant, $\overline{U}_i$ is the four-dimensional vector of the average velocity in the equilibrium state, and T is temperature.

To change from the distribution (13.63) to (13.48), one needs to select the frame of reference in which U_i is $(0, i\varepsilon/c)$, to integrate (13.63) over ε, and then use (13.61) which relates the functions F_a and f_a.

14. Stationary Space–Time Correlations in a Plasma†

In the foregoing sections it has been shown that if $\varepsilon = (r_{av}/r_d)^3 \ll 1$, for a statistical description of the processes in a plasma one can use the closed set of equations for the first distribution functions f_a and the correlation functions g_{ab} or second moments. The higher correlation functions in this case are small (of the order of ε^2).

If, furthermore, the functions f_a are slowly varying functions of their coordinates and time (vary little during the correlation time and over distances of the order of the correlation radius), then "simultaneous" second moments can be given in terms of the first distribution functions. As a result we get a closed set of kinetic equations — equations for the first distribution functions.

The functions $\overline{\delta N_a(\boldsymbol{x}, t)\, \delta N_b(\boldsymbol{x}', t)}$ characterize the statistical relation of the values of the coordinates and momenta for a pair of charged particles at a particular instant of time t.

However, in some cases it is necessary to know the statistical relation between the values of the coordinates and momenta of a pair of particles (or of the distribution of the particles at two points in phase space) not at the same instant, but at two different instants of time.

To solve this problem it is sufficient to determine the mean value of the product of the functions $N_a(\boldsymbol{x}, t)$ and $N_b(\boldsymbol{x}', t')$ at two different instants t and t', i.e. the function

$$\overline{N_a(\boldsymbol{x}, t)\, N_b(\boldsymbol{x}', t')}. \tag{14.1}$$

One can immediately separate out the part which is expressed by the first distribution functions f_a and f_b. For this we substitute

† Klimontovich and Silin (1963), Rostoker (1961), Akhiezer, Akhiezer and Sitenko (1962), and Klimontovich (1961).

into formula (14.1) the expressions $N_a = \overline{N}_a + \delta N_a$ and $N_b = \overline{N}_b + \delta N_b$. Considering that $\overline{\delta N_a} = 0$ and $\overline{\delta N_b} = 0$, we get

$$\overline{N_a(\boldsymbol{x}, t) N_b(\boldsymbol{x}', t')} = \overline{N}_a(\boldsymbol{x}, t) \overline{N}_b(\boldsymbol{x}', t') + \overline{\delta N_a(\boldsymbol{x}, t)\, \delta N_b(\boldsymbol{x}', t')}. \tag{14.2}$$

The first term on the right-hand side of this formula is given by the first distribution functions since the functions $\overline{N}_a$, $\overline{N}_b$ are proportional to f_a and f_b.

The second term, however, represents the correlation of the fluctuations (deviations about the mean) of the phase densities at different instants. In the present section we show that the expression

$$\overline{\delta N_a(\boldsymbol{x}, t)\, \delta N_b(\boldsymbol{x}', t')} \tag{14.3}$$

on the same assumptions as in § 10 regarding slow variation of the functions f_a, is also determined by the first distribution functions f_a.

This result is very important. In fact, by using the function (14.3) one can find the space–time correlations of electrodynamic functions: fluctuations of the densities of the charges $\delta\varrho$, of the currents $\delta\boldsymbol{j}$ and of other characteristics of a plasma determined by the motion of charged particles.

Thus, for example, for the correlation of the fluctuations of the charge density at different points and at different instants of time, we have

$$\overline{\delta\varrho(\boldsymbol{q}, t)\, \delta\varrho(\boldsymbol{q}', t')} = \sum_{ab} e_a e_b \int \overline{\delta N_a(\boldsymbol{q}, \boldsymbol{p}, t)\, \delta N_b(\boldsymbol{q}', \boldsymbol{p}', t')}\, d^3\boldsymbol{p}\, d^3\boldsymbol{p}'. \tag{14.4}$$

Furthermore, by using (14.3), one can determine the correlations between fluctuations of gas-dynamic functions, such as the densities of the individual components, their velocities, temperatures, and moments of velocities and so on, and also the cross-correlations of the fluctuations of electrodynamic and gas-dynamic functions.

Thus all binary statistical characterizations of a non-equilibrium plasma can be found by the use of (14.3).

In the present section we form expressions for the spectral functions for a wide frequency band compared with the "collision" frequency, i.e. for $\omega \gg 1/\tau_r$, where τ_r is the time taken to establish equilibrium. Slow fluctuations, i.e. at frequencies $\omega \lesssim 1/\tau_r$, constitute a separate problem and therefore will not be considered in the present section.

We now turn to the problem posed. To find the function (14.3) for a non-relativistic plasma, one can use eqn. (5.33) for the function δN_a.

Accordingly we multiply (5.33) by $\delta N_a(\boldsymbol{q}', \boldsymbol{p}', t')$ and average out. We then get

$$\frac{\partial}{\partial t}\overline{(\delta N_a\,\delta N_b)}_{t,\,t'}+\left(\boldsymbol{v}\cdot\frac{\partial}{\partial \boldsymbol{q}}\overline{(\delta N_a\,\delta N_b)}_{t,\,t'}\right)$$
$$-n_a\sum_c\left(\frac{\partial}{\partial \boldsymbol{q}}\cdot\int\frac{e_a e_c}{|\boldsymbol{q}-\boldsymbol{q}''|}\overline{(\delta N_c\,\delta N_b)}_{t,\,t'}\,d^3\boldsymbol{q}''\,d^3\boldsymbol{p}''\,\frac{\partial f_a}{\partial \boldsymbol{p}}\right)=0, \quad (14.5)$$

as required. Here $\overline{(\delta N_a\,\delta N_b)}_{t,\,t'}$ is an abbreviation for the function (14.3).

In the case of statistical equilibrium the functions $\overline{(\delta N_a\,\delta N_b)}_{t,\,t'}$ depend only on the difference between the coordinates $\boldsymbol{q}$ and $\boldsymbol{q}'$ and on the difference between t and t'.

In non-equilibrium conditions for which the requirement of slow variation of the distribution functions f_a is satisfied (see § 10), it can be assumed that expressions (14.3) also depend on the differences between the coordinates and between the instants of time, and only on the coordinates and time proper through the first distribution functions f_a.

Thus one can look for the solution of (14.5) which explicitly depends only on $\boldsymbol{q}-\boldsymbol{q}'$, $t-t'$:

$$\overline{\delta N_a(\boldsymbol{q}, \boldsymbol{p}, t)\,\delta N_b(\boldsymbol{q}', \boldsymbol{p}', t')}=\overline{(\delta N_a\,\delta N_b)}_{\boldsymbol{q}-\boldsymbol{q}',\,t-t'}\,. \quad (14.6)$$

If these conditions are satisfied, (14.6) is a rapidly varying function of $\boldsymbol{q}-\boldsymbol{q}'$ and $t-t'$, whereas the f_a are slowly varying functions of $\boldsymbol{q}$, $\boldsymbol{q}'$, t, t'.

Therefore for solving eqns. (14.5) one can assume as a first approximation that the functions f_a are functions of the momenta and that they do not depend on the coordinates and time.

Considering our assumptions, eqn. (14.5) needs to be solved on the following "initial" condition: the function (14.6) is the same as the expression for a simultaneous correlation of the fluctuations of the phase densities. Knowing that the phase densities are associated with the correlation functions g_{ab}, we write this "initial" condition in the form: if $t-t' = 0$

$$(\overline{\delta N_a \, \delta N_b})_{t,t'} = (\overline{\delta N_a \, \delta N_b})_t \equiv n_a n_b g_{ab}(\boldsymbol{x}, \boldsymbol{x}', t) + \delta_{ab} n_a \, \delta(\boldsymbol{x}-\boldsymbol{x}') \, f_a(\boldsymbol{x}, t). \tag{14.7}$$

To solve the set of eqns. (14.5) with the initial condition (14.7), it is expedient to use the one-sided Fourier transform in the independent variable $t-t'$ and then the two-sided Fourier transform in the variables $\boldsymbol{q}-\boldsymbol{q}'$.

The solution so obtained enables the two-time functions (14.3) to be expressed in terms of the one-time functions $(\overline{\delta N_a \, \delta N_b})_t$, the expressions for which have already been found in § 10.

But since the one-time functions $(\overline{\delta N_a \, \delta N_b})_t$, under the conditions under consideration, are given in terms of the first distribution functions (see § 10), in the last analysis we obtain formulae which express the space–time correlations in terms of the first distribution functions.

We say that the space–time correlations obtained in such an approximation are *stationary* and *uniform* since they are explicitly independent of time and the coordinates. Dependence on the coordinates and time enters only through the functions f_a.

Slight non-uniformity can be treated in the same way as in § 11 (formulae (11.48–56)). Non-stationarity will be considered in §§ 16 and 17.

The proposed method of calculation was carried out at length by Klimontovich and Silin [1962]. The method appears rather cumbersome. This is especially evident in the relativistic case. For this reason in the present section we shall consider another method which enables expressions to be formed for stationary space–time correlations in a simpler way.

As the initial equations we take the set (5.41–43) for the random deviations δN_a, $\delta \boldsymbol{E}$ and $\delta \boldsymbol{B}$.

Using these equations we express the values of the random functions δN_a, $\delta \boldsymbol{E}$, $\delta \boldsymbol{B}$ at the instant t in terms of their value at the earlier instant $t = 0$. For this we use the one-sided Fourier transform with respect to time and the two-sided transform in the coordinates. For the respective Fourier components one may put, for instance,

$$\delta N_a(\omega, \boldsymbol{k}, \boldsymbol{p}) = \int_0^{\infty} \int_{-\infty}^{\infty} \delta N_a(\boldsymbol{q}, \boldsymbol{p}, t) e^{-\Delta t + i(\omega t - (\boldsymbol{k} \cdot \boldsymbol{q}))}\, dt\, d^3\boldsymbol{q}.$$

The functions $\delta N_a(\omega, \boldsymbol{k}, \boldsymbol{p})$, $\delta \boldsymbol{E}(\omega, \boldsymbol{k})$, $\delta \boldsymbol{B}(\omega, \boldsymbol{k})$ are analytic in the upper half-plane of the complex frequency $\omega + i\Delta$.

From eqns. (5.41–43) we obtain, after straightforward algebraic transformations, the following expressions for these functions

$$\delta N_a(\omega, \boldsymbol{k}, \boldsymbol{p}) = \frac{i}{\omega - (\boldsymbol{k} \cdot \boldsymbol{v}) + i\Delta} \left\{ \delta N_a(\boldsymbol{k}, \boldsymbol{p}, t = 0) - e_a n_a \left(\delta \boldsymbol{E}(\omega, \boldsymbol{k}) \cdot \frac{\partial f_a}{\partial \boldsymbol{p}} \right) \right\}. \tag{14.8}$$

$$\delta \boldsymbol{E}(\omega, \boldsymbol{k}) = \frac{i\omega \big[\boldsymbol{k} \wedge [\delta \boldsymbol{E}(\boldsymbol{k}, t = 0) \wedge \boldsymbol{k}]\big] - ic[\boldsymbol{k} \wedge \delta \boldsymbol{B}(\boldsymbol{k}, t = 0)] k^2}{k^2\big((\omega + i\Delta)^2\, \varepsilon^{\perp}(\omega + i\Delta, \boldsymbol{k}) - c^2 k^2\big)}$$
$$+ 4\pi \sum_a e_a \int \frac{\delta N_a(\boldsymbol{k}, \boldsymbol{p}, t = 0)}{\omega - (\boldsymbol{k} \cdot \boldsymbol{v}) + i\Delta} \left\{ \frac{\boldsymbol{k}}{k^2 \varepsilon^{\parallel}(\omega + i\Delta, \boldsymbol{k})} + \frac{\omega \big[\boldsymbol{k} \wedge [\boldsymbol{v} \wedge \boldsymbol{k}]\big]}{k^2\big((\omega + i\Delta)^2\, \varepsilon^{\perp}(\omega + i\Delta, \boldsymbol{k}) - c^2 k^2\big)} \right\} d^3\boldsymbol{p}. \tag{14.9}$$

$$\delta \boldsymbol{B}(\omega, \boldsymbol{k}) = \frac{c}{\omega + i\Delta} [\boldsymbol{k} \wedge \delta \boldsymbol{E}(\omega, \boldsymbol{k})] + \frac{i}{\omega + i\Delta} \delta \boldsymbol{B}(\boldsymbol{k}, t = 0). \tag{14.10}$$

Here $\varepsilon^{\|}(\omega, \boldsymbol{k})$, $\varepsilon^{\perp}(\omega, \boldsymbol{k})$ are the longitudinal and transverse dielectric constants, as defined by (10.19) and (13.17).

The formulae (14.8–10) enable the functions δN_a, $\delta \boldsymbol{E}$ and $\delta \boldsymbol{B}$ to be found from their values at the instant $t = 0$.

By using the functions $\delta N_a(\boldsymbol{k}, \boldsymbol{p}, t)$, $\delta \boldsymbol{E}(\boldsymbol{k}, t)$ and $\delta \boldsymbol{B}(\boldsymbol{k}, t)$ one can find the spatial spectral functions for the correlations at two instants. For example,

$$\overline{\delta N_a(\boldsymbol{k}, \boldsymbol{p}, t)\, \delta N_b(\boldsymbol{k}', \boldsymbol{p}', t')} = (2\pi)^3\, \delta(\boldsymbol{k}-\boldsymbol{k}')\, (\overline{\delta N_a\, \delta N_b})_{\boldsymbol{k}, t, t'}\,. \tag{14.11}$$

The function $\delta(\boldsymbol{k}-\boldsymbol{k}')$ appears in formula (14.11) owing to spatial homogeneity.

In the equilibrium and stationary cases the correlations at two instants depend only on the difference $t-t'$.

Hence space-time spectral functions do not depend explicitly on time. They are associated with the corresponding two-time correlations by a Fourier transform. For instance,

$$(2\pi)^3\, \delta(\boldsymbol{k}-\boldsymbol{k}')\, (\delta N_a(\boldsymbol{p})\, \delta N_b(\boldsymbol{p}'))_{\omega, \boldsymbol{k}} = \int_{-\infty}^{\infty} \overline{\delta N_a(\boldsymbol{k}, \boldsymbol{p}, t)\, \delta N_b(\boldsymbol{k}', \boldsymbol{p}', t')} e^{i\omega(t-t')}\, d(t-t'). \tag{14.12}$$

Comparing the formulae (14.11, 12), we get

$$(\delta N_a\, \delta N_b)_{\omega, \boldsymbol{k}} = \int_{-\infty}^{\infty} (\delta N_a\, \delta N_b)_{\boldsymbol{k}, t-t'} e^{i\omega(t-t')}\, d(t-t'). \tag{14.12a}$$

Analogous formulae hold for the functions $(\delta \boldsymbol{E} \cdot \delta \boldsymbol{E})_{\omega, \boldsymbol{k}}$, $(\delta \boldsymbol{B} \cdot \delta \boldsymbol{B})_{\omega, \boldsymbol{k}}$ and other spectral functions.

We will use expressions (14.8–10) for finding the space–time spectral functions.

For this we show that, for example, the spectral function $(\delta N_a\, \delta N_b)_{\omega, \boldsymbol{k}}$ is expressible in terms of the functions $\delta N_a(\omega, \boldsymbol{k}, \boldsymbol{p})$ and $\delta N_b(\omega, \boldsymbol{k}', \boldsymbol{p}')$:

$$(2\pi)^3\, \delta(\boldsymbol{k}-\boldsymbol{k}')\, (\delta N_a\, \delta N_b)_{\omega, \boldsymbol{k}} = \lim_{\Delta \to 0} 2\Delta\, \overline{\delta N_a(\omega, \boldsymbol{k}, \boldsymbol{p})\, \delta N_b^*(\omega, \boldsymbol{k}', \boldsymbol{p}')}. \tag{14.13}$$

Likewise

$$(2\pi)^3\, \delta(\boldsymbol{k}-\boldsymbol{k}')\, (\delta \boldsymbol{E}\cdot\delta \boldsymbol{E})_{\omega,\,\boldsymbol{k}} = \lim_{\Delta\to 0} 2\Delta\, \overline{(\delta \boldsymbol{E}(\omega,\, \boldsymbol{k})\cdot \delta \boldsymbol{E}^*(\omega,\, \boldsymbol{k}'))} \tag{14.14}$$

and so on.

We obtain the formula (14.14), for which we consider the expression

$$\overline{(\delta \boldsymbol{E}(\omega,\, \boldsymbol{k})\cdot \delta \boldsymbol{E}^*(\omega,\, \boldsymbol{k}'))} = \int_0^\infty dt' \int_0^\infty dt'' e^{-\Delta t'+i\omega t'}\, e^{-\Delta t''-i\omega t''}\, \overline{(\delta \boldsymbol{E}(\boldsymbol{k},\, t')\cdot \delta \boldsymbol{E}(\boldsymbol{k}',\, t''))}. \tag{14.15}$$

By virtue of the stationarity and uniformity of the expression, $\overline{(\delta \boldsymbol{E}(\boldsymbol{k},\, t')\cdot \delta \boldsymbol{E}(\boldsymbol{k}',\, t''))}$ depends on $t'-t''$ and so is non-zero only if $\boldsymbol{k} = \boldsymbol{k}'$.

We introduce the new variables $t'-t'' = \tau$ and $(t'+t'')/2 = t$, and then

$$\overline{(\delta \boldsymbol{E}(\omega,\, \boldsymbol{k})\cdot \delta \boldsymbol{E}^*(\omega,\, \boldsymbol{k}'))} = \int_{-\infty}^\infty d\tau \int_{\frac{|\tau|}{2}}^\infty dt\, e^{-2\Delta t+i\omega\tau}\, \overline{(\delta \boldsymbol{E}(\boldsymbol{k},\, t')\cdot \delta \boldsymbol{E}(\boldsymbol{k}',\, t''))}. \tag{14.16}$$

Integrating over t, we get

$$\overline{(\delta \boldsymbol{E}(\omega,\, \boldsymbol{k})\cdot \delta \boldsymbol{E}^*(\omega,\, \boldsymbol{k}'))} = \frac{1}{2\Delta} \int_{-\infty}^\infty \overline{(\delta \boldsymbol{E}(\boldsymbol{k},\, t)\cdot \delta \boldsymbol{E}(\boldsymbol{k}',\, t''))}\, e^{i\omega(t'-t'')}\, d(t'-t'').$$

By using formula (14.12a), we get (14.14).

Formulae analogous to (14.13, 14) are used in statistical radio physics (see, for example, Stratonovich, 1961).

We find, first, an expression for the spectral function $(\delta \boldsymbol{E}\cdot\delta \boldsymbol{E})_{\omega,\,\boldsymbol{k}}$. To do this we substitute into the right-hand side of the formula (14.14) the expression (14.9) for $\delta \boldsymbol{E}(\omega,\, \boldsymbol{k})$ and the corresponding expression for $\delta \boldsymbol{E}^*(\omega,\, \boldsymbol{k})$.

We shall consider stable stationary states for which the equations

$$\varepsilon^{||}(\omega, \boldsymbol{k}) = 0, \quad \omega^2\varepsilon^{\perp}(\omega, \boldsymbol{k}) - c^2k^2 = 0 \tag{14.17}$$

do not have real roots.

Consider the contribution to (14.14) of the individual terms of the product $(\delta\boldsymbol{E}(\omega, \boldsymbol{k})\cdot\delta\boldsymbol{E}^*(\omega, \boldsymbol{k}'))$. First of all we cancel out the common factor $(2\pi)^3\,\delta(\boldsymbol{k}-\boldsymbol{k}')$.

The product of the first terms of the expressions $\delta\boldsymbol{E}(\omega, \boldsymbol{k})\cdot\delta\boldsymbol{E}^*(\omega, \boldsymbol{k}')$, after averaging and dividing by $(2\pi)^3\,\delta(\boldsymbol{k}-\boldsymbol{k}')$, contains terms of the kind

$$\frac{(\delta E_i\,\delta E_j)_{\boldsymbol{k}}}{|\omega^2\varepsilon^{\perp}(\omega, \boldsymbol{k}) - c^2k^2|^2} \tag{14.18}$$

and also analogous terms with the functions $(\delta E_i\,\delta B_j)_{\boldsymbol{k}}, (\delta B_i\,\delta B_j)_{\boldsymbol{k}}$.

Simultaneous spatial correlation functions in the equilibrium state are always finite.

For states, near to equilibrium, when the conditions (10.12, 13) are fulfilled,

$$\lim_{\Delta\to 0} \Delta(\delta E_i\,\delta E_j)_{\boldsymbol{k}} = 0. \tag{14.19}$$

The limiting transition $\Delta \to 0$ implies, as previously, that Δ is much smaller than all the characteristic times of the spectral functions. In this case, according to (10.13),

$$\tau_{\max} \ll 1/\Delta \ll \tau_r, \tag{14.20}$$

where $\tau_{\max}$ is the characteristically maximum time of the spectral functions. For example, $\tau_{\max} \sim 1/\gamma_{\min}$, where $\gamma_{\min}$ is the damping increment of the plasma excitations at $k \sim k_{\min}$. Here $k_{\min}$ is the boundary of the space spectrum on the side of low wave numbers.

If conditions (14.19, 20) are fulfilled, and also the condition (14.17), expressions of the kind (14.18) become vanishingly small after multiplying by Δ as $\Delta \to 0$, and so they make no contribution to the expression for the function $(\delta\boldsymbol{E}\cdot\delta\boldsymbol{E})_{\omega, \boldsymbol{k}}$.

The cross terms of the product $(\delta\boldsymbol{E}(\omega, \boldsymbol{k})\cdot\delta\boldsymbol{E}^*(\omega, \boldsymbol{k}'))$ also make no contribution to the expression for the function $(\delta\boldsymbol{E}\cdot\delta\boldsymbol{E})_{\omega, \boldsymbol{k}}$ for the same reasons. The only difference is that instead of expressions of the kind (14.18), we have expressions which contain, instead of spatial spectral functions, space–time functions of the kind

$$\int \frac{(\delta \boldsymbol{E}\, \delta N_a(\boldsymbol{p}))_{\boldsymbol{k}}}{\omega-(\boldsymbol{k}\cdot\boldsymbol{v})+i\Delta}\, d^3\boldsymbol{p} = (\delta \boldsymbol{E}\, \delta U)_{\omega,\, \boldsymbol{k}},$$

where

$$U(\omega, \boldsymbol{k}) = \int [\delta N_a(\boldsymbol{p}, 0)/(\omega-(\boldsymbol{k}\cdot\boldsymbol{v})+i\Delta)]\, d^3\boldsymbol{p}.$$

The space–time spectral functions satisfy the condition

$$\lim_{\Delta\to 0} \Delta(\delta \boldsymbol{E}\cdot\delta \boldsymbol{E})_{\omega,\, \boldsymbol{k}} = 0, \tag{14.21}$$

which corresponds to (14.19). Similar conditions hold for the other functions.

We have still to consider the contribution of the second terms to the product $(\delta\boldsymbol{E}(\omega, \boldsymbol{k})\cdot\delta\boldsymbol{E}^*(\omega, \boldsymbol{k}'))$.

After multiplying the second terms we obtain the following expression for the function:

$$(\delta \boldsymbol{E}\cdot\delta \boldsymbol{E})_{\omega,\, \boldsymbol{k}} = (\delta \boldsymbol{E}^{||}\cdot\delta \boldsymbol{E}^{||})_{\omega,\, \boldsymbol{k}} + (\delta \boldsymbol{E}^{\perp}\cdot\delta \boldsymbol{E}^{\perp})_{\omega,\, \boldsymbol{k}}, \tag{14.22}$$

where

$$(\delta \boldsymbol{E}^{||}\cdot\delta \boldsymbol{E}^{||})_{\omega,\, \boldsymbol{k}} = \sum_{ab} \frac{(4\pi)^2 e_a e_b}{k^2} \lim_{\Delta\to 0} 2\Delta \int \frac{(\delta N_a\, \delta N_b)_{\boldsymbol{k}}\, d^3\boldsymbol{p}\, d^3\boldsymbol{p}'}{(\omega-(\boldsymbol{k}\cdot\boldsymbol{v})+i\Delta)\,(\omega-(\boldsymbol{k}\cdot\boldsymbol{v}')-i\Delta)} \times \frac{1}{|\varepsilon^{||}(\omega, \boldsymbol{k})|^2}. \tag{14.23}$$

$$(\delta \boldsymbol{E}^{\perp}\cdot\delta \boldsymbol{E}^{\perp})_{\omega,\, \boldsymbol{k}} = \sum_{ab} \frac{(4\pi)^2 e_a e_b}{k^4} \lim_{\Delta\to 0} 2\Delta \times \int \frac{([[\boldsymbol{k}\wedge\boldsymbol{v}]\wedge\boldsymbol{k}]\cdot[[\boldsymbol{k}\wedge\boldsymbol{v}']\wedge\boldsymbol{k}])\,(\delta N_a\, \delta N_b)_{\boldsymbol{k}}}{(\omega-(\boldsymbol{k}\cdot\boldsymbol{v})+i\Delta)\,(\omega-(\boldsymbol{k}\cdot\boldsymbol{v}')-i\Delta)}\, d^3\boldsymbol{p}\, d^3\boldsymbol{p}' \times \frac{\omega^2}{|\omega^2\varepsilon^{\perp} - c^2k^2|^2}. \tag{14.24}$$

The expression (14.23) determines the spectral function of the longitudinal fields, whilst (14.24) determines that of the transverse fields. From these relations it follows that the space–time functions are also given by the simultaneous spatial spectral function $(\delta N_a(\boldsymbol{p})\,\delta N_b(p'))_{\boldsymbol{k},t}$.

This function is connected with the Fourier components of the simultaneous correlation functions by the relation

$$(\delta N_a\,\delta N_b)_{\boldsymbol{k}} = n_a n_b g_{ab}(\boldsymbol{k},\boldsymbol{p},\boldsymbol{p}')+\delta_{ab} n_a\,\delta(\boldsymbol{p}-\boldsymbol{p}')f_a\,.$$

We substitute this expression in the formulae (14.23, 24). In the terms containing the functions g_{ab}, in this case we have the integrals

$$\int \frac{g_{ab}(\boldsymbol{k},\boldsymbol{p},\boldsymbol{p}')}{(\omega-(\boldsymbol{k}\cdot\boldsymbol{v})+i\Delta)\,(\omega-(\boldsymbol{k}\cdot\boldsymbol{v}')-i\Delta)}\,d^3\boldsymbol{p}\,d^3\boldsymbol{p}';$$

$$\int \frac{([[\boldsymbol{k}\wedge\boldsymbol{v}]\wedge\boldsymbol{k}]\cdot[[\boldsymbol{k}\wedge\boldsymbol{v}']\wedge\boldsymbol{k}])\,g_{ab}(\boldsymbol{k},\boldsymbol{p},\boldsymbol{p}')}{(\omega-(\boldsymbol{k}\cdot\boldsymbol{v})+i\Delta)\,(\omega-(\boldsymbol{k}\cdot\boldsymbol{v}')-i\Delta)}\,d^3\boldsymbol{p}\,d^3\boldsymbol{p}'. \tag{14.25}$$

From the ensemble density it follows that in the equilibrium case the function $g_{ab}(\boldsymbol{k},\boldsymbol{p},\boldsymbol{p}')$ can be represented as

$$g_{ab}(\boldsymbol{k},\boldsymbol{p},\boldsymbol{p}') = g_{ab}(\boldsymbol{k})\,f_a(\boldsymbol{p})\,f_b(\boldsymbol{p}'),$$

where f_a, f_b are Maxwell distributions.

Integrals of the following kind enter into the formulae (14.25):

$$\int \frac{\varphi(\boldsymbol{p},\boldsymbol{p}')\,g_{ab}(\boldsymbol{k},\boldsymbol{p},\boldsymbol{p}')}{(\omega-(\boldsymbol{k}\cdot\boldsymbol{v})+i\Delta)\,(\omega-(\boldsymbol{k}\cdot\boldsymbol{v}')-i\Delta)}\,d^3\boldsymbol{p}\,d^3\boldsymbol{p}', \tag{14.26}$$

where the $\varphi(\boldsymbol{p},\boldsymbol{p}')$ are functions which are integrated with $g_{ab}(\boldsymbol{k},\boldsymbol{p},\boldsymbol{p}')$, for example polynomials in $\boldsymbol{p}$ and $\boldsymbol{p}'$.

In the equilibrium case the integrals (14.26) for given $\varphi(\boldsymbol{p},\boldsymbol{p}')$ can be evaluated. They are finite functions of ω and $\boldsymbol{k}$.

Consider the non-equilibrium state, when

$$\lim_{\Delta\to 0}\Delta\int \frac{\varphi(\boldsymbol{p},\boldsymbol{p}')\,g_{ab}(\boldsymbol{k},\boldsymbol{p},\boldsymbol{p}')}{(\omega-(\boldsymbol{k}\cdot\boldsymbol{v})+i\Delta)\,(\omega-(\boldsymbol{k}\cdot\boldsymbol{v}')-i\Delta)}\,d^3\boldsymbol{p}\,d^3\boldsymbol{p}' = 0, \tag{14.27}$$

the quantitity Δ here satisfying conditions (14.20), as above.

Using this condition and the formula

$$\lim_{\Delta\to 0}\frac{\Delta}{(\varphi(x))^2+\Delta^2} = \pi\delta(\varphi(x)), \tag{14.28}$$

we obtain from (14.23, 24) the following expressions for the spectral functions of the longitudinal and transverse electric fields:

$$(\delta \boldsymbol{E}^{\|} \cdot \delta \boldsymbol{E}^{\|})_{\omega, \boldsymbol{k}} = \sum_a \frac{(4\pi)^2 e_a^2 n_a}{k^2} \int \frac{2\pi\delta(\omega - (\boldsymbol{k} \cdot \boldsymbol{v}))}{|\varepsilon^{\|}(\omega, \boldsymbol{k})|^2} f_a \, d^3\boldsymbol{p}; \tag{14.29}$$

$$(\delta \boldsymbol{E}^{\perp} \cdot \delta \boldsymbol{E}^{\perp})_{\omega, \boldsymbol{k}} = \sum_a \frac{(4\pi)^2 e_a^2 n_a \omega^2}{k^2} \int \frac{2\pi\delta(\omega - (\boldsymbol{k} \cdot \boldsymbol{v})) \, [\boldsymbol{k} \wedge \boldsymbol{v}]^2 f_a}{|\omega^2 \varepsilon^{\perp}(\omega, \boldsymbol{k}) - c^2 k^2|^2} d^3\boldsymbol{p}. \tag{14.30}$$

In the isotropic case the tensors $(\delta \boldsymbol{E}^{\|} \cdot \delta \boldsymbol{E}^{\|})_{\omega, \boldsymbol{k}}$, $(\delta \boldsymbol{E}^{\perp} \cdot \delta \boldsymbol{E}^{\perp})_{\omega, \boldsymbol{k}}$ can be represented as

$$(\delta E_i^{\|} \, \delta E_j^{\|})_{\omega, \boldsymbol{k}} = \frac{k_i k_j}{k^2} (\delta \boldsymbol{E}^{\|} \cdot \delta \boldsymbol{E}^{\|})_{\omega, \boldsymbol{k}};$$

$$(\delta E_i^{\perp} \, \delta E_j^{\perp})_{\omega, \boldsymbol{k}} = \frac{1}{2} \left(\delta_{ij} - \frac{k_i k_j}{k^2} \right) (\delta \boldsymbol{E}^{\perp} \cdot \delta \boldsymbol{E}^{\perp})_{\omega, \boldsymbol{k}}; \tag{14.31}$$

$$(\delta E_i \delta E_j)_{\omega, \boldsymbol{k}} = (\delta E_i^{\|} \, \delta E_j^{\|})_{\omega, \boldsymbol{k}} + (\delta E_i^{\perp} \, \delta E_j^{\perp})_{\omega, \boldsymbol{k}}, \tag{14.32}$$

and they are therefore determined by formulae (14.29, 30).

In the same way, by using the conditions (14.19–21, 25), we can form expressions for more complicated spectral functions.

Later we shall require the spectral function $(\delta N_a \, \delta \boldsymbol{E})_{\omega, \boldsymbol{k}}$. It is determined by the expression

$$(\delta N_a \delta E_i)_{\omega, \boldsymbol{k}} = -\frac{i e_a n_a}{\omega - (\boldsymbol{k} \cdot \boldsymbol{v}) + i\Delta} (\delta E_j \, \delta E_i)_{\omega, \boldsymbol{k}} \frac{\partial f_a}{\partial p_j} + i 4\pi e_a n_a 2\pi\delta(\omega - (\boldsymbol{k} \cdot \boldsymbol{v})) \left\{ \frac{k_i}{k^2 \varepsilon^{\|}(\omega - i\Delta, \boldsymbol{k})} + \frac{\omega [[\boldsymbol{k} \wedge \boldsymbol{v}] \wedge \boldsymbol{k}]_i}{k^2((\omega - i\Delta)^2 \, \varepsilon^{\perp}(\omega - i\Delta, \boldsymbol{k}) - c^2 k^2)} \right\} f_a. \tag{14.33}$$

We introduce the expression for the real part of this spectral function

$$\text{Re}\,(\delta N_a\,\delta E_i)_{\omega,\,\boldsymbol{k}} = -\pi e_a n_a\,\delta(\omega-(\boldsymbol{k}\cdot\boldsymbol{v}))\,(\delta E_j\,\delta E_i)_{\omega,\,\boldsymbol{k}}\frac{\partial f_a}{\partial p_j}$$
$$-4\pi e_a n_a 2\pi\,\delta(\omega-(\boldsymbol{k}\cdot\boldsymbol{v}))\left\{\frac{k_i\,\text{Im}\,\varepsilon^{||}(\omega,\,\boldsymbol{k})}{|\varepsilon^{||}(\omega,\,\boldsymbol{k}|^2\,k^2}\right.$$
$$\left.+\frac{\omega^3[[\boldsymbol{k}\wedge\boldsymbol{v}]\wedge\boldsymbol{k}]_i\,\text{Im}\,\varepsilon^{\perp}(\omega,\,\boldsymbol{k})}{k^2\,|\omega^2\varepsilon^{\perp}(\omega,\,\boldsymbol{k})-c^2k^2|^2}\right\}f_a. \tag{14.34}$$

This expression contains the spectral function $(\delta E_i\,\delta E_j)_{\omega,\,\boldsymbol{k}}$ of the fields, which is given by (14.22, 29–32).

In the same way we form the expression for the most general spectral function of phase distributions of particles in a plasma:

$$(\delta N_a\delta N_b)_{\omega,\,\boldsymbol{k}} = 2\pi\delta_{ab}\delta(\omega-(\boldsymbol{k}\cdot\boldsymbol{v}))\,\delta(\boldsymbol{p}-\boldsymbol{p}')\,n_a f_a$$
$$+\frac{e_a e_b n_a n_b(\delta E_i\delta E_j)_{\omega,\,\boldsymbol{k}}}{(\omega-(\boldsymbol{k}\cdot\boldsymbol{v})+i\Delta)\,(\omega-(\boldsymbol{k}\cdot\boldsymbol{v}')-i\Delta)}\cdot\frac{\partial f_a}{\partial p_i}\cdot\frac{\partial f_b}{\partial p'_j}$$
$$-\frac{4\pi e_a e_b n_a n_b}{\omega-(\boldsymbol{k}\cdot\boldsymbol{v})+i\Delta}\cdot\frac{2\pi\delta(\omega-(\boldsymbol{k}\cdot\boldsymbol{v}'))}{k^2}\left[\frac{k_i}{\varepsilon^{\parallel}(\omega+i\Delta,\,\boldsymbol{k})}\right.$$
$$\left.+\frac{\omega[[\boldsymbol{k}\wedge\boldsymbol{v}']\wedge\boldsymbol{k}]_i}{\omega^2\varepsilon^{\perp}(\omega+i\Delta,\,\boldsymbol{k})-c^2k^2}\right]\frac{\partial f_a}{\partial p_i}f_b$$
$$-\frac{4\pi e_a e_b n_a n_b}{\omega-(\boldsymbol{k}\cdot\boldsymbol{v}')-i\Delta}\cdot\frac{2\pi\delta(\omega-(\boldsymbol{k}\cdot\boldsymbol{v}))}{k^2}\left[\frac{k_i}{\varepsilon^{\parallel}(\omega-i\Delta,\,\boldsymbol{k})}\right.$$
$$\left.+\frac{\omega[[\boldsymbol{k}\wedge\boldsymbol{v}]\wedge\boldsymbol{k}]_i}{\omega^2\varepsilon^{\perp}(\omega-i\Delta,\,\boldsymbol{k})-c^2k^2}\right]\frac{\partial f_b}{\partial p'_i}f_a. \tag{14.35}$$

We have thus formed expressions for space–time correlation functions without solving the equations for the simultaneous correlation functions. Moreover, by using our expressions, the corresponding simultaneous correlation functions or spatial correlation functions can be found.

From (14.12), for instance, the relation between the spatial and space–time spectral functions of the phase densities is

$$(\delta N_a\delta N_b)_{\boldsymbol{k}} = \frac{1}{2\pi}\int_{-\infty}^{\infty}(\delta N_a\delta N_b)_{\omega,\,\boldsymbol{k}}\,d\omega. \tag{14.36}$$

By using (14.29–32) the expressions for the spatial spectral functions are

$$(\delta E_i^{\parallel}\,\delta E_j^{\parallel})_{\boldsymbol{k}} = \frac{k_i k_j}{k^2} \sum_a \frac{(4\pi)^2 e_a^2 n_a}{k^2} \int \frac{f_a}{|\varepsilon^{\parallel}((\boldsymbol{k}\cdot\boldsymbol{v})\cdot\boldsymbol{k})|^2}\, d^3\boldsymbol{p}; \tag{14.37}$$

$$(\delta E_i^{\perp}\,\delta E_j^{\perp})_{\boldsymbol{k}} = \sum_a \frac{(4\pi)^2 e_a^2 n_a}{k^4}$$

$$\times \int \frac{(\boldsymbol{k}\cdot\boldsymbol{v})^2\,[[\boldsymbol{k}\wedge\boldsymbol{v}]\wedge\boldsymbol{k}]_i\,[[\boldsymbol{k}\wedge\boldsymbol{v}]\wedge\boldsymbol{k}]_j}{|(\boldsymbol{k}\cdot\boldsymbol{v})^2\,\varepsilon^{\perp}((\boldsymbol{k}\cdot\boldsymbol{v})\cdot\boldsymbol{k}) - c^2k^2|^2} f_a\, d^3\boldsymbol{p}. \tag{14.38}$$

Formula (14.37), for the spatial spectral function of longitudinal fields is the same as (10.36), though formed in another way. It can also be shown without difficulty that the same expressions can also be formed for the other spatial spectral functions in two different ways.

Let us form the corresponding expressions for the case of statistical equilibrium.

We substitute Maxwell distributions in (14.29, 30). Using (13.44, 45) for the functions Im $\varepsilon^{\parallel}(\omega, \boldsymbol{k})$ and Im $\varepsilon^{\perp}(\omega, \boldsymbol{k})$, we get

$$(\delta\boldsymbol{E}^{\parallel}\cdot\delta\boldsymbol{E}^{\parallel})_{\omega,\boldsymbol{k}} = \frac{8\pi}{\omega}\,\frac{\operatorname{Im}\varepsilon^{\parallel}(\omega,\boldsymbol{k})}{|\varepsilon^{\parallel}(\omega,\boldsymbol{k})|^2}\,\varkappa T; \tag{14.39}$$

$$(\delta\boldsymbol{E}^{\perp}\cdot\delta\boldsymbol{E}^{\perp})_{\omega,\boldsymbol{k}} = \frac{16\pi\omega^3\operatorname{Im}\varepsilon^{\perp}(\omega,\boldsymbol{k})}{|\omega^2\varepsilon^{\perp}(\omega,\boldsymbol{k}) - c^2k^2|^2}\,\varkappa T. \tag{14.40}$$

Consider now the case of the longitudinal field in more detail. The $||$ sign is omitted.

We substitute Maxwell's distribution in the expression for $\varepsilon(\omega, \boldsymbol{k})$. The expression for Im $\varepsilon(\omega, \boldsymbol{k})$ in the equilibrium non-relativistic case is

$$\operatorname{Im}\varepsilon(\omega,\boldsymbol{k}) = \pi\sum_a \frac{4\pi e_a^2 n_a}{k^2\varkappa T}\cdot\frac{m_a\omega}{k\sqrt{(2\pi m_a\varkappa T)}}\, e^{-\frac{m_a\omega^3}{2k^2\varkappa T}}. \tag{14.41}$$

From this formula it follows that if $\omega \neq 0$, then

$$\operatorname{Im}\varepsilon(\omega,\boldsymbol{k}) \to 0 \quad \text{as} \quad k \to 0. \tag{14.42}$$

We apply the formula

$$\lim_{\Delta \to 0} \frac{\Delta}{\varphi^2(x)+\Delta^2} = \pi\delta(\varphi(x)), \qquad \Delta > 0. \tag{14.43}$$

By applying it and using (14.41, 42) for small k we get

$$\frac{\omega \operatorname{Im} \varepsilon(\omega, \boldsymbol{k})}{|\omega\varepsilon(\omega, \boldsymbol{k})|^2} \to \pi\delta(\omega \operatorname{Re} \varepsilon(\omega, \boldsymbol{k})). \tag{14.44}$$

So, for small k the expression (14.39) becomes

$$(\delta \boldsymbol{E}^{\parallel} \cdot \delta \boldsymbol{E}^{\parallel})_{\omega, \boldsymbol{k}} = 8\pi^2\delta(\omega \operatorname{Re} \varepsilon^{\parallel}(\omega, \boldsymbol{k}))\varkappa T. \tag{14.45}$$

This implies that the spectral function is in this case non-zero at those values of ω and $\boldsymbol{k}$ for which

$$\operatorname{Re} \varepsilon^{\parallel}(\omega, \boldsymbol{k}) = 0. \tag{14.46}$$

In the zeroth approximation in k, the expression (10.19) for $\varepsilon^{\parallel}(\omega, \boldsymbol{k})$ becomes

$$\varepsilon^{\parallel} = 1 - \frac{\omega_{\mathrm{L}}^2}{\omega^2}; \qquad \omega_{\mathrm{L}}^2 = \sum_a \frac{4\pi e_a^2 n_a}{m_a}. \tag{14.47}$$

Using the formula

$$\delta(\varphi(x)) = \sum_s \frac{\delta(x-x_s)}{|\varphi'(x)|_{x=x_s}}, \tag{14.48}$$

where x_s are simple roots of the equation $\varphi(x) = 0$, in this approximation we get

$$\delta(\omega \operatorname{Re} \varepsilon^{\parallel}(\omega, \boldsymbol{k})) = \frac{1}{2}[\delta(\omega-\omega_{\mathrm{L}})+\delta(\omega+\omega_{\mathrm{L}})]. \tag{14.49}$$

From (14.45, 49), therefore

$$(\delta \boldsymbol{E}^{\parallel} \cdot \delta \boldsymbol{E}^{\parallel})_{\omega, \boldsymbol{k}} = 4\pi^2[\delta(\omega-\omega_{\mathrm{L}})+\delta(\omega+\omega_{\mathrm{L}})]\varkappa T. \tag{14.50}$$

Thus the spectral function is non-zero at frequencies coinciding with the plasma oscillation frequency.

Likewise from (14.40) we get

$$(\delta \boldsymbol{E}^{\perp} \cdot \delta \boldsymbol{E}^{\perp})_{\omega, \boldsymbol{k}} = 16\pi^2\delta(\omega^2 \operatorname{Re} \varepsilon^{\perp}(\omega, \boldsymbol{k}) - c^2k^2)\,|\omega|\,\varkappa T. \tag{14.51}$$

By using solution (8.49) of the dispersion relation (8.47) for the transverse field at low values of k, we get

$$(\delta\boldsymbol{E}^{\perp}\cdot\delta\boldsymbol{E}^{\perp})_{\omega,\,\boldsymbol{k}} = 8\pi^2[\delta(\omega-\omega_k)+\delta(\omega+\omega_k)]\,\varkappa T,$$
$$\omega_k = \sqrt{(\omega_{\mathrm{L}}^2+c^2k^2)}. \tag{14.52}$$

For the spatial spectral functions, using (14.60, 52), we obtain the following expressions:

$$(\delta\boldsymbol{E}^{\parallel}\cdot\delta\boldsymbol{E}^{\parallel})_{\boldsymbol{k}} = \frac{1}{2\pi}\int(\delta\boldsymbol{E}^{\parallel}\cdot\delta\boldsymbol{E}^{\parallel})_{\omega,\,\boldsymbol{k}}\,d\omega = 4\pi\varkappa T, \tag{14.53}$$

$$(\delta\boldsymbol{E}^{\perp}\cdot\delta\boldsymbol{E}^{\perp})_{\boldsymbol{k}} = 8\pi\varkappa T. \tag{14.54}$$

The results (14.45, 49, 51–54) hold when the imaginary parts of the functions $\varepsilon^{\parallel}(\omega, \boldsymbol{k})$ and $\varepsilon^{\perp}(\omega, \boldsymbol{k})$ are small. Under this condition the attenuation is also small and so we may say that the results relate to the "pass band", or radiation region.

It follows from (14.53, 54) that for the radiation region the energy both of the longitudinal field and also of the transverse field, referred to a particular value of the vector k, is independent of this entity, and is determined solely by the temperature.

The expression for the function $(\delta\boldsymbol{E}\cdot\delta\boldsymbol{E})_{\boldsymbol{k}}$ from (14.39) is the same as (10.39) for any $\boldsymbol{k}$:

$$(\delta\boldsymbol{E}^{\parallel}\cdot\delta\boldsymbol{E}^{\parallel})_{\boldsymbol{k}} = 4\pi\frac{\varkappa T}{1+r_d^2k^2}\cdot \tag{14.55}$$

Hence (14.53) holds if $kr_d \ll 1$. On this particular condition the damping is small, which follows from (14.41) if $\omega \approx \omega_{\mathrm{L}}$.

It is seen from (14.55) that the longitudinal field's energy, referred to a particular $\boldsymbol{k}$, depends in the general case on $\boldsymbol{k}$ and decreases with increasing $\boldsymbol{k}$.

We now show that there is no such relationship for the function $(\delta\boldsymbol{E}^{\perp}\cdot\delta\boldsymbol{E}^{\perp})_{\boldsymbol{k}}$.

Integrating the expression (14.40) over ω and considering that

$$\mathrm{Im}\,\varepsilon^{\perp}(\omega, \boldsymbol{k}) = \frac{1}{2i}\left(\varepsilon^{\perp}(\omega+i\Delta, \boldsymbol{k})-\varepsilon^{\perp}(\omega-i\Delta, \boldsymbol{k})\right),$$

we write the integral as

$$(\delta \boldsymbol{E}^{\perp} \cdot \delta \boldsymbol{E}^{\perp})_{\boldsymbol{k}} = -8\pi\varkappa T \frac{1}{2\pi i} \int \left(\frac{1}{(\omega + i\Delta)^2 \varepsilon^{\perp}(\omega + i\Delta, \boldsymbol{k}) - c^2 k^2} \right.$$

$$\left. - \frac{1}{(\omega - i\Delta)^2 \varepsilon^{\perp}(\omega - i\Delta, \boldsymbol{k}) - c^2 k^2} \right) \omega \, d\omega. \tag{14.56}$$

The first of these integrals contains singularities only in the lower half-plane, whilst the second contains singularities only in the upper half-plane; therefore in the former we close the contour in the upper half-plane, but in the lower half-plane in the latter.

Taking into account that

$$\omega^2 \varepsilon^{\perp}(\omega, \boldsymbol{k}) - c^2 k^2 \to \omega^2 \quad \text{as} \quad \omega \to \infty, \tag{14.57}$$

and then using the value of the integral

$$\frac{1}{2\pi i} \int \frac{d\omega}{\omega \pm i\Delta} = \pm \frac{1}{2}, \tag{14.58}$$

we obtain the result

$$(\delta \boldsymbol{E}^{\perp} \cdot \delta \boldsymbol{E}^{\perp})_{\boldsymbol{k}} = 8\pi\varkappa T, \tag{14.59}$$

which is the same as (14.54) for the radiation region.

This is due to the following reasons. The integral (14.56) depends on the value of $\varepsilon^{\perp}$ as $\omega \to \infty$. Therefore, for fixed k, $\omega > ck$, and so the phase velocity $\omega/k > c$.

From (13.45) it follows that

$$\operatorname{Im} \varepsilon^{\perp}(\omega + i\Delta, \boldsymbol{k}) \to 0 \quad \text{as} \quad \Delta \to 0, \quad \text{if} \quad \omega/k > c, \tag{14.60}$$

since the condition $\omega = (\boldsymbol{k} \cdot \boldsymbol{v})$ under which the integrand in (13.45) is non-zero for $\omega/k > c$, cannot be fulfilled, i. e. all charged particles have velocities less than the speed of light.

Therefore the contribution to (14.59) in the equilibrium case relates only to the radiation region and so (14.59) and (14.54) coincide.

We show that the form of the correlation function is not affected in the equilibrium state by considering the transverse field.

From (14.35) we find the expression for the spatial spectral function

$$(\delta N_a \delta N_b)_{\boldsymbol{k}} = \frac{1}{2\pi}\int (\delta N_a \delta N_b)_{\omega,\,\boldsymbol{k}}\, d\omega.$$

Bearing in mind that

$$n_a n_b g_{ab}(\boldsymbol{k}, \boldsymbol{p}, \boldsymbol{p}') = (\delta N_a \delta N_b)_{\boldsymbol{k}} - \delta_{ab} n_a \delta(\boldsymbol{p}-\boldsymbol{p}') f_a,$$

we find an expression for the function $g_{ab}(\boldsymbol{k}, \boldsymbol{p}, \boldsymbol{p}')$ and then substitute into it the Maxwell distribution (13.48). Here all the terms associated with the transverse field drop out, and so the expression for the function $g_{ab}(\boldsymbol{k}, \boldsymbol{p}, \boldsymbol{p}')$ is

$$g_{ab}(\boldsymbol{k}, \boldsymbol{p}, \boldsymbol{p}') = -\frac{e_a e_b}{\sum\limits_c e_c^2 n_c (1 + r_d^2 k^2)} f_a(\boldsymbol{p}) f_b(\boldsymbol{p}'). \qquad (14.61)$$

This differs from the non-relativistic expression in that here f_a and f_b are the relativistic Maxwell distributions (13.48).

Using the foregoing formulae one can find spectral functions of the strange currents $\delta \boldsymbol{j}^{\mathrm{e}}$, charges $\delta \varrho^{\mathrm{e}}$ and flux densities $\delta \boldsymbol{D}$, the action of each of which is equivalent to thermal motion.

For example, for the longitudinal field, when

$$\delta \boldsymbol{D}(\omega, \boldsymbol{k}) = \varepsilon^{\parallel}(\omega, \boldsymbol{k})\, \delta \boldsymbol{E}^{\parallel}(\omega, \boldsymbol{k}),$$

(14.39) yields the following expression for the spectral function

$$(\delta \boldsymbol{D} \cdot \delta \boldsymbol{D})_{\omega,\,\boldsymbol{k}} = \frac{8\pi}{\omega} \operatorname{Im} \varepsilon^{\parallel}(\omega, \boldsymbol{k})\, \varkappa T$$

or

$$(\delta \boldsymbol{D} \cdot \delta \boldsymbol{D})_{\omega,\,\boldsymbol{k}} = \frac{32\pi^2}{\omega^2} \sigma(\omega, \boldsymbol{k})\, \varkappa T, \qquad (14.62)$$

where $\sigma(\omega, \boldsymbol{k})$ is the electric conductivity.

This formula is analogous to Nyquist's formula for the spectral function of a "strange" electromotive force equivalent to the action of thermal motion in an electric circuit:

$$(\varepsilon^2)_\omega = 2R(\omega)\, \varkappa T, \qquad (14.63)$$

where $R(\omega)$ is the ohmic impedance.

Corresponding formulae can be produced without difficulty for the spectral functions of external ("strange") charges and currents.

From Maxwell's equations we find that

$$\delta \boldsymbol{j}^{\mathrm{e}}(\omega, \boldsymbol{k}) = \frac{i\omega}{4\pi}\,\delta \boldsymbol{D}(\omega, \boldsymbol{k}), \quad \delta \varrho^{\mathrm{e}}(\omega, \boldsymbol{k}) = \frac{i}{4\pi}\,(\boldsymbol{k}\cdot\delta \boldsymbol{D}(\omega, \boldsymbol{k})). \tag{14.64}$$

Using these relations and also formulae (14.62), we obtain expressions for the corresponding spectral functions:

$$(\delta \boldsymbol{j}_{\mathrm{e}}^{\parallel}\cdot\delta \boldsymbol{j}_{\mathrm{e}}^{\parallel})_{\omega,\, \boldsymbol{k}} = 2\sigma(\omega, \boldsymbol{k})\,\varkappa T = \frac{\omega}{2\pi}\,\mathrm{Im}\,\varepsilon^{\parallel}(\omega, \boldsymbol{k})\,\varkappa T; \tag{14.65}$$

$$(\delta \varrho^{\mathrm{e}}\,\delta \varrho^{\mathrm{e}})_{\omega,\, \boldsymbol{k}} = 2\,\frac{k^2}{\omega^2}\,\sigma(\omega, \boldsymbol{k})\,\varkappa T = \frac{k^2}{2\pi\omega}\,\mathrm{Im}\,\varepsilon^{\parallel}(\omega, \boldsymbol{k})\,\varkappa T. \tag{14.66}$$

These formulae were first obtained by Leontovich and Rytov in a phenomenological way [Leontovich and Rytov, 1952; and Rytov, 1953].

The results given in this section refer to the case of a spatially homogeneous plasma, isotropic in momentum space, when the distribution functions f_a depend on the absolute magnitude of the momentum, i.e. $f_a = f_a(|\boldsymbol{p}|, t)$.

Anisotropy occurs in momentum space, for instance, if the components of a plasma move in relation to each other under the action of an external magnetic field and so on.

In the anisotropic state the dielectric constant tensor depends not only on the vector $\boldsymbol{k}$, but also on other vectors. The separation of the fields into longitudinal and transverse therefore appears impossible in the general case and so the tensor $\varepsilon_{ij}(\omega, \boldsymbol{k})$ is no longer determined by the two functions $\varepsilon^{\parallel}(\omega, \boldsymbol{k})$ and $\varepsilon^{\perp}(\omega, \boldsymbol{k})$.

We must mention the changes in the initial expressions (14.8–10) in the anisotropic case.

In eqn. (5.41) it is now impossible to neglect the term which contains $([\boldsymbol{v}\wedge\delta\boldsymbol{B}]\cdot\partial f_a/\partial\boldsymbol{p})$, therefore eqn. (14.8) in the anisotropic case becomes

$$\delta N_a(\omega, \boldsymbol{k}, \boldsymbol{p}) = \frac{i}{\omega - (\boldsymbol{k}\cdot\boldsymbol{v}) + i\Delta} \Bigg\{ \delta N_a(\boldsymbol{k}, \boldsymbol{p}, t = 0)$$

$$- e_a n_a \left(\left\{ \delta \boldsymbol{E}(\omega, \boldsymbol{k}) + \frac{1}{c} [v \wedge \delta \boldsymbol{B}(\omega, \boldsymbol{k})] \right\} \cdot \frac{\partial f_a}{\partial \boldsymbol{p}} \right) \Bigg\}. \quad (14.67)$$

We introduce the tensor

$$A_{ij} = \frac{\omega^2}{c^2} \varepsilon_{ij} + k_i k_j - \delta_{ij} k^2. \quad (14.68)$$

The dielectric-constant tensor is now given by the expression

$$\varepsilon_{ij} = \delta_{ij} + \sum_a \frac{4\pi e_a^2 n_a}{\omega} \int \frac{v_i \left(1 - \frac{(\boldsymbol{k}\cdot\boldsymbol{v})}{\omega}\right) \frac{\partial f_a}{\partial p_j} + \frac{v_i v_j}{\omega} \left(\boldsymbol{k} \cdot \frac{\partial f_a}{\partial \boldsymbol{p}}\right)}{\omega - (\boldsymbol{k}\cdot\boldsymbol{v}) + i\Delta} \, d^3\boldsymbol{p}. \quad (14.69)$$

In the isotropic case this formula changes into (7.27). Instead of (14.9) we now have

$$\delta E_i(\omega, \boldsymbol{k}) = -i A_{ij}^{-1} \Bigg(\frac{4\pi\omega}{c^2} \delta j_j^{\mathrm{e}}(\omega, \boldsymbol{k}) - \frac{\omega}{c^2} \delta E_j(\boldsymbol{k}, 0) + \frac{1}{c} [\boldsymbol{k} \wedge \delta \boldsymbol{B}(\boldsymbol{k}, 0)]_j + \sum_a \frac{4\pi e_a^2 n_a}{c^3} \int \frac{v_j \left([\boldsymbol{v} \wedge \delta \boldsymbol{B}(\boldsymbol{k}, 0)] \cdot \frac{\partial f_a}{\partial \boldsymbol{p}} \right)}{\omega - (\boldsymbol{k}\cdot\boldsymbol{v}) + i\Delta} \, d^3\boldsymbol{p} \Bigg), \quad (14.70)$$

where A_{ij}^{-1} is the inverse tensor of A_{ij}, and

$$\boldsymbol{j}^{\mathrm{e}} = i \sum_a e_a \int \frac{\boldsymbol{v} \delta N_a(\boldsymbol{k}, \boldsymbol{p}, 0)}{\omega - (\boldsymbol{k}\cdot\boldsymbol{p}) + i\Delta} \, d^3\boldsymbol{p}.$$

In the isotropic case

$$A_{ij}^{-1} = \frac{c^2}{\omega^2} \left\{ \frac{k_i k_j}{\varepsilon^{\parallel}(\omega, \boldsymbol{k})\, k^2} + \frac{\delta_{ij} k^2 - k_i k_j}{k^2 \left(\varepsilon^{\perp}(\omega, \boldsymbol{k}) - \frac{c^2 k^2}{\omega^2} \right)} \right\} \quad (14.71)$$

and so (14.70) agrees with (14.9). In the anisotropic case (14.10) remains unchanged.

Equations (14.67, 69, 10) serve as the initial equations for finding the space–time correlation functions in the anisotropic case. The way of forming the expressions for the spectral functions is still the same.

The results obtained in this section can be generalized to the case of a slightly inhomogeneous plasma in the same way as in § 11 (see expressions (11.48–56)).

Finally, we make one more important observation. The foregoing expressions for the spectral functions in the equilibrium state hold good both for the radiation region when the functions $\operatorname{Im}\varepsilon^{\parallel}$ and $\operatorname{Im}\varepsilon^{\perp}$ are small, and also for the "stop band" (the "collision region"). In the latter case the imaginary part of the tensor ε_{ij} is largish, and so the thermal losses are not small either; they are proportional to $\operatorname{Im}\varepsilon_{ij}$.

If the plasma is not in the equilibrium state and the functions f_a depend on time, the resulting expressions hold only for those regions of the space–time spectrum for which the conditions (10.12, 13) are satisfied.

These conditions can be written

$$\frac{\partial f_a}{\partial t} \ll \frac{f_a}{\tau_{\max}}, \tag{14.72}$$

i. e. the first functions vary little in the maximum correlation time $\tau_{\max} \equiv \tau(k_{\min})$ for non-equilibrium processes in a plasma.

Inequality (14.72) is satisfied if the spectral functions are small for $k < k_{\min}$.

Unless the conditions (10.12, 13) and (14.72) are fulfilled, it is impossible to express the spatial and space–time correlation functions in terms of the first distribution functions over the entire spectrum.

In this case we divide the spatial spectrum into two parts, viz. the short wave part (large k) and the long wave part (small k). The first part we call the "stop band" or "collision region" (in this region large damping decrements occur). The latter term is justified because only for this region can the right-hand side of eqn. (10.9) be expressed in terms of the first distribution functions and so be written in the form of the "collision integral".

The other region we call the "pass band" or "radiation region" since for small k the damping decrements are small and so the existence of waves in the plasma is possible.

Before tackling the description of non-equilibrium processes in a plasma with regard to radiation processes (see § 16), we shall consider the kinetic equation for a plasma in a permanent magnetic field.

15. Correlation Functions and Collision Integral in the Presence of an External Magnetic Field

Consider a non-relativistic plasma. In this case the transverse-field strengths are small and so we can use the set of equations for the functions $\delta N_a(q, \boldsymbol{p}, t)$ and also the longitudinal electric field strength $\delta \boldsymbol{E}$.

We put $\boldsymbol{B}$ for the average magnetic field strength in the plasma. It is assumed that

$$\boldsymbol{B} = \text{const}, \quad \boldsymbol{E} = 0. \tag{15.1}$$

We shall consider the spatially homogeneous case. Slight inhomogeneity can be treated as in § 11. The functions f_a thus depend only on the momentum $\boldsymbol{p}$ and time t.

To determine the spectral functions and the collision integral, we use the method propounded in § 14, for which the functions f_a are required to be slowly varying functions.

To satisfy this requirement, we confine ourselves to processes for which the functions f_a have the form

$$f_a(\boldsymbol{p}, t) = f_a(p^{\perp}, p^{\parallel}, t). \tag{15.2}$$

Here $p^{\perp}$ and $p^{\parallel}$ are the transverse and longitudinal components of the momentum relative to the vector $\boldsymbol{B}$, i. e.

$$(\boldsymbol{p}^{\perp} \cdot \boldsymbol{B}) = 0, [\boldsymbol{p}^{\parallel} \wedge \boldsymbol{B}] = 0. \tag{15.3}$$

It is thus assumed that the functions f_a are independent of the angular variable in momentum space.

By making these assumptions the set of equations for the functions δN_a and $\delta \boldsymbol{E}$ becomes

$$\frac{\partial \delta N_a}{\partial t} + \left(\boldsymbol{v} \cdot \frac{\partial \delta N_a}{\partial \boldsymbol{q}}\right) + \frac{e_a}{c}\left([\boldsymbol{v} \wedge \boldsymbol{B}] \cdot \frac{\partial \delta N_a}{\partial \boldsymbol{p}}\right)$$

$$+ e_a n_a \left(\delta \boldsymbol{E} \cdot \frac{\partial f_a}{\partial \boldsymbol{p}}\right) = 0, \qquad (15.4)$$

$$\operatorname{div} \delta \boldsymbol{E} = 4\pi \sum_a e_a n_a \int \delta N_a \, d^3\boldsymbol{p}; \qquad \operatorname{curl} \delta \boldsymbol{E} = 0.$$

Equation (15.4) does not have a term

$$\frac{e_a n_a}{c}\left([\boldsymbol{v} \wedge \boldsymbol{B}] \cdot \frac{\partial f_a}{\partial \boldsymbol{p}}\right),$$

since it vanishes by dint of (15.2).

The equation for the function f_a in the homogeneous case is

$$\frac{\partial f_a}{\partial t} + \frac{e_a}{c}\left([\boldsymbol{v} \wedge \boldsymbol{B}] \cdot \frac{\partial f_a}{\partial \boldsymbol{p}}\right) = -\frac{e_a}{n_a} \cdot \frac{\partial}{\partial \boldsymbol{p}} \overline{\delta N_a \, \delta \boldsymbol{E}} =$$

$$-\frac{e_a}{n_a (2\pi)^3}\left(\frac{\partial}{\partial \boldsymbol{p}} \cdot \int \operatorname{Re} \, (\delta N_a \; \delta \boldsymbol{E})_{\boldsymbol{k}}\right) d^3\boldsymbol{k}. \qquad (15.5)$$

It differs from (10.9) in the term which contains the magnetic field.

The same problem arises of determining the spectral function $(\delta N_a \, \delta \boldsymbol{E})_{\boldsymbol{k}}$, but now in the presence of an external magnetic field.

We use the method of § 14. It is required to express, using eqns. (15.4), the function $\delta N_a(\boldsymbol{q}, \boldsymbol{p}, t)$ at the instant t through its value at the initial instant $t = 0$.

Note that eqn. (15.4) for δN_a agrees with (9.4) after the substitution

$$\delta N_a \to f_a^1, \quad \delta \boldsymbol{E} \to \boldsymbol{E}, \quad \boldsymbol{B} \to \boldsymbol{B}^0, \qquad (15.6)$$

so the expression (9.12) can be used directly. Putting $t_0 = 0$ therein, when considered with (15.6), we get

$$\delta N_a(\boldsymbol{q}, \boldsymbol{p}, t) = \delta N_a(\boldsymbol{R}_a(0, t, \boldsymbol{p}, \boldsymbol{q}), \boldsymbol{P}_a(0, t, \boldsymbol{p}), 0)$$

$$- e_a n_a \int_0^t dt' \left(\delta \boldsymbol{E}(\boldsymbol{R}_a(0, t-t' \boldsymbol{p}, \boldsymbol{q}), t') \cdot \left(\frac{\partial f_a(\boldsymbol{p})}{\partial \boldsymbol{p}}\right)_{\boldsymbol{p} \to \boldsymbol{P}_a(0,\, t-t',\, \boldsymbol{p})}\right)$$

$$(15.7)$$

We assume that the conditions (10.12, 13) and (14.72) are fulfilled, and so the dependence of the functions f_a on time cannot be taken into account here.

The functions $\boldsymbol{R}_a(0. t, \boldsymbol{p}, \boldsymbol{q})$ and $\boldsymbol{P}_a(0, t, \boldsymbol{p})$ are determined by formulae (9.9, 10).

In (15.7) we carry out the one-sided Fourier transformation with respect to t and the two-sided transformation with respect to the coordinates. The resulting expression is

$$\delta N_a(\omega, \boldsymbol{k}, \boldsymbol{p})+e_a n_a \int_0^\infty e^{-\Delta t+i[\omega t+(\boldsymbol{k}\cdot\boldsymbol{R}_a(0,\,t,\,\boldsymbol{p},\,0))]}\left(\delta\boldsymbol{E}(\omega, \boldsymbol{k})\cdot\left(\frac{\partial f_a(\boldsymbol{p})}{\partial \boldsymbol{p}}\right)_{\boldsymbol{p}\to\boldsymbol{P}_a(0,\,t,\,\boldsymbol{p})}\right)dt$$
$$= \int_0^\infty e^{-\Delta t+i[\omega t+(\boldsymbol{k}\cdot\boldsymbol{R}_a(0,\,t,\,\boldsymbol{p},\,0))]}\,\delta N_a\big(\boldsymbol{k}, \boldsymbol{P}_a(0, t, \boldsymbol{p})\big)\,dt. \tag{15.8}$$

From this expression we can find the function $\delta\boldsymbol{E}(\omega, \boldsymbol{k})$. We multiply (15.8) with $-i4\pi e_a\boldsymbol{k}/k^2$, sum over a and then integrate over $\boldsymbol{p}$.

Using the relation between the functions $\delta\boldsymbol{E}(\omega, \boldsymbol{k})$ and $\delta N_a(\omega, \boldsymbol{k}, \boldsymbol{p})$:

$$\delta\boldsymbol{E}(\omega, \boldsymbol{k}) = -i\sum_a 4\pi e_a\frac{\boldsymbol{k}}{k^2}\int \delta N_a(\omega, \boldsymbol{k}, \boldsymbol{p})\,d^3\boldsymbol{p}, \tag{15.9}$$

which is implied by the second equation of (15.4), the required expression is

$$\delta\boldsymbol{E}(\omega, \boldsymbol{k}) = -i\sum_a \frac{4\pi e_a\boldsymbol{k}}{k^2\varepsilon^+(\omega, \boldsymbol{k})}$$
$$\times\int_0^\infty\int e^{-\Delta t+i[\omega t+(\boldsymbol{k}\cdot\boldsymbol{R}_a(0,\,t,\,\boldsymbol{p},\,0))]}\,\delta N_a\big(\boldsymbol{k}, \boldsymbol{P}_a(0, t, \boldsymbol{p})\big)\,dt\,d^3\boldsymbol{p}. \tag{15.10}$$

For the dielectric constant of a "Coulomb" plasma in a constant magnetic field, we have

$$\varepsilon^{\pm}(\omega, \boldsymbol{k}) = 1 - i\sum_a \frac{4\pi e_a^2 n_a}{k^2} \int_0^{\pm\infty} \int e^{\mp\Delta t + i[\omega t + (\boldsymbol{k}\cdot\boldsymbol{R}_a(0,\,t,\,\boldsymbol{p}\,0))]}$$
$$\times \left(\boldsymbol{k}\cdot\frac{\partial f_a(\boldsymbol{p})}{\partial \boldsymbol{p}}\right)_{\boldsymbol{p}\to\boldsymbol{P}_a(0,\,t,\,\boldsymbol{p})} dt\, d^3\boldsymbol{p}. \tag{15.11}$$

The term "Coulomb" emphasizes that this expression is suitable for those cases when the rotational electromagnetic field can be neglected.

If $\boldsymbol{B} = 0$, (15.11) agrees with (10.19) for the longitudinal dielectric constant.

We transform (15.11) under the condition (15.2):

$$\left(\boldsymbol{k}\cdot\frac{\partial f_a}{\partial \boldsymbol{p}}\right)_{\boldsymbol{p}\to\boldsymbol{P}_a(0,\,t,\,\boldsymbol{p})} = \frac{\partial f_a}{\partial p_i} k_j \frac{dp_i}{dP_{aj}}$$
$$= \left(\boldsymbol{P}_a(0, t, \boldsymbol{k})\cdot\frac{\partial f_a(\boldsymbol{p})}{\partial \boldsymbol{p}}\right). \tag{15.12}$$

The vector $\boldsymbol{P}_a(0, t, \boldsymbol{k})$ is given by the expression (9.9) if in it $\boldsymbol{p} \to \boldsymbol{k}$.

We introduce cylindrical coordinates with the z-direction along the vector $\boldsymbol{B}$:

$$k_x = k^{\perp}\cos\psi, \quad p_x = p^{\perp}\cos\varphi,$$
$$k_y = k^{\perp}\sin\psi, \quad p_y = p^{\perp}\sin\varphi. \tag{15.13}$$

Using these coordinates, we get

$$(\boldsymbol{k}\cdot\boldsymbol{R}_a(0, t, \boldsymbol{p}, \boldsymbol{q}) = (\boldsymbol{k}\cdot\boldsymbol{q}) - k^{\parallel} v^{\parallel} t$$
$$-\frac{k^{\perp}v^{\perp}}{\Omega_a}[\sin(\varphi-\psi+\Omega_a t) - \sin(\varphi-\psi)]. \tag{15.14}$$

$$\left(\boldsymbol{P}_a(0, t, \boldsymbol{k})\cdot\frac{\partial f_a}{\partial \boldsymbol{p}}\right) = \left(k^{\parallel}\frac{\partial}{\partial p^{\parallel}} + \cos(\varphi-\psi+\Omega_a t)\, k^{\perp}\frac{\partial}{\partial p^{\perp}}\right) f_a. \tag{15.15}$$

We substitute the expressions (15.12, 14, 15) into the formula (15.11) and use the formula

$$e^{i\alpha\sin(\varphi-\psi)} = \sum_n I_n(\alpha) e^{in(\varphi-\psi)} \text{ with } \alpha = \frac{k^{\perp}v^{\perp}}{\Omega_a}. \tag{15.16}$$

Then we perform integration with respect to the angle φ, using the expressions:

$$\frac{1}{2\pi}\sum_{m,\,m'}\int_0^{2\pi} I_m(\alpha)\,I_{m'}(\alpha)e^{-im(\varphi+\Omega_a\tau-\psi)+im'(\varphi-\psi)}\,d\varphi$$
$$=\sum_m I_m^2(\alpha)\,e^{-im\Omega_a\tau}; \tag{15.17}$$

$$\frac{1}{2\pi}\sum_{m,\,m'}\int_0^{2\pi} I_m(\alpha)\,I_{m'}(\alpha)\,e^{im(\varphi-\psi+\Omega_a\tau)-im'(\varphi-\psi)}\cos(\varphi-\psi+\Omega_a\tau)\,d\varphi$$
$$=\sum_m e^{im\Omega_a\tau}\,I_m^2(\alpha)\,\frac{m}{\alpha};\quad \alpha=\frac{k^{\perp}v^{\perp}}{\Omega_a}. \tag{15.18}$$

We finally integrate with respect to τ. We use the value of the integral

$$-i\int_0^{\pm\infty} e^{\mp\Delta\tau+i(\omega-m\Omega_a-k^{\parallel}v^{\parallel})\tau}\,d\tau=\frac{1}{\omega-m\Omega_a-k^{\parallel}v^{\parallel}\pm i\Delta}. \tag{15.19}$$

The resulting expression for the dielectric constant is

$$\varepsilon^{\pm}(\omega,\boldsymbol{k})=1+\sum_b\frac{4\pi e_b^2 n_b}{k^2}\sum_m\int_0^{\infty}2\pi p^{\perp}\,dp^{\perp}\int_{-\infty}^{\infty}dp^{\parallel}\,I_m^2\left(\frac{k^{\perp}v^{\perp}}{\Omega_b}\right)$$
$$\times\frac{\left[k^{\parallel}\dfrac{\partial}{\partial p^{\parallel}}+\dfrac{m\Omega_b}{v^{\perp}}\dfrac{\partial}{\partial p^{\perp}}\right]f_b}{\omega-k^{\parallel}v^{\parallel}-m\Omega_b\pm i\Delta}. \tag{15.20}$$

By using the expressions (15.8, 10) we find the spectral functions $(\delta N_a\delta\boldsymbol{E})_{\omega,\,\boldsymbol{k}}$ and $(\delta\boldsymbol{E}\cdot\delta\boldsymbol{E})_{\omega,\,\boldsymbol{k}}$ in the stationary case when the time-dependence of the functions $f_a(\boldsymbol{p},t)$ can be neglected.

By means of the formulae (15.10) and (14.14) we find that

$$(\delta\boldsymbol{E}\cdot\delta\boldsymbol{E})_{\omega,\,\boldsymbol{k}}=\sum_{ab}\frac{(4\pi)^2e_ae_b}{k^2}\lim_{\Delta\to 0}\frac{2\Delta}{|\varepsilon(\omega,\boldsymbol{k})|^2}\int_0^{\infty}dt\int_0^{\infty}dt'$$
$$\times\int d^3\boldsymbol{p}\int d^3\boldsymbol{p}'e^{-\Delta(t+t')+i\omega(t-t')}\,e^{i(\boldsymbol{k}\cdot\boldsymbol{R}_a(0,\,t,\,\boldsymbol{p},\,0)-\boldsymbol{R}_b(0,\,t',\,0))}$$
$$\times\big(\delta N_a(\boldsymbol{P}_a(0,t,\boldsymbol{p}))\,\delta N_b(\boldsymbol{P}_b(0,t',\boldsymbol{p}'))\big)_{\boldsymbol{k}}. \tag{15.21}$$

We substitute the variables of integration

$$\boldsymbol{p},\boldsymbol{p}'\to\boldsymbol{P}_a,\boldsymbol{P}_b. \tag{15.22}$$

The Jacobian of the transformation from $\boldsymbol{p}$ to $\boldsymbol{P}$ is equal to unity. In this connexion we use the transformation formulae

$$\boldsymbol{P}_a(0, t, \boldsymbol{P}_a(0, \tau, \boldsymbol{p})) = \boldsymbol{P}_a(0, t+\tau, \boldsymbol{p}); \tag{15.23}$$

$$\boldsymbol{R}_a(0, t, \boldsymbol{P}_a(0, \tau, \boldsymbol{p}), 0) = \boldsymbol{R}_a(0, t+\tau, \boldsymbol{p}, 0) - R_a(0, \tau, \boldsymbol{p}, 0). \tag{15.24}$$

The transformation (15.22) corresponds to a change from the variables at the instant t to the variables at the instant 0, and so in (15.23, 24) one puts $\tau = -t$.

Considering that

$$\boldsymbol{P}_a(0, 0, \boldsymbol{p}) = \boldsymbol{p}; \quad \boldsymbol{R}_a(0, 0, \boldsymbol{p}, 0) = 0, \tag{15.25}$$

we obtain from (15.24)

$$\boldsymbol{R}_a(0, t, \boldsymbol{P}_a(0, -t, \boldsymbol{p}), 0) = -\boldsymbol{R}_a(0, -t, \boldsymbol{p}, 0). \tag{15.26}$$

As a result the expression (15.21) becomes

$$(\delta \boldsymbol{E} \cdot \delta \boldsymbol{E})_{\omega, \boldsymbol{k}} = \sum_{ab} \frac{(4\pi)^2 e_a e_b}{k^2} \lim_{\varDelta \to 0} \frac{2\varDelta}{|\varepsilon(\omega, \boldsymbol{k})|^2} \int_0^\infty dt \int_0^\infty dt'$$

$$\times \int d^3\boldsymbol{p}\, d^3\boldsymbol{p}' e^{-\varDelta(t+t')+i\omega(t-t')} e^{-i(\boldsymbol{k}\cdot\boldsymbol{R}_a(0, -t, \boldsymbol{p}, 0) - \boldsymbol{R}_b(0, -t', \boldsymbol{p}', 0))}$$

$$\times (\delta N_a(\boldsymbol{p})\, \delta N_b(\boldsymbol{p}'))_{\boldsymbol{k}}. \tag{15.27}$$

From now onwards we continue as in § 14.

Using the formula

$$(\delta N_a \delta N_b)_{\boldsymbol{k}} = n_a n_b g_{ab}(\boldsymbol{k}, \boldsymbol{p}, \boldsymbol{p}') + \delta_{ab} n_a \delta(\boldsymbol{p} - \boldsymbol{p}') f_a, \tag{15.28}$$

we divide the expression (15.27) into two parts.

For the collision region, whenever the conditions formulated in §§ 10 and 14 are fulfilled, the first term, which contains the function g_{ab}, becomes vanishingly small as $\varDelta \to 0$.

As a result the expression (15.27) becomes

$$(\delta \boldsymbol{E} \cdot \delta \boldsymbol{E})_{\omega, \boldsymbol{k}} = \sum_{a} \frac{(4\pi)^2 e_a^2 n_a}{k^2} \lim_{\varDelta \to 0} \frac{2\varDelta}{|\varepsilon(\omega, \boldsymbol{k})|^2} \int_0^\infty dt \int_0^\infty dt'$$

$$\times \int d^3\boldsymbol{p} e^{-\varDelta(t+t')+i\omega(t-t')} e^{-i(\boldsymbol{k}\cdot\boldsymbol{R}_a(0, -t, \boldsymbol{p}, 0) - \boldsymbol{R}_a(0, -t', \boldsymbol{p}, 0))} f_a(\boldsymbol{p}). \tag{15.29}$$

We change, in this expression, to cylindrical coordinates. From (15.14) it follows that

$$(\boldsymbol{k}\cdot\boldsymbol{R}_a(0,-t,\boldsymbol{p},0))-(\boldsymbol{k}\cdot\boldsymbol{R}_a(0,-t',\boldsymbol{p},0)$$
$$= k^{\parallel}v^{\parallel}(t-t')-\frac{k^{\perp}v^{\perp}}{\Omega_a}(\sin(\varphi-\Omega_a t-\psi)$$
$$-\sin(\varphi-\Omega_a t'-\psi)). \tag{15.30}$$

We substitute the expression (15.30) into (15.29). Using (15.16, 17), we perform integration over φ, t and t'. After this we carry out the limiting transition $\Delta\to 0$. Here we use the formula

$$\lim_{\Delta\to 0}\frac{2\Delta}{(\omega-m\Omega_a-k^{\parallel}v^{\parallel})^2+\Delta^2} = 2\pi\delta(\omega-m\Omega_a-k^{\parallel}v^{\parallel}). \tag{15.31}$$

As a result the final expression is

$$(\delta\boldsymbol{E}\cdot\delta\boldsymbol{E})_{\omega,\boldsymbol{k}} = \sum_a\frac{(4\pi)^2e_a^2n_a}{k^2}\sum_m\int_0^{\infty}\int_{-\infty}^{\infty}I_m^2\left(\frac{k^{\perp}v^{\perp}}{\Omega_a}\right)$$
$$\times\frac{\delta(\omega-k^{\parallel}v^{\parallel}-m\Omega_a)}{|\varepsilon(\omega,\boldsymbol{k})|^2}f_a(\boldsymbol{p})2\pi p^{\perp}\,dp^{\perp}\,dp^{\parallel}. \tag{15.32}$$

If $\boldsymbol{B}=0$ this expression agrees with (14.29). The limiting transition $\boldsymbol{B}\to 0$ is simpler in (15.29).

To form an expression for the spectral function $(\delta N_a\delta\boldsymbol{E})_{\omega,\boldsymbol{k}}$ we need formulae (15.8, 10) and (14.13, 14).

Consider the formula resulting from multiplication of the right-hand sides. Discarding the term containing the function $g_{ab}(\boldsymbol{k},\boldsymbol{p},\boldsymbol{p}')$, we obtain

$$i\frac{4\pi e_a n_a}{\varepsilon^-(\omega,\boldsymbol{k})}\frac{\boldsymbol{k}}{k^2}\lim_{\Delta\to 0}2\Delta\int_0^{\infty}dt\int_0^{\infty}dt'\int d^3\boldsymbol{p}'e^{-\Delta(t+t')+i\omega(t-t')}$$
$$\times e^{i(\boldsymbol{k}\cdot\boldsymbol{R}_a(0,t,\boldsymbol{p},0)-\boldsymbol{R}_a(0,t',\boldsymbol{p}',0))}\,\delta(\boldsymbol{P}_a(0,t,\boldsymbol{p})-\boldsymbol{P}_a(0,t',\boldsymbol{p}'))f_a(\boldsymbol{p}'). \tag{15.33}$$

We have to integrate this expression over $\boldsymbol{p}'$. For this we first of all introduce within the integral the new variable

$$\boldsymbol{p}'\to\boldsymbol{P}_a(0,t,\boldsymbol{p}'). \tag{15.34}$$

The Jacobian of this transformation is equal to unity. Using the formula (15.26) we rewrite the integrals in (15.33) as

$$\int_0^\infty dt \int_0^\infty dt' \int d^3\boldsymbol{p}' e^{-\Delta(t+t')+i\omega(t-t')+i(\boldsymbol{k}\cdot\boldsymbol{R}_a(0,t,\boldsymbol{p},0)+\boldsymbol{R}_a(0,-t',\boldsymbol{p}',0))}$$
$$\times\delta(\boldsymbol{P}_a(0,t,\boldsymbol{p})-\boldsymbol{p}'). \qquad (15.35)$$

From formula (15.24)

$$\boldsymbol{R}_a(0,-t',\boldsymbol{P}_a(0,t,\boldsymbol{p},0)) = \boldsymbol{R}_a(0,t-t',\boldsymbol{p},0)$$
$$-\boldsymbol{R}_a(0,t,\boldsymbol{p},0). \qquad (15.36)$$

Bearing this relation in mind, we integrate (15.35) over $\boldsymbol{p}'$. As a result for (15.33) we get

$$i\frac{4\pi e_a n_a}{\varepsilon^-(\omega,\boldsymbol{k})}\cdot\frac{\boldsymbol{k}}{k^2}\lim_{\Delta\to 0} 2\Delta\int_0^\infty dt$$
$$\times\int_0^\infty dt'\, e^{-\Delta(t+t')+i\omega(t-t')+i(\boldsymbol{k}\cdot\boldsymbol{R}_a(0,t-t',\boldsymbol{p},0))} f_a. \qquad (15.37)$$

We substitute the variables $t-t'=\tau$ and $(t+t')/2=\theta$ into this expression, and then integrate over θ. Here the quantity 2Δ cancels out and so we get

$$i\frac{4\pi e_a n_a}{\varepsilon^-(\omega,\boldsymbol{k})}\frac{\boldsymbol{k}}{k^2}\int_{-\infty}^\infty d\tau e^{i[\omega\tau+(\boldsymbol{k}\cdot\boldsymbol{R}_a(0,\tau,\boldsymbol{p},0))]} f_a(\boldsymbol{p}). \qquad (15.38)$$

This formula was produced by multiplying the right-hand sides of the expressions (15.8, 10), multiplying by 2Δ and then carrying out the limiting transition $\Delta\to 0$.

We now multiply together the left-hand sides of the expressions (15.8, 10) and use (14.13, 14). The resulting expression consists of two terms, viz. one equal to $(\delta N_a\delta\boldsymbol{E})_{\omega,\boldsymbol{k}}$, whilst the other contains the function $(\delta E_i\delta E_j)_{\omega,\boldsymbol{k}}$. We transfer it to the right-hand side. Using (15.38) we get the following expression for the spectral function $(\delta N_a\delta\boldsymbol{E})_{\omega,\boldsymbol{k}}$:

$$(\delta N_a\,\delta E_i)_{\omega,\boldsymbol{k}} = -e_a n_a\int_0^\infty e^{-\Delta t+i[\omega t+(\boldsymbol{k}\cdot\boldsymbol{R}_a(0,t,\boldsymbol{p},0))]}$$
$$\times(\delta E_j\,\delta E_i)_{\omega,\boldsymbol{k}}\left(\frac{\partial f_a}{\partial p_j}\right)_{p_j\to P_{aj}(0,t,\boldsymbol{p})} + i\frac{4\pi k_i e_a n_a}{k^2\varepsilon(\omega-i\Delta,\boldsymbol{k})}$$
$$\times\int_{-\infty}^\infty e^{-i[\omega t+(\boldsymbol{k}\cdot\boldsymbol{R}_a(0,t,\boldsymbol{p},0))]} f_a\,dt,\ \Delta\to 0, \qquad (15.39)$$

where

$$(\delta E_i \delta E_j)_{\omega, \boldsymbol{k}} = \frac{k_i k_j}{k^2} (\delta \boldsymbol{E} \cdot \delta \boldsymbol{E})_{\omega, \boldsymbol{k}}. \tag{15.40}$$

If $\boldsymbol{B} = 0$ this expression is the same as the longitudinal part of the expression (14.33).

By using (15.32) the spectral function $(\delta N_a \delta \boldsymbol{E})_{\omega, \boldsymbol{k}}$ can be given in the stationary case in terms of the functions f_a.

The spatial spectral function is found from (15.39) by integration over ω

$$(\delta N_a \delta \boldsymbol{E})_{\boldsymbol{k}} = \frac{1}{2\pi} \int_{-\infty}^{\infty} (\delta N_a \delta \boldsymbol{E})_{\omega, \boldsymbol{k}} \, d\omega. \tag{15.41}$$

In order to form the kinetic equations for the functions f_a, the expression obtained in this way for the function $(\delta N_a \delta \boldsymbol{E})_{\boldsymbol{k}}$ needs to be substituted into (15.5).

Since it is assumed that the f_a have the form (15.2), i.e. are independent of the angular variable φ, to obtain the collision integral it is sufficient to know the expression, averaged over the angle φ, for the spectral function.

We do the averaging over φ in (15.39). For this we use expressions which are obtained by means of the formulae (15.14–18),

$$\int_0^{2\pi} \frac{d\varphi}{2\pi} \int_0^{\infty} dt e^{-\Delta t + i[\omega t + (\boldsymbol{k} \cdot \boldsymbol{R}_a(0, t, \boldsymbol{p}, 0))]} = \sum_m I_m^2 \left(\frac{k^{\perp} v^{\perp}}{\Omega_a} \right) \frac{i}{\omega - k^{\parallel} v^{\parallel} - m\Omega_a + i\Delta}, \tag{15.42}$$

$$\int_0^{2\pi} \frac{d\varphi}{2\pi} \int_{-\infty}^{\infty} dt e^{i[\omega t + (\boldsymbol{k} \cdot \boldsymbol{R}_a(0, t, \boldsymbol{p}, 0))]} = \sum_m I_m^2 \left(\frac{k^{\perp} v^{\perp}}{\Omega_a} \right) 2\pi \delta(\omega - k^{\parallel} v^{\parallel} - m\Omega_a). \tag{15.43}$$

Using these formulae, from (15.39) we get the expression

$$\frac{1}{2\pi} \int_0^{2\pi} (\delta N_a (\boldsymbol{k} \cdot \delta \boldsymbol{E}))_{\omega, \boldsymbol{k}} \, d\varphi = -i e_a n_a \sum_m I_m^2 \left(\frac{k^{\perp} v^{\perp}}{\Omega_a} \right) \times \left\{ \frac{(\delta \boldsymbol{E} \cdot \delta \boldsymbol{E})_{\omega, \boldsymbol{k}}}{\omega - k^{\parallel} v^{\parallel} - m\Omega_a + i\Delta} \left(\boldsymbol{k} \cdot \frac{\partial}{\partial \boldsymbol{p}} \right) f_a - \frac{8\pi^2}{\varepsilon(\omega - i\Delta, \boldsymbol{k})} \delta(\omega - k^{\parallel} v^{\parallel} - m\Omega_a) f_a \right\}. \tag{15.44}$$

Here and below $\left(\boldsymbol{k}\cdot\frac{\partial}{\partial \boldsymbol{p}}\right) \equiv k^{\parallel}\frac{\partial}{\partial p^{\parallel}}+\frac{m\Omega_a}{v^{\perp}}\cdot\frac{\partial}{\partial p^{\perp}}$.

Using (15.41, 44), the expression for the real part of the spatial spectral function, averaged over φ, is

$$\frac{1}{2\pi}\int_0^{2\pi} d\varphi \,\mathrm{Re}\,(\delta N_a(\boldsymbol{k}\cdot\delta \boldsymbol{E}))_{\boldsymbol{k}} = -\pi e_a n_a \sum_m I_m^2\left(\frac{k^{\perp}v^{\perp}}{\Omega_a}\right)$$
$$\times\int_{-\infty}^{\infty}\frac{d\omega}{2\pi}\,\delta(\omega-k^{\parallel}v^{\parallel}-m\Omega_a)$$
$$\times\left\{(\delta \boldsymbol{E}\cdot\delta \boldsymbol{E})_{\omega\omega,\boldsymbol{k}}\left(\boldsymbol{k}\cdot\frac{\partial}{\partial \boldsymbol{p}}f_a+\frac{8\pi^2\,\mathrm{Im}\,\varepsilon(\omega,\boldsymbol{k})}{|\varepsilon(\omega,\boldsymbol{k})|^2}f_a\right)\right\}. \quad (15.45)$$

To obtain the equation for the functions f_a, we need to consider the expression

$$-\frac{e_a}{n_a}\frac{1}{(2\pi)^4}\int_0^{2\pi}d\varphi\int d^3\boldsymbol{k}\left(\frac{\boldsymbol{k}}{k^2}\cdot\frac{\partial}{\partial \boldsymbol{p}}\,\mathrm{Re}\,(\delta N_a(\boldsymbol{k}\cdot\delta \boldsymbol{E}))_{\boldsymbol{k}}\right)$$
$$\equiv S_a(p^{\perp},p^{\parallel},t). \quad (15.46)$$

In cylindrical coordinates

$$\left(\boldsymbol{k}\cdot\frac{\partial}{\partial \boldsymbol{p}}\right) = k^{\parallel}\frac{\partial}{\partial p^{\parallel}}+\cos(\varphi-\psi)\,k^{\perp}\frac{\partial}{\partial p^{\perp}}$$
$$-\sin(\varphi-\psi)\frac{k^{\perp}}{p^{\perp}}\cdot\frac{\partial}{\partial \varphi}. \quad (15.47)$$

To evaluate the integral over φ in (15.46), consider the expansion of the function $(\delta N_a(\boldsymbol{k}\cdot\delta \boldsymbol{E}))_{\boldsymbol{k}}$ as a series in $\varphi-\psi$

$$(\delta N_a(\boldsymbol{k}\cdot\delta \boldsymbol{E}))_{\boldsymbol{k}} = e^{i\alpha\sin(\varphi-\psi)}\sum_m e^{-im(\varphi-\psi)}\,(\delta N_a(\boldsymbol{k}\cdot\delta \boldsymbol{E})),$$
$$\alpha = \frac{k^{\perp}v^{\perp}}{\Omega_a}. \quad (15.48)$$

Using the formula (15.16), the series in (15.48) becomes

$$(\delta N_a(\boldsymbol{k}\cdot\delta \boldsymbol{E}))_{\boldsymbol{k}} = \sum_{m,m'} I_{m'}(\alpha)e^{i(m'-m)(\varphi-\psi)}\,(\delta N_a(\boldsymbol{k}\cdot\delta \boldsymbol{E}))_{\boldsymbol{k}}^m. \quad (15.49)$$

Averaging over φ, from (15.49) we get

$$\frac{1}{2\pi}\int_0^{2\pi}(\delta N_a(\boldsymbol{k}\cdot\delta\boldsymbol{E}))_{\boldsymbol{k}}\,d\varphi=\sum_m I_m(\alpha)\,(\delta N_a(\boldsymbol{k}\cdot\delta\boldsymbol{E}))_{\boldsymbol{k}}^m. \tag{15.50}$$

Comparing the expressions (15.50) and (15.41, 44), we find the expression for the Fourier coefficient of $(\delta N_a(\boldsymbol{k}\cdot\delta\boldsymbol{E}))_{\boldsymbol{k}}^m$.

We substitute the series (15.49) into (15.46). We use the expression (15.47), and the value of the integral

$$\frac{1}{2\pi}\sum_{m,\,m'}\int_0^{2\pi}\cos(\varphi-\psi)\,e^{i(m'-m)(\varphi-\psi)}\,I_{m'}(\alpha)\,d\varphi$$

$$=\frac{1}{2}\left(I_{m+1}(\alpha)+I_{m-1}(\alpha)\right)=\frac{m}{\alpha}\,I_m(\alpha). \tag{15.51}$$

As a result for the "collision" integral $S_a(p^{\perp}, p^{\parallel}, t)$ of (15.46) we get the expression

$$S_a=-\frac{e_a}{n_a(2\pi)^3}\sum_m\int\left(\boldsymbol{k}\cdot\frac{\partial}{\partial\boldsymbol{p}}\right)I_m\left[\frac{k^{\perp}v^{\perp}}{\Omega_a}\right]$$

$$\times(\delta N_a(\boldsymbol{k}\cdot\delta\boldsymbol{E}))_{\boldsymbol{k}}^m\,d^3\boldsymbol{k}. \tag{15.52}$$

Comparing the formulae (15.50, 45), we write the expression for the function

$$\operatorname{Re}(\delta N_a(\boldsymbol{k}\cdot\delta\boldsymbol{E}))_{\boldsymbol{k}}^m=-\frac{e_a n_a}{2}\,I_m\left(\frac{k^{\perp}v^{\perp}}{\Omega_a}\right)$$

$$\times\left\{(\delta\boldsymbol{E}\cdot\delta\boldsymbol{E})_{k^{\parallel}v^{\parallel}+m\Omega_a,\,\boldsymbol{k}}\left(\boldsymbol{k}\cdot\frac{\partial}{\partial\boldsymbol{p}}\right)f_a\right.$$

$$\left.+\frac{8\pi\operatorname{Im}\varepsilon(k^{\parallel}v^{\parallel}+m\Omega_a,\boldsymbol{k})}{|\varepsilon(k^{\parallel}v^{\parallel}+m\Omega_a,\boldsymbol{k})|^2}\,f_a\right\}. \tag{15.53}$$

We substitute this expression into (15.52). We represent the "collision" integral in two forms as in §§ 11 and 13.

Firstly, we write eqns. (15.5) for the functions f_a as Fokker–Planck equations. In this case the "collision" integral S_a is

$$S_a(p^\perp, p^\parallel, t) = \sum_m \int \left\{ \left(\boldsymbol{k}\cdot\frac{\partial}{\partial \boldsymbol{p}}\right) D_a^m(p^\perp, p^\parallel) \right.$$

$$\times \left(\boldsymbol{k}\cdot\frac{\partial}{\partial \boldsymbol{p}}\right) f_a(p^\perp, p^\parallel, t) + \left(\boldsymbol{k}\cdot\frac{\partial}{\partial \boldsymbol{p}}\right) A_a^m(p^\perp, p^\parallel)$$

$$\left. \times f_a(p^\perp, p^\parallel, t) \right\} d^3\boldsymbol{k}. \tag{15.54}$$

The coefficients D_a^m and A_a^m are given by the expressions

$$D_a^m = \frac{e_a^2}{16\pi^3 k^2} I_m^2 \left(\frac{k^\perp v^\perp}{\Omega_a}\right) (\delta\boldsymbol{E}\cdot\delta\boldsymbol{E})_{k^\parallel v^\parallel + m\Omega_a,\, \boldsymbol{k}}, \tag{15.55}$$

$$A_a^m = \frac{e_a^2}{2\pi^2 k^2} I_m^2 \left(\frac{k^\perp v^\perp}{\Omega_a}\right) \frac{\operatorname{Im} \varepsilon(k^\parallel v^\parallel + m\Omega_a, \boldsymbol{k})}{|\varepsilon(k^\parallel v^\parallel + m\Omega_a, \boldsymbol{k})|^2}. \tag{15.56}$$

Thus the diffusion coefficient in momentum space is determined by the spectral function $(\delta\boldsymbol{E}\cdot\delta\boldsymbol{E})_{\omega,\boldsymbol{k}}$ at the frequency $\omega = k^\parallel v^\parallel + m\Omega_a$.

The frictional coefficient A_a^m is proportional to the imaginary part of the dielectric constant at that same frequency. If $\boldsymbol{B} = 0$, the expressions (15.54–56) agree with (11.6–8).

For the other form of the collision integral we substitute into (15.53) the expression (15.32) for the function $(\delta\boldsymbol{E}\cdot\delta\boldsymbol{E})_{\omega,\boldsymbol{k}}$ and also the corresponding expression for the imaginary part of the dielectric constant. We get

$$S_a = \sum_b n_b \sum_{m,\, m'} \int \left(\boldsymbol{k}\cdot\frac{\partial}{\partial \boldsymbol{p}}\right)_m Q_{a,b}^{m,m'} \left\{ \left(\boldsymbol{k}\cdot\frac{\partial}{\partial \boldsymbol{p}}\right)_m \right.$$

$$\left. - \left(\boldsymbol{k}\cdot\frac{\partial}{\partial \boldsymbol{p}_1}\right)_{m'} \right\} f_a(p^\perp, p^\parallel, t) f_b(p_1^\perp, p_1^\parallel, t)$$

$$\times 2\pi p_1^\perp \, dp_1^\perp \, dp_1^\parallel \, 2\pi k^\perp \, dk^\perp \, dk^\parallel, \tag{15.57}$$

where

$$Q_{a,b}^{m,m'} = 2e_a^2 e_b^2 I_m^2 \left(\frac{k^\perp v^\perp}{\Omega_a}\right) I_{m'}^2 \left(\frac{k^\perp v_1^\perp}{\Omega_a}\right)$$

$$\times \frac{\delta(k^\parallel v^\parallel + m\Omega_a - k^\parallel v_1^\parallel - m'\Omega_b)}{k^4 |\varepsilon(k^\parallel v^\parallel + m\Omega_a, \boldsymbol{k})|^2}. \tag{15.58}$$

The expression (15.57) agrees with that given by Yeleonskii, Zyryanov and Silin [1962].

The collision integral in a magnetic field is studied in various papers [Belyayev, 1958; Rostoker, 1960; and Yeleonskii, Zyryanov and Silin, 1962].

CHAPTER V

The Kinetic Equations and Expressions for Spectral Functions when the Radiation by Plasma Waves Is Taken into Account

---

16. Non-stationarity. Spectral Functions for the Radiation Region

In §§ 10, 13 and 14 it was shown that for the short-wave region of the spatial spectrum (the collision region or "stop band") single- and double-time correlations in the case of slowly varying processes can be expressed in terms of the first distribution functions $f_a(\boldsymbol{q}, \boldsymbol{p}, t)$.

For the long-wave region this appears to be impossible in the general case. Actually, for quite small wave numbers, the correlation times of the plasma excitations $\tau(k)$ become comparable with, or greater than, the relaxation time τ_r for the f_a. In solving spectral function equations one cannot therefore ever assume that the spectral functions do not depend explicitly on time. But also in this region one may simplify the initial set of equations for the first and second moments and so express more complex moments in terms of simpler moments, though not only by first moments [Klimontovich, 1959, 1962a, 1962b, 1963, 1961].

In § 14 expressions were obtained for space–time spectral functions for the spectral region where conditions (10.12, 16) and (14.63) are satisfied. More general expressions will now be found for the spectral functions which hold also for the radiation region.

So as not to over-complicate the calculations, consider firstly the case of a Coulomb plasma, i.e., we neglect the transverse electromagnetic field.

On this condition, as the initial equations we may take (5.31) for the random deviations δN_a and $\delta \boldsymbol{E}$.

As also in § 14, we are attempting to form expressions for the space–time spectral functions without having to solve equations for our single-time correlations.

We write the first equation (5.31) for the time variable $t' = t+\tau$ and then, by means of this equation, we express the function δN_a at the instant $t+\tau$ in terms of its value at the instant t. We use for this the Fourier transform in $\boldsymbol{q}$ and τ

$$\delta N_a(\omega, \boldsymbol{k}, \boldsymbol{p}, t) = \int_0^\infty d\tau \int d^3\boldsymbol{q} e^{-\Delta\tau+i(\omega\tau-(\boldsymbol{k}\cdot\boldsymbol{q}))}\, \delta N_a(\boldsymbol{q}, \boldsymbol{p}, t+\tau). \quad (16.1)$$

As a result we find from the first equation of (5.31)

$$\delta N_a(\boldsymbol{k}, \omega, \boldsymbol{p}, t) = i\frac{\delta N_a(\boldsymbol{k}, \boldsymbol{p}, t)}{\omega-(\boldsymbol{k}\cdot\boldsymbol{v})+i\Delta} - \frac{ie_a n_a}{\omega-(\boldsymbol{k}\cdot\boldsymbol{v})+i\Delta}\int_0^\infty \left(\delta\boldsymbol{E}(\boldsymbol{k}, t+\tau)\cdot\frac{\partial f_a}{\partial \boldsymbol{p}}(t+\tau, \boldsymbol{p})\right)e^{-\Delta\tau+i\omega\tau}\, d\tau. \quad (16.2)$$

Using the second and third equations of (5.31), we obtain

$$\delta\boldsymbol{E}(\omega, \boldsymbol{k}, t) = -i\,4\pi\frac{\boldsymbol{k}}{k^2}\sum_a e_a \int \delta N_a(\omega, \boldsymbol{k}, \boldsymbol{p}, t)\, d^3\boldsymbol{p}. \quad (16.3)$$

We eliminate the function δN_a from this equation by means of (16.2). Using the expression (10.19), we obtain the equation

$$\int_0^\infty \varepsilon^+(\omega, \boldsymbol{k}, t+\tau)\, \delta\boldsymbol{E}(\boldsymbol{k}, t+\tau)e^{-\Delta\tau+i\omega\tau}\, d\tau = \sum_a \frac{4\pi e_a \boldsymbol{k}}{k^2}\int \frac{\delta N_a(\boldsymbol{k}, \boldsymbol{p}, t)}{\omega-(\boldsymbol{k}\cdot\boldsymbol{v})+i\Delta}\, d^3\boldsymbol{p}. \quad (16.4)$$

In the stationary case eqns. (16.2, 4) coincide with the longitudinal part of eqns. (14.8, 9).

Consider first eqn. (16.4). We write it in the form of Poisson's equation for the Fourier components of a random variation in the induction

$$\delta \boldsymbol{D}(\omega, \boldsymbol{k}, t) = \sum_a \frac{4\pi e_a \boldsymbol{k}}{k^2} \int \frac{\delta N_a(\boldsymbol{k}, \boldsymbol{p}, t)}{\omega - (\boldsymbol{k}\cdot\boldsymbol{v}) + i\Delta} d^3\boldsymbol{p}, \tag{16.5}$$

where

$$\delta \boldsymbol{D}(\omega, \boldsymbol{k}, t) = \int_0^\infty d\tau e^{-\Delta\tau + i\omega\tau} \varepsilon^+(\omega, \boldsymbol{k}, t+\tau)\, \delta \boldsymbol{E}(\boldsymbol{k}, t+\tau). \tag{16.6}$$

Performing in this latter expression the inverse Fourier transformation with respect to time, we get

$$\delta \boldsymbol{D}(\boldsymbol{k}, t+\tau) = \frac{1}{2\pi} \int_{-\infty}^\infty d\omega e^{\Delta\tau - i\omega\tau}\, \delta \boldsymbol{D}(\omega, \boldsymbol{k}, t)$$

$$= \frac{1}{2\pi} \int_{-\infty}^\infty d\omega \int_0^\infty \delta\tau' e^{\Delta(\tau-\tau') - i\omega(\tau-\tau')} \varepsilon^+(\omega, \boldsymbol{k}, t+\tau')\, \delta \boldsymbol{E}(\boldsymbol{k}, t+\tau'). \tag{16.7}$$

Let us now try to simplify these expressions.

In the radiation region one may suppose that the function $\delta \boldsymbol{E}(\boldsymbol{k}, t+\tau)$ varies at two rates, i.e. fast and slow variation with time. The fast variation is due to oscillatory processes in the plasma, and the slow variation to relaxation processes.

If the spectrum of the oscillations in the plasma is discrete, then under such a condition (cf. (2.76))

$$\delta \boldsymbol{E}(\boldsymbol{k}, t) = \sum_l \delta \boldsymbol{E}^l(\boldsymbol{k}, t) e^{-i\omega_l(\boldsymbol{k})t}. \tag{16.8}$$

The complex amplitudes δE^l are slowly varying time functions. We shall see below that they are non-zero at those frequencies ω_l which satisfy the equation

$$\varepsilon'(\omega_l, \boldsymbol{k}, t) = 0. \tag{16.9}$$

By substituting (16.8) into the right-hand side of (16.7), this expression can be simplified the same as (2.72). Here we use another method.

The function $\varepsilon(\omega, \boldsymbol{k}, t)$ depends on time through the function $f_a(\boldsymbol{p}, t)$ and so in the spatially homogeneous case it varies slowly with time. We put μt for the slowly varying argument of the function $\delta \boldsymbol{E}$. Thus, in the radiation region

$$\delta \boldsymbol{E}(\boldsymbol{k}, t) = \delta \boldsymbol{E}(\boldsymbol{k}, \mu t, t).$$

We write the "slow" arguments in (16.7) as

$$t+\tau' = t+\tau+(\tau'-\tau)$$

and then expand them as a series in $\tau'-\tau$. Keeping the first two terms of the expression, we get

$$\delta \boldsymbol{D}(\boldsymbol{k}, t+\tau) = \frac{1}{2\pi}\int_{-\infty}^{\infty} d\omega \int_{0}^{\infty} d\tau' e^{-\Delta(\tau'-\tau)+i\omega(\tau'-\tau)}$$
$$\times\left(1+(\tau'-\tau)\frac{\partial}{\partial(t+\tau)}\right)\varepsilon^{+}(\omega, \boldsymbol{k}, t+\tau)\,\delta \boldsymbol{E}(\boldsymbol{k}, \mu(t+\tau), t+\tau'). \tag{16.10}$$

But

$$(\tau'-\tau)e^{i\omega(\tau'-\tau)} = -i\frac{\partial}{\partial\omega}e^{i\omega(\tau'-\tau)},$$

and so we integrate by parts over ω and get

$$\delta \boldsymbol{D}(\boldsymbol{k}, t+\tau) = \frac{1}{2\pi}\int_{-\infty}^{\infty} d\omega \int_{0}^{\infty} d\tau' e^{-\Delta(\tau'-\tau)+i\omega(\tau'-\tau)}$$
$$\times\left(1+i\frac{\partial^2}{\partial\omega\,\partial(t+\tau)}\right)\varepsilon^{+}(\omega, \boldsymbol{k}, t+\tau)\,\delta \boldsymbol{E}(\boldsymbol{k}, \mu(t+\tau), t+\tau'). \tag{16.11}$$

We write

$$\delta \boldsymbol{E}(\boldsymbol{k}, t, \omega, \mu(t+\tau))$$
$$= \int_{0}^{\infty} d\tau' e^{-\Delta\tau'+i\omega\tau'}\,\delta \boldsymbol{E}(\boldsymbol{k}, \mu(t+\tau), t+\tau') \tag{16.12}$$

for the Fourier component with respect to the fast time. In accordance with this expansion as a Fourier integral in the fast time, the function $\delta D(\boldsymbol{k}, t+\tau)$ has the form

$$\delta \boldsymbol{D}(\boldsymbol{k}, t+\tau) = \frac{1}{2\pi}\int_{-\infty}^{\infty} d\omega e^{\Delta\tau-i\omega\tau}\,\delta \boldsymbol{D}(\boldsymbol{k}, \omega, t, \mu(t+\tau)). \tag{16.13}$$

Using (16.11–13) we find the expression for the Fourier component $\delta\boldsymbol{D}$ of the induction taking non-stationarity into account

$$\begin{aligned}\delta\boldsymbol{D}(\omega, \boldsymbol{k}, t, \mu(t+\tau)) \\ = \varepsilon^{+}(\omega, \boldsymbol{k}, \mu(t+\tau))\, \delta\boldsymbol{E}(\omega, \boldsymbol{k}, t, \mu(t+\tau)) \\ +i\frac{\partial}{\partial(t+\tau)}\left(\frac{\partial\varepsilon^{+}}{\partial\omega}\,\delta\boldsymbol{E}\right).\end{aligned} \tag{16.14}$$

In the stationary case the Fourier components do not depend on the slow time, therefore the second term in (16.14) vanishes and

$$\delta\boldsymbol{D}(\omega, \boldsymbol{k}, t) = \varepsilon^{+}(\omega, \boldsymbol{k})\, \delta\boldsymbol{E}(\omega, \boldsymbol{k}, t). \tag{16.15}$$

The argument t in (16.14, 15) plays the part of the "initial moment" when using the Fourier transformation. In some formulae this argument is omitted.

The second term in (16.14) takes the non-stationarity into account†.

Our isolation of the radiation region corresponds to dividing the spatial spectrum into two regions, viz. the "collision" region (or stop band) and the radiation region (or pass band). We use the superscript "rad" to denote functions relating to the radiation region, and "coll" for the collision region.

As previously, τ_r is the relaxation time of the distribution function f_a, and $\tau(\boldsymbol{k})$ is the relaxation time of a plasma wave with wave vector k; $\gamma(\boldsymbol{k}) \sim 1/\tau(\boldsymbol{k})$ is the decrement of attenuation; $\omega(\boldsymbol{k})$ is the corresponding frequency.

It is assumed that the following condition is fulfilled for all the wave vectors of waves which play a notable rôle in non-

† If in the Fourier integral expansion one has regard to the dependence of the frequency on time, a further term appears on the right-hand side of (16.14):

$$\frac{i}{2}\frac{\partial\omega}{\partial t}\frac{\partial^2\varepsilon}{\partial\omega^2}\delta E, \quad \text{where} \quad \frac{\partial\omega}{\partial t} = -\frac{\partial\varepsilon'}{\partial t}\Big/\frac{\partial\varepsilon'}{\partial\omega}.$$

In this case, for instance, the formula (16.29) for the effective decrement of attenuation becomes (see Klimontovich, 1965):

$$\gamma' = \gamma+\left(\frac{\partial^2\varepsilon'}{\partial t\,\partial\omega}+\frac{1}{2}\frac{\partial\omega}{\partial t}\frac{\partial^2\varepsilon'}{\partial\omega^2}\right)\Big/\frac{\partial\varepsilon'}{\partial\omega}.$$

By using this expression the form of the adiabatic invariant can be established for various actual cases.

equilibrium processes in a plasma

$$\omega(\boldsymbol{k}) \gg 1/\tau_r, \tag{16.16}$$

i.e. the relaxation time of the functions f_a is much greater than the maximum oscillation period in a plasma. In particular, this condition is satisfied when it is not essential to have regard to the radiation of plasma waves and we can therefore confine ourselves to the collisions (see (11.43)).

In the collision region

$$\omega(\boldsymbol{k}) \gtrsim \gamma^{\text{coll}}(\boldsymbol{k}) \gg 1/\tau_r,$$

i.e. the damping time is much less than τ_r. In the radiation region (pass band):

$$\omega(\boldsymbol{k}) \gg \gamma^{\text{rad}}(\boldsymbol{k}) \sim 1/\tau_r. \tag{16.17}$$

In formula (16.14) $\tau \sim 1/\omega(\boldsymbol{k})$ and so, in accord with (16.17), the functions $\varepsilon^+(\omega, \boldsymbol{k}, t+\tau)$ and $\delta\boldsymbol{E}(\omega, \boldsymbol{k}, \mu(t+\tau))$ vary little during the time τ. Hence we expand (16.14) as a series in τ and confine ourselves to the first non-vanishing terms in the "stationary" term and the "non-stationary" term. We then get

$$\delta\boldsymbol{D}(\omega, \boldsymbol{k}, t, \mu t) = \varepsilon^+(\omega, \boldsymbol{k}, \mu t)\, \delta\boldsymbol{E}(\omega, \boldsymbol{k}, t, \mu t) + i\frac{\partial}{\partial t}\left(\frac{\partial \varepsilon^+}{\partial \omega}\, \delta\boldsymbol{E}\right). \tag{16.18}$$

This formula also provides an approximate expression for the left-hand side of (16.4) with regard to the non-stationarity of radiation, and so eqn. (16.4) thus becomes

$$\varepsilon^+(\omega, \boldsymbol{k}, \mu t)\, \delta\boldsymbol{E}(\omega, \boldsymbol{k}, t, \mu t) + i\frac{\partial}{\partial t}\left(\frac{\partial \varepsilon^+}{\partial \omega}\, \delta\boldsymbol{E}\right) = \sum_a \frac{4\pi e_a \boldsymbol{k}}{k^2} \int \frac{\delta N_a(\boldsymbol{k}, \boldsymbol{p}, t)}{\omega - (\boldsymbol{k}\cdot\boldsymbol{v}) + i\Delta}\, d^3\boldsymbol{p}. \tag{16.19}$$

The right-hand side of this equation depends not only on the "initial instant" t, but also on the slow time μt through f_a.

The expressions for the spectral functions only retain the slow variation with t through f_a (see below), and so the one argument μt can take the place of the two arguments t and μt.

By an analogous transformation of (16.2), we get

$$\begin{aligned}
&\delta N_a(\omega, \boldsymbol{k}, p, t, \mu t)\\
&\quad + \frac{ie_a n_a}{\omega-(\boldsymbol{k}\cdot\boldsymbol{v})+i\Delta}\left(\delta \boldsymbol{E}(\omega, \boldsymbol{k}, t, \mu t)\cdot\frac{\partial f_a(\boldsymbol{p}, \mu t)}{\partial \boldsymbol{p}}\right)\\
&\quad - \frac{\partial}{\partial t}\left(\frac{\partial}{\partial\omega}\,\frac{e_a n_a}{\omega-(\boldsymbol{k}\cdot\boldsymbol{v})+i\Delta}\left(\delta\boldsymbol{E}\cdot\frac{\partial f_a}{\partial \boldsymbol{p}}\right)\right)\\
&= i\,\frac{\delta N_a(\boldsymbol{k}, \boldsymbol{p}, t)}{\omega-(\boldsymbol{k}\cdot\boldsymbol{v})+i\Delta}\,. \qquad (16.20)
\end{aligned}$$

Clearly, when considered with (16.3), eqn. (16.20) implies (16.19). We use (16.19) to form an equation for the spectral function $(\delta\boldsymbol{E}\cdot\delta\boldsymbol{E})_{\omega,\,\boldsymbol{k}}$. For this, along with (16.19), we consider the complex conjugate equation

$$\begin{aligned}
&\delta\boldsymbol{E}^* + \frac{i}{\varepsilon^-}\cdot\frac{\partial}{\partial t}\left(\frac{\partial\varepsilon^-}{\partial\omega}\,\delta\boldsymbol{E}^*\right)\\
&= \frac{1}{\varepsilon^-}\sum_a \frac{4\pi e_a \boldsymbol{k}}{k^2}\int \frac{\delta N_a^*(\boldsymbol{k}, \boldsymbol{p}, t)}{\omega-(\boldsymbol{k}\cdot\boldsymbol{v})-i\Delta}\,d^3\boldsymbol{p}. \qquad (16.21)
\end{aligned}$$

In eqn. (16.21) we have divided by ε and used the fact that $(\varepsilon^+)^* = \varepsilon^-$.

In the stationary case eqns. (16.19, 21) imply the expression (14.23) which in § 14 yielded the expression (14.29) for the spectral function $(\delta\boldsymbol{E}\cdot\delta\boldsymbol{E})_{\omega,\,\boldsymbol{k}}$ in the collision region.

We multiply together the left- and right-hand sides of eqns. (16.19, 21). The resulting expression yields two equations after equating in succession the real and imaginary parts of the left and right-hand sides.

Consider first the equation obtained by equating the real parts.

We leave only terms of the order μ and therefore discard the terms which contain the product of time derivatives.

Later we shall require a definition of the damping decrement

$$\gamma(\omega, \boldsymbol{k}) = \varepsilon''(\omega, \boldsymbol{k})\Big/\frac{\partial\varepsilon'}{\partial\omega}\,. \qquad (16.22)$$

In the radiation region $\gamma^{\text{rad}} \sim \mu$ and so terms containing the product ε'' and the time derivative are neglected. We then get

$$\varepsilon' \delta \boldsymbol{E}(\omega, \boldsymbol{k}, \mu t)\, \delta \boldsymbol{E}^*(\omega, \boldsymbol{k}, \mu t) = \frac{\varepsilon'}{|\varepsilon(\omega, \boldsymbol{k}, \mu t)|^2} \sum_{ab} \frac{(4\pi)^2 e_a e_b}{k^2} \times \int \frac{\delta N_a(\boldsymbol{k}, \boldsymbol{p}, t)\, \delta N_b^*(\boldsymbol{k}, \boldsymbol{p}', t)}{(\omega - (\boldsymbol{k} \cdot \boldsymbol{v}) + i\Delta)(\omega - (\boldsymbol{k} \cdot \boldsymbol{v}') - i\Delta)}\, d^3\boldsymbol{p}\, d^3\boldsymbol{p}'. \tag{16.23}$$

We multiply this equation by 2Δ and pass to the limit $\Delta \to 0$, and then avail ourselves of the formulae (14.13, 14). Consider the right-hand side of (16.23).

As previously in § 14, by means of the formula

$$(\delta N_a \delta N_b)_{\boldsymbol{k},\, t} = n_a n_b g_{ab}(\boldsymbol{k}, \boldsymbol{p}, \boldsymbol{p}', t) + n_a \delta_{ab} \delta(\boldsymbol{p} - \boldsymbol{p}') f_a$$

we divide the right-hand side of (16.23) into two.

The second part, which does not contain the function g_{ab}, after integration over $\boldsymbol{p}'$ as $\Delta \to 0$ within the integral, becomes

$$\frac{\varepsilon'}{|\varepsilon|^2} \sum_a \frac{(4\pi)^2 e_a^2 n_a}{k^2} \int 2\pi \delta(\omega - (\boldsymbol{k} \cdot \boldsymbol{v})) f_a\, d^3\boldsymbol{p}.$$

Here the following formula is used

$$\lim \frac{2\Delta}{(\omega - (\boldsymbol{k} \cdot \boldsymbol{v}))^2 + \Delta^2} = 2\pi \delta(\omega - (\boldsymbol{k} \cdot \boldsymbol{v})).$$

Consider now the term containing the correlation function.

It contains an integral of type (14.26).

As in § 14, we consider non-equilibrium states for which the condition (14.27) is satisfied. To show what restrictions are imposed by this condition in the non-stationary case, we divide this integral into three parts.

The first is the non-resonant part. The integrals are taken over the range of values $\boldsymbol{p}$ and $\boldsymbol{p}'$ such that $(\boldsymbol{k} \cdot \boldsymbol{v}) \ll \omega$ and $(\boldsymbol{k} \cdot \boldsymbol{v}') \ll \omega$. This part then takes into account the contribution from slow particles which do not interact with the waves. By virtue of the condition (14.19) one can put

$$\lim_{\Delta \to 0} \Delta \int g_{ab}(\boldsymbol{k}, \boldsymbol{p}, \boldsymbol{p}')\, d^3\boldsymbol{p}\, d^3\boldsymbol{p}' = 0,$$

and this term therefore drops out.

The second part is the resonant part. In this case

$$\omega \sim (\boldsymbol{k}\cdot\boldsymbol{v}), \quad \omega \sim (\boldsymbol{k}\cdot\boldsymbol{v}'),$$

i.e. the contribution from the particles having velocity close to the phase velocities of the waves arising in the plasma, is taken into account.

In this region

$$\lim_{\Delta \to 0} \frac{2\Delta}{(\omega-(\boldsymbol{k}\cdot\boldsymbol{v})+i\Delta)\,(\omega-(\boldsymbol{k}\cdot\boldsymbol{v}')-i\Delta)} = 2\pi\delta(\omega-(\boldsymbol{k}\cdot\boldsymbol{v}))\,\delta_{(\boldsymbol{k}\cdot\boldsymbol{v}),\,(\boldsymbol{k}\cdot\boldsymbol{v}')},$$

where $\delta_{(\boldsymbol{k}\cdot\boldsymbol{v}),\,(\boldsymbol{k}\cdot\boldsymbol{v}')}$ is Kronecker's symbol. The integral over this region in (16.23) may therefore be written as

$$2\pi \int \delta(\omega-(\boldsymbol{k}\cdot\boldsymbol{v}))\,\delta_{(\boldsymbol{k}\cdot\boldsymbol{v}),\,(\boldsymbol{k}\cdot\boldsymbol{v}')}\, g_{ab}(\boldsymbol{k}, \boldsymbol{p}, \boldsymbol{p}')\, d^3\boldsymbol{p}\, d^3\boldsymbol{p}'.$$

Thus, in this integral the contribution from the correlation function of the resonant particles is taken into account.

For slight non-stationarity it is presupposed, in particular, that the decrement (or increment) $\gamma(\boldsymbol{k})$ must be small, i.e. there are few resonant particles for which $\omega \sim (\boldsymbol{k}\cdot\boldsymbol{v})$.

For a few resonant particles the correlation between them can be ignored and then the integral over the resonant region also drops out.

Finally, the last part is the overlap region, the contribution of which is negligible too. This is readily seen by means of the isotropy condition.

As a result we obtain the following equation from (16.23);

$$\varepsilon'(\omega, \boldsymbol{k}, \mu t) \Big\{ (\delta\boldsymbol{E}\cdot\delta\boldsymbol{E})_{\omega,\, \boldsymbol{k},\, \mu t} - \sum_a \frac{(4\pi)^2 e_a^2 n_a}{k^2} \int \frac{2\pi\delta(\omega-(\boldsymbol{k}\cdot\boldsymbol{v}))\, f_a(\boldsymbol{p}, \mu t)}{|\varepsilon(\omega, \boldsymbol{k}, \mu t)|^2}\, d^3\boldsymbol{p} \Big\} = 0. \tag{16.24}$$

This equation implies that the spectral function $(\delta \boldsymbol{E} \cdot \delta \boldsymbol{E})_{\omega, \boldsymbol{k}, \mu t}$ can only differ from its stationary value (14.29) at frequencies $\omega(\boldsymbol{k})$ which satisfy the equation

$$\varepsilon'(\omega, \boldsymbol{k}, \mu t) = 0. \tag{16.25}$$

We now equate the imaginary parts of the equation formed by cross-multiplying (16.19) and (16.21).

We also multiply this equation by 2Δ and pass to the limit $\Delta \to 0$. We leave only terms of order μ and use eqn. (16.25). As a result we arrive at the equation:

$$\begin{aligned} \frac{\partial \varepsilon'}{\partial \omega} \cdot \frac{\partial}{\partial t} (\delta \boldsymbol{E} \cdot \delta \boldsymbol{E})^{\text{rad}}_{\omega, \boldsymbol{k}, \mu t} &= -2\left(\varepsilon'' + \frac{\partial}{\partial t} \cdot \frac{\partial \varepsilon'}{\partial \omega}\right) (\delta \boldsymbol{E} \cdot \delta \boldsymbol{E})^{\text{rad}}_{\omega, \boldsymbol{k}, \mu t} \\ &\quad - \lim_{\Delta \to 0} \operatorname{Re} \frac{4i\Delta}{\varepsilon^{-}(\omega, \boldsymbol{k}, \mu t)} \sum_{ab} \frac{(4\pi)^2 e_a e_b}{k^2} \\ &\quad \times \int \frac{(\delta N_a\, \delta N_b)_{\boldsymbol{k}, \mu t}}{(\omega - (\boldsymbol{k} \cdot \boldsymbol{v}) + i\Delta)(\omega - (\boldsymbol{k} \cdot \boldsymbol{v}') - i\Delta)} d^3\boldsymbol{p}\, d^3\boldsymbol{p}'. \end{aligned} \tag{16.26}$$

We divide by $\partial\varepsilon'/\partial\omega$, discard the integral with g_{ab} and have regard to the fact that

$$\operatorname{Re} \frac{-i}{\varepsilon^{-}(\omega, \boldsymbol{k}, \mu t)} = \pi \operatorname{sign} \frac{\partial \varepsilon'}{\partial \omega}\, \delta\big(\varepsilon'(\omega, \boldsymbol{k}, \mu t)\big). \tag{16.27}$$

To obtain this formula, it is necessary to expand the function $\varepsilon^{-}(\omega - i\Delta, \boldsymbol{k})$ in Δ and then use the expression

$$\lim_{\Delta \to 0} \frac{\dfrac{\Delta\, \partial \varepsilon'}{\partial \omega}}{\varepsilon'^2 + \Delta^2 \left(\dfrac{\partial \varepsilon'}{\partial \omega}\right)^2} = \pi \operatorname{sign} \frac{\partial \varepsilon'}{\partial \omega}\, \delta\big(\varepsilon'(\omega, \boldsymbol{k})\big).$$

After these transformations eqn. (16.26) becomes (below the parameter μ is omitted):

$$\frac{\partial}{\partial t}(\delta \boldsymbol{E} \cdot \delta \boldsymbol{E})^{\text{rad}}_{\omega, \boldsymbol{k}, t} = -2\gamma'(\omega, \boldsymbol{k}, t)(\delta \boldsymbol{E} \cdot \delta \boldsymbol{E})^{\text{rad}}_{\omega, \boldsymbol{k}, t}$$

$$+(2\pi)^2 \frac{\delta\big(\varepsilon'(\omega, \boldsymbol{k}, t)\big)}{\left|\dfrac{\partial \varepsilon'}{\partial \omega}\right|} \sum_a \frac{(4\pi)^2 e_a^2 n_a}{k^2} \int \delta(\omega - (\boldsymbol{k} \cdot \boldsymbol{v})) f_a \, d^3\boldsymbol{p}. \tag{16.28}$$

Here

$$\gamma' = \gamma + \frac{\partial}{\partial t} \ln \frac{\partial \varepsilon'}{\partial \omega}, \tag{16.29}$$

where γ is the damping decrement (16.22).

The second term in formula (16.29) takes into account the time variation of the function f_a. In some cases the second term in (16.29) can be neglected. For instance, if the roots of eqn. (16.25) are close to the plasma frequency, the relationship $\omega(\boldsymbol{k})$ is determined by the time variation of the density $n_a = \int f_a \, d^3\boldsymbol{p}$. In a spatially homogeneous plasma the n_a are constant and so $\partial\omega(\boldsymbol{k})/\partial t = 0$. In the following we drop the prime on γ', assuming that the second term in (16.29) is included in γ.

Also eqn. (16.28) takes the place in the radiation region of expression (14.29) for the spectral function $(\delta \boldsymbol{E} \cdot \delta \boldsymbol{E})_{\omega, \boldsymbol{k}}$.

We show now that the more complex spectral functions can be expressed in terms of the functions $(\delta \boldsymbol{E} \cdot \delta \boldsymbol{E})_{\omega, \boldsymbol{k}}$ and f_a. For this we return to eqn. (16.20).

We multiply the left- and right-hand sides of eqn. (16.20, 21). We then equate the real parts on the left and right, multiply by 2Δ and pass to the limit $\Delta \to 0$.

As a result, from the right-hand sides of (16.20, 21) we obtain the expression

$$\lim_{\Delta \to 0} \operatorname{Re} \frac{2\Delta i}{\varepsilon^-(\omega, \boldsymbol{k}, t)} \sum_b \frac{4\pi e_b \boldsymbol{k}}{k^2} \cdot$$

$$\times \int \frac{(\delta N_a \delta N_b)_{\boldsymbol{k}, t}}{\big(\omega - (\boldsymbol{k} \cdot \boldsymbol{v}) + i\Delta\big)\big(\omega - (\boldsymbol{k} \cdot \boldsymbol{v}') - i\Delta\big)} d^3\boldsymbol{p}'. \tag{16.30}$$

This can be simplified if the state of the plasma differs little from equilibrium. In this case the term in (16.30) with the correlation function vanishes (see (14.27)) and so (16.30), when considered with (16.27), becomes

$$-8\pi^3 \operatorname{sign}\frac{\partial \varepsilon'}{\partial \omega}\,\delta(\varepsilon'(\omega, \boldsymbol{k}, t))\,\frac{e_a n_a}{k^2}\,\boldsymbol{k}\delta(\omega-(\boldsymbol{k}\cdot\boldsymbol{v}))f_a. \tag{16.31}$$

After the transformations we obtain two terms from the left-hand sides of eqn. (16.20, 21). The first is $\mathrm{Re}(\delta N_a \delta \boldsymbol{E})_{\omega, \boldsymbol{k}, t}$; the other is determined by the spectral function $(\delta \boldsymbol{E}\cdot\delta \boldsymbol{E})_{\omega, \boldsymbol{k}, t}$. We take it onto the right-hand side and so get the following expression for the real part of the spectral function $(\delta N_a \delta \boldsymbol{E})_{\omega, \boldsymbol{k}, t}$ in the radiation region:

$$\begin{aligned}\mathrm{Re}\,(\delta N_a\,\delta E_i)_{\omega\ \boldsymbol{k}, t} &= -e_a n_a \pi\delta(\omega-(\boldsymbol{k}\cdot\boldsymbol{v}))\,(\delta E_j\,\delta E_i)_{\omega, \boldsymbol{k}, t}\,\frac{\partial f_a}{\partial p_j}\\ &+\frac{1}{2}\cdot\frac{\partial}{\partial \omega}\cdot P\,\frac{e_a n_a}{\omega-(\boldsymbol{k}\cdot\boldsymbol{v})}\left[\frac{\partial}{\partial t}(\delta E_j \delta \boldsymbol{E})_{\omega, \boldsymbol{k}, t}\,\frac{\partial f_a}{\partial p_j}\right.\\ &\left.+2(\delta E_j \delta \boldsymbol{E})_{i\omega, \boldsymbol{k}, t}\,\frac{\partial^2 f_a}{\partial p_j\,\partial t}\right]\\ &-8\pi^3 \operatorname{sign}\frac{\partial \varepsilon'}{\partial \omega}\,\delta(\varepsilon'(\omega, \boldsymbol{k}, t))\,\frac{e_a n_a}{k^2}\,k_i\delta(\omega-(\boldsymbol{k}\cdot\boldsymbol{v}))f_a.\end{aligned} \tag{16.32}$$

By using (16.32) one can, of course, obtain eqn. (16.28).

Thus, in the non-stationary case, for the radiation region the spectral function $(\delta N_a \delta \boldsymbol{E})_{\omega, \boldsymbol{k}, t}$ is not determined entirely by the functions f_a. It is also necessary to know the spectral function $(\delta \boldsymbol{E}\cdot\delta \boldsymbol{E})_{\omega, \boldsymbol{k}, t}$.

One can similarly express still more complex spectral functions in terms of f_a and $(\delta \boldsymbol{E}\cdot\delta \boldsymbol{E})_{\omega, \boldsymbol{k}, t}$, for example, the function $(\delta N_a \delta N_b)_{\omega, \boldsymbol{k}, t}$.

In the next section we shall see that for the functions f_a and $(\delta \boldsymbol{E}\cdot\delta \boldsymbol{E})^{\mathrm{rad}}_{\omega, \boldsymbol{k}, t}$ we are able to obtain a closed set of equations which generalizes the set of kinetic equations for f_a (see §§ 11 and 13) to the case when it is necessary to consider the radiation.

Using the solution of this set of equations, and by making the same assumptions, we can find the spectral function for any characteristic of a plasma.

A very interesting case is that when only two roots of identical magnitude of the dispersion equation (16.25) are important. Any spectral functions of a plasma may then be expressed in terms of the functions f_a and the spatial spectral function $(\delta\boldsymbol{E}\cdot\delta\boldsymbol{E})^{\text{rad}}_{\boldsymbol{k},t}$.

To show this, we represent the function $\delta\boldsymbol{E}(\boldsymbol{k}, t)$ for the radiation region in the form of (16.8).

Substituting (16.8) into the expression for the space–time spectral function

$$(2\pi)^3\,\delta(\boldsymbol{k}-\boldsymbol{k}')\,(\delta\boldsymbol{E}\cdot\delta\boldsymbol{E})^{\text{rad}}_{\omega,\boldsymbol{k},t} = \int \overline{\delta\boldsymbol{E}(\boldsymbol{k}, t+\tau)\,\delta\boldsymbol{E}(\boldsymbol{k}', t)} \times e^{i\omega\tau}\,d\tau, \tag{16.33}$$

we average it over in the interval $T\sim 1/\Delta$.

Leaving the principal terms, after integrating over t and τ, and then cancelling by $(2\pi)^3\,\delta(\boldsymbol{k}-\boldsymbol{k}')$ we obtain:

$$(\delta\boldsymbol{E}\cdot\delta\boldsymbol{E})^{\text{rad}}_{\omega,\boldsymbol{k},t} = 2\pi\sum_{l}\delta(\omega-\omega^{l}_{\boldsymbol{k}})\,(\delta\boldsymbol{E}^{l}\cdot\delta\boldsymbol{E}^{l})_{\boldsymbol{k},t}. \tag{16.34}$$

Considering the two identical roots when $\omega' = \pm\omega_k$, we find that

$$2(\delta\boldsymbol{E}^{l}\cdot\delta\boldsymbol{E}^{l})_{\boldsymbol{k},t} = \frac{1}{2\pi}\int(\delta\boldsymbol{E}\cdot\delta\boldsymbol{E})^{\text{rad}}_{\omega,\boldsymbol{k},t}\,d\omega = (\delta\boldsymbol{E}\cdot\delta\boldsymbol{E})^{\text{rad}}_{\boldsymbol{k},t}, \tag{16.35}$$

$$(\delta\boldsymbol{E}\cdot\delta\boldsymbol{E})^{\text{rad}}_{\omega,\boldsymbol{k},t} = 2\pi\,\frac{\delta(\omega-\omega_{\boldsymbol{k}})+\delta(\omega+\omega_{\boldsymbol{k}})}{2}\,(\delta\boldsymbol{E}\cdot\delta\boldsymbol{E})^{\text{rad}}_{\boldsymbol{k},t}. \tag{16.36}$$

It follows from (16.35) that the function $(\delta\boldsymbol{E}\cdot\delta\boldsymbol{E})^{\text{rad}}_{\boldsymbol{k},t}$ is the spatial spectral function for the radiation region.

Substituting (16.36) into (16.32), we express the spectral function $(\delta N_a\delta\boldsymbol{E})_{\omega,\boldsymbol{k},t}$ in terms of the functions f_a and $(\delta\boldsymbol{E}\cdot\delta\boldsymbol{E})^{\text{rad}}_{\boldsymbol{k},t}$. The most general spectral function $(\delta N_a\delta N_b)_{\omega,\boldsymbol{k},t}$ is also expressible in terms of these functions too.

Though the function $(\delta\boldsymbol{E}\cdot\delta\boldsymbol{E})_{\boldsymbol{k},t}$ is expressible through the first distribution functions f_a for the collision region (see (14.37)), the radiation region's function $(\delta\boldsymbol{E}\cdot\delta\boldsymbol{E})^{\text{rad}}_{\boldsymbol{k},t}$ in the non-stationary case is not expressible through f_a. Substituting the expression

(16.36) into (16.28) and performing integration over ω, the equation for $(\delta\boldsymbol{E}\cdot\delta\boldsymbol{E})^{\text{rad}}_{\boldsymbol{k},t}$ is

$$\frac{\partial}{\partial t}(\delta\boldsymbol{E}\cdot\delta\boldsymbol{E})^{\text{rad}}_{\boldsymbol{k},t} = -2\gamma(\omega_{\boldsymbol{k}},\boldsymbol{k})(\delta\boldsymbol{E}\cdot\delta\boldsymbol{E})^{\text{rad}}_{\boldsymbol{k},t}$$

$$+\pi\sum_a \frac{(4\pi)^2 e_a^2 n_a}{k^2}\omega_{\boldsymbol{k}}^2 \int \delta(\omega_{\boldsymbol{k}}-(\boldsymbol{k}\cdot\boldsymbol{v}))f_a\,d^3\boldsymbol{p}. \tag{16.37}$$

In the last term it is taken into account that

$$\delta(\varepsilon'(\omega,\boldsymbol{k})) = |\omega|\frac{\delta(\omega-\omega_{\boldsymbol{k}})+\delta(\omega+\omega_{\boldsymbol{k}})}{2};$$

$$\left|\frac{\partial\varepsilon'}{\partial\omega}\right| = \frac{2}{\omega_{\boldsymbol{k}}}.$$

This is not a closed equation since it contains the functions f_a. The closed set for $(\delta\boldsymbol{E}\cdot\delta\boldsymbol{E})^{\text{rad}}_{\boldsymbol{k},t}$ and f_a is formed in the next section.

The foregoing results may be generalized without difficulty to the case of a relativistic plasma. The relevant results are given elsewhere [Klimontovich, 1961, 1963].

It is very important to take non-stationarity into account when an external magnetic field is present. So as not to encumber the exposition by complicated formulae, we give the relevant results for a Coulomb plasma.

Using the foregoing method, the expression for the spectral function $(\delta\boldsymbol{E}\cdot\delta\boldsymbol{E})^{\text{rad}}_{\omega,\boldsymbol{k},t}$ is

$$\frac{\partial}{\partial t}(\delta\boldsymbol{E}\cdot\delta\boldsymbol{E})^{\text{rad}}_{\omega,\boldsymbol{k},t} = -2\gamma(\omega,\boldsymbol{k},t)(\delta\boldsymbol{E}\cdot\delta\boldsymbol{E})^{\text{rad}}_{\omega,\boldsymbol{k},t}$$

$$+(2\pi)^2\frac{\delta(\varepsilon'(\omega,\boldsymbol{k}))}{\left|\frac{\partial\varepsilon'}{\partial\omega}\right|}\sum_a\frac{(4\pi)^2e_a^2n_a}{k^2}\sum_a\int 2\pi p^{\perp}\,dp^{\perp}\,dp^{\parallel}$$

$$\times I_n^2\left(\frac{k^{\perp}v^{\perp}}{\Omega_a}\right)\delta(\omega-k^{\parallel}v^{\parallel}-n\Omega_a)f_a. \tag{16.38}$$

Here γ is the damping decrement connected with the dielectric constant by formula (16.22). The dielectric constant with a magnetic field present is determined by formula (15.20).

As when $\boldsymbol{B} = 0$, the spectral function $(\delta \boldsymbol{E} \cdot \delta \boldsymbol{E})^{\text{rad}}_{\omega, \boldsymbol{k}, t}$ for a fixed value of the vector $\boldsymbol{k}$ is non-zero at frequencies which satisfy the dispersion equation (16.9).

If we can confine ourselves to the two roots of the dispersion equation (16.9), by using formula (16.36) an equation for the spatial spectral function $(\delta \boldsymbol{E} \cdot \delta \boldsymbol{E})^{\text{rad}}_{\boldsymbol{k}, t}$ can be obtained from (16.38).

As when $\boldsymbol{B} = 0$, the spectral function $(\delta N_a \delta \boldsymbol{E})_{\omega, \boldsymbol{k}, t}$ is expressible in terms of the functions $(\delta \boldsymbol{E} \cdot \delta \boldsymbol{E})_{\omega, \boldsymbol{k}, t}$ and f_a.

We now show that a closed set of equations can be obtained for these functions.

17. Allowing for Radiation in the Kinetic Equations. Set of Equations for the First Distribution Functions and for the Spectral Field Function†

We begin with the case of a Coulomb plasma.

We obtain firstly the equations for the functions f_a. We substitute into (11.3) the expression for the real part of the spectral function $(\delta N_a \delta \boldsymbol{E})_{\boldsymbol{k}, t}$ and represent it as the sum of the two parts relating to the "collision" region and radiation region respectively:

$$\operatorname{Re} (\delta N_a \delta \boldsymbol{E})_{\boldsymbol{k}, t} = \operatorname{Re} (\delta N_a \delta \boldsymbol{E})^{\text{coll}}_{\boldsymbol{k}, t} + \operatorname{Re} (\delta N_a \delta \boldsymbol{E})^{\text{rad}}_{\boldsymbol{k}, t}. \tag{17.1}$$

The first term on the right-hand side of (17.1) is determined by (10.35); the other comes from (16.32) by integrating‡ over ω:

$$\operatorname{Re} (\delta N_a \delta \boldsymbol{E})^{\text{rad}}_{\boldsymbol{k}, t} = -4\pi^2 e_a n_a \frac{\boldsymbol{k}}{k^2} B((\boldsymbol{k} \cdot \boldsymbol{v}) \cdot \boldsymbol{k}) f_a - \frac{e_a n_a \boldsymbol{k}}{2\pi k^2}$$
$$\times \int \Big[\pi \delta(\omega - (\boldsymbol{k} \cdot \boldsymbol{v})) (\delta \boldsymbol{E} \cdot \delta \boldsymbol{E})_{\omega, \boldsymbol{k}, t}$$
$$- \frac{1}{2} \cdot \frac{\partial}{\partial \omega} P \frac{1}{\omega - (\boldsymbol{k} \cdot \boldsymbol{v})} \frac{\partial (\delta \boldsymbol{E} \cdot \delta \boldsymbol{E})_{\omega, \boldsymbol{k}, t}}{\partial t} \Big] \left(\boldsymbol{k} \cdot \frac{\partial f_a}{\partial \boldsymbol{p}} \right) d\omega. \tag{17.2}$$

We introduced the notation

$$B(\omega, \boldsymbol{k}) = \operatorname{sign} \frac{\partial \varepsilon'}{\partial \omega} \delta(\varepsilon'(\omega, \boldsymbol{k})). \tag{17.3}$$

† Klimontovich (1959, 1962, 1963a, 1963b).

‡ In §§ 17 and 22 for simplicity terms containing the time derivatives $\partial f_a / \partial t$ and $\partial \varepsilon'(\omega, \boldsymbol{k}) / \partial t$ are omitted.

Substituting into (11.3) the expression thus found for $\mathrm{Re}(\delta N_a \delta \boldsymbol{E})_{\boldsymbol{k}, t}$, we get

$$\frac{\partial f_a}{\partial t} = \frac{\partial}{\partial p_i} D^a_{ij} \frac{\partial f_a}{\partial p_j} + \frac{\partial}{\partial p_i} (A^a_i f_a). \tag{17.4}$$

This equation differs from (11.3, 6) in that now the coefficients D^a_{ij} and A^a_i each consist of two parts:

$$D^a_{ij} = D^{(a)\,\mathrm{coll}}_{ij} + D^{(a)\,\mathrm{rad}}_{ij}, \tag{17.5}$$

$$A^a_i = A^{(a)\,\mathrm{coll}}_i + A^{(a)\,\mathrm{rad}}_i. \tag{17.6}$$

The first terms on the right-hand sides of these expressions refer to the "collision" region. They are determined by the expressions (11.7, 8) in which the integration is over $\boldsymbol{k}$ in the collision region (stop band) and the decrements are much greater than the collision frequency:

$$\gamma(\boldsymbol{k}) \gg \frac{1}{\tau_r},$$

The $D^{(a)\,\mathrm{rad}}_{ij}$ and $A^{(a)\,\mathrm{rad}}_i$ describe the contribution to the diffusion and friction coefficients in momentum space from the radiation region.

Using (17.2), the expressions for these factors are:

$$D^{(a)\,\mathrm{rad}}_{ij} = \frac{e_a^2}{16\pi^3} \int \frac{k_i k_j}{k^2} \delta(\omega - (\boldsymbol{k}\cdot\boldsymbol{v}))\, (\delta\boldsymbol{E}\cdot\delta\boldsymbol{E})^{\mathrm{rad}}_{\omega, \boldsymbol{k}, t}\, d\omega\, d^3\boldsymbol{k}$$

$$- \frac{e_a^2}{32\pi^4} \int \frac{k_i k_j}{k^2} \cdot \frac{\partial}{\partial\omega} \left(P \frac{1}{\omega - (\boldsymbol{k}\cdot\boldsymbol{v})} \right) \frac{\partial}{\partial t} (\delta\boldsymbol{E}\cdot\delta\boldsymbol{E})^{\mathrm{rad}}_{\omega, \boldsymbol{k}, t}\, d\omega d^3\boldsymbol{k} \tag{17.7}$$

$$A^{(a)\,\mathrm{rad}}_i = \frac{e_a^2}{2\pi} \int \frac{k_i}{k^2} B((\boldsymbol{k}\cdot\boldsymbol{v})\cdot\boldsymbol{k})\, d^3\boldsymbol{k}. \tag{17.8}$$

Equations (17.4) for the f_a with factors (17.5, 6) defined by (11.7, 8) and (17.7, 8), are not closed equations, since (17.7) contains the function $(\delta\boldsymbol{E}\cdot\delta\boldsymbol{E})_{\omega, \boldsymbol{k}, t}$, which is not expressed in terms of the f_a. To form a closed set of equations, it is further necessary to use eqn. (16.28) for the function $(\delta\boldsymbol{E}\cdot\delta\boldsymbol{E})^{\mathrm{rad}}_{\omega, \boldsymbol{k}, t}$.

Equations (17.4) and (16.28) for the f_a and $(\delta\boldsymbol{E}\cdot\delta\boldsymbol{E})^{\mathrm{rad}}_{\omega, \boldsymbol{k}, t}$ with coefficients (11.7, 8) and (17.7, 8) can be used as the initial set to describe nonequilibrium processes in a homogeneous Coulomb plasma with regard to the radiation of longitudinal waves. If the contribution of the radiation region is neglected, this set coincides with the kinetic equations (11.3, 6).

The integration over ω in (17.7) can be replaced by summation over the roots of eqn. (16.25). Substituting the expression (16.34) into (17.7) and integrating over ω, we get

$$D_{ij}^{(a)\,\mathrm{rad}} = \frac{e_a^2}{8\pi^2}\sum_l \int \frac{k_i k_j}{k^2}\,\delta(\omega_{\boldsymbol{k}}^l-(\boldsymbol{k}\cdot\boldsymbol{v}))\,(\delta\boldsymbol{E}^l\cdot\delta\boldsymbol{E}^l)_{\boldsymbol{k},t}\,d^3\boldsymbol{k}$$

$$-\frac{e_a^2}{16\pi^3}\sum_l \frac{k_i k_j}{k^2}\,\frac{\partial}{\partial\omega_l}\left(P\frac{1}{\omega_l-(\boldsymbol{k}\cdot\boldsymbol{v})}\right)\frac{\partial}{\partial t}(\delta\boldsymbol{E}^l\cdot\delta\boldsymbol{E}^l)_{\boldsymbol{k},t}\,d^3\boldsymbol{k}. \tag{17.9a}$$

Confining ourselves to the two roots of (16.25) for fixed $\boldsymbol{k}$ in the isotropic case when

$$|\omega_{\boldsymbol{k}}^1| = |\omega_{\boldsymbol{k}}^2| = \omega_{\boldsymbol{k}} \quad \text{and} \quad D_{ij}^a(\boldsymbol{p}) = D_{ij}^a(-\boldsymbol{p}),$$

the expression (17.9) can be written as

$$D_{ij}^{(a)\,\mathrm{rad}} = \frac{e_a^2}{8\pi^2}\int \frac{k_i k_j}{k^2}\,\delta(\omega_{\boldsymbol{k}}-(\boldsymbol{k}\cdot\boldsymbol{v}))\,(\delta\boldsymbol{E}\cdot\delta\boldsymbol{E})_{\boldsymbol{k},t}^{\mathrm{rad}}\,d^3\boldsymbol{k}$$

$$-\frac{e_a^2}{32\pi^3}\int \frac{k_i k_j}{k^2}\sum_{l=1,2}\frac{\partial}{\partial\omega_{\boldsymbol{k}}^l}\left(P\frac{1}{\omega_{\boldsymbol{k}}^l-(\boldsymbol{k}\cdot\boldsymbol{v})}\right)\frac{\partial}{\partial t}(\delta\boldsymbol{E}\cdot\delta\boldsymbol{E})_{\boldsymbol{k},t}^{\mathrm{rad}}\,d^3\boldsymbol{k} \tag{17.9}$$

Here it is assumed that $(\delta\boldsymbol{E}^l\cdot\delta\boldsymbol{E}^l)_{\boldsymbol{k},t} = \frac{1}{2}(\delta\boldsymbol{E}\cdot\delta\boldsymbol{E})_{\boldsymbol{k},t}^{\mathrm{rad}}$ if $l = 1, 2$.

The first term in (17.9) can be written as

$$\frac{e_a^2}{8\pi^2}\int \frac{k_i k_j}{k^2}\cdot\frac{B((\boldsymbol{k}\cdot\boldsymbol{v})\cdot\boldsymbol{k})}{(\boldsymbol{k}\cdot\boldsymbol{v})}\,(\delta\boldsymbol{E}\cdot\delta\boldsymbol{E})_{\boldsymbol{k},t}^{\mathrm{rad}}\,d^3\boldsymbol{k},$$

considering that for two roots the function (17.3) is

$$B(\omega,\boldsymbol{k}) = \omega\,\frac{(\delta(\omega-\omega_{\boldsymbol{k}})+\delta(\omega+\omega_{\boldsymbol{k}}))}{2}. \tag{17.10}$$

To close the set of equations when only two roots are taken into account, the simpler equation (16.37) for the function $(\delta\boldsymbol{E}\cdot\delta\boldsymbol{E})_{\boldsymbol{k},t}$ can be used instead of (16.28).

Substituting into (16.37) the expression for the damping decrement

$$\gamma(\omega_{\boldsymbol{k}}, \boldsymbol{k}) = -\frac{\pi}{2}\sum_a \frac{4\pi e_a^2 n_a}{k^2}\omega_{\boldsymbol{k}} \int \delta(\omega_{\boldsymbol{k}} - (\boldsymbol{k}\cdot\boldsymbol{v})) \times\left(\boldsymbol{k}\cdot\frac{\partial f_a}{\partial \boldsymbol{p}}\right) d^3\boldsymbol{p}, \tag{17.11}$$

and using (17.10), eqn. (16.37) becomes

$$\frac{\partial}{\partial t}(\delta\boldsymbol{E}\cdot\delta\boldsymbol{E})^{\text{rad}}_{\boldsymbol{k},t} = \pi\sum_a \frac{(4\pi)^2 e_a^2 n_a}{k^2}\int\left[\left(\boldsymbol{k}\cdot\frac{\partial f_a}{\partial \boldsymbol{p}}\right)\frac{(\delta\boldsymbol{E}\cdot\delta\boldsymbol{E})_{\boldsymbol{k},t}}{4\pi} + (\boldsymbol{k}\cdot\boldsymbol{v})f_a B((\boldsymbol{k}\cdot\boldsymbol{v})\cdot\boldsymbol{k})\right] d^3\boldsymbol{p}. \tag{17.12}$$

Let us now consider some properties of this set of equations. We start with the simpler equations (17.4, 12) for f_a and $(\delta\boldsymbol{E}\cdot\delta\boldsymbol{E})^{\text{rad}}_{\boldsymbol{k},t}$.

In the equilibrium case the solution of this set is

$$f_a = \frac{1}{(2\pi m_a \varkappa T_a)^{\frac{3}{2}}}\exp\left(-\frac{p^2}{2m_a\varkappa T}\right);$$

$$(\delta\boldsymbol{E}\cdot\delta\boldsymbol{E})^{\text{rad}}_{\boldsymbol{k},t} = 4\pi\varkappa T. \tag{17.13}$$

Thus, in the equilibrium case the velocity distribution is a Maxwell distribution, and so the radiation temperature,

$$\varkappa T^{\text{rad}}_{\boldsymbol{k}} \equiv \frac{(\delta\boldsymbol{E}\cdot\delta\boldsymbol{E})^{\text{rad}}_{\boldsymbol{k}}}{4\pi}, \tag{17.14}$$

is the same as the temperature of the particles.

The Maxwell distribution separately turns to zero the terms on the right-hand side of (17.4) describing the "collisions" of the charged particles and the radiation respectively. These two processes may have different relaxation times.

Consider the equilibrium solution of the more general set of equations (17.4) and (16.28). From (16.28) it follows that in the equilibrium case the function $(\delta\boldsymbol{E}\cdot\delta\boldsymbol{E})^{\text{rad}}_{\omega,\boldsymbol{k}}$ is determined by the expression

$$(\delta\boldsymbol{E}\cdot\delta\boldsymbol{E})^{\text{rad}}_{\omega,\boldsymbol{k}} = \frac{8\pi^2}{\omega}\,\text{sign}\frac{\partial\varepsilon'}{\partial\omega}\,\delta(\varepsilon'(\omega,\boldsymbol{k}))\varkappa T. \tag{17.15}$$

Formula (16.22) was used in obtaining this result. For the two roots of (16.25) the expression (17.15) coincides with (14.50)

Clearly, the right-hand side of eqn. (17.4) with the coefficients (11.7, 8) and (17.7, 8) vanishes when f_a is a Maxwell distribution, and $(\delta \boldsymbol{E} \cdot \delta \boldsymbol{E})^{\text{rad}}_{\omega, \boldsymbol{k}}$ is determined by (17.15).

If the radiation temperature $T^{\text{rad}}_{\boldsymbol{k}}$ is constant, the second term in expressions (17.7, 9) vanishes. When the two roots $\boldsymbol{k}$ are taken into account the expressions (17.9, 8) for $D^{(a)\,\text{rad}}_{ij}$ and $A^{(a)\,\text{rad}}_{i}$ can be written as

$$D^{(a)\,\text{rad}}_{ij} = \frac{e_a^2}{2\pi} \int \varkappa T^{\text{rad}}_{k} \frac{k_i k_j}{k^2} \delta(\omega_{\boldsymbol{k}} - (\boldsymbol{k} \cdot \boldsymbol{v}))\, d^3\boldsymbol{k},$$

$$T^{\text{rad}}_{k} = \text{const};$$

$$A^{(a)\,\text{rad}}_{ij} = \frac{e_a^2}{2\pi} \int \frac{k_i}{k^2} (\boldsymbol{k} \cdot \boldsymbol{v})\, \delta(\omega_{\boldsymbol{k}} - (\boldsymbol{k} \cdot \boldsymbol{v}))\, d^3\boldsymbol{k}. \tag{17.16}$$

The equations (17.4) and (16.28) for f_a and $(\delta \boldsymbol{E} \cdot \delta \boldsymbol{E})^{\text{rad}}_{\omega, \boldsymbol{k}, t}$ yield the law of the conservation of the total energy of a plasma

$$W = \sum_a n_a \int \frac{p^2}{2m_a} f_a\, d^3\boldsymbol{p} + \frac{1}{(2\pi)^4} \int \frac{(\delta \boldsymbol{E} \cdot \delta \boldsymbol{E})^{\text{rad}}_{\omega, \boldsymbol{k}, t}}{8\pi}\, d\omega\, d^3\boldsymbol{k}. \tag{17.17}$$

By using the formula

$$(\delta \boldsymbol{E} \cdot \delta \boldsymbol{E})^{\text{rad}}_{\boldsymbol{k}, t} = \frac{1}{2\pi} \int (\delta \boldsymbol{E} \cdot \delta \boldsymbol{E})^{\text{rad}}_{\omega, \boldsymbol{k}, t}\, d\omega,$$

the expression (17.17) can be written as

$$W = \sum_a n_a \int \frac{p^2}{2m_a} f_a\, d^3\boldsymbol{p} + \frac{1}{(2\pi)^3} \int \frac{(\delta \boldsymbol{E} \cdot \delta \boldsymbol{E})^{\text{rad}}_{\boldsymbol{k}}}{8\pi}\, d^3\boldsymbol{k}. \tag{17.18}$$

The integration over $\boldsymbol{k}$ is carried out over the radiation region.

If the radiation is not taken into account in the kinetic equations, and we confine ourselves to the "collisions" (see § 11), instead of (17.17, 18), we get

$$W = \sum_a n_a \int \frac{p^2}{2m_a} f_a\, d^3\boldsymbol{p} = \text{const}.$$

For a relativistic plasma also one can form a closed set of equations for f_a and $(\delta \boldsymbol{E} \cdot \delta \boldsymbol{E})_{\omega, \boldsymbol{k}}$.

Also in this case the equations for f_a can be written as (17.4). Here the coefficients $D_{ij}^{(a)\,\text{coll}}$ and $A_i^{(a)\,\text{coll}}$ are found by the formulae (13.39, 40), whilst for $D_{ij}^{(a)\,\text{rad}}$ and $A_i^{(a)\,\text{rad}}$ we have:

$$D_{ij}^{(a)\,\text{rad}} = \frac{e_a^2}{16\pi^3}\int \delta(\omega-(\boldsymbol{k}\cdot\boldsymbol{v}))\,(\delta E_i\delta E_j)^{\text{rad}}_{\omega,\boldsymbol{k},t}\,d\omega\,d^3\boldsymbol{k}$$

$$-\frac{e_a^2}{32\pi^4}\int \frac{\partial}{\partial\omega}\left(P\frac{1}{\omega-(\boldsymbol{k}\cdot\boldsymbol{v})}\right)\frac{\partial}{\partial t}(\delta E_i\delta E_j)^{\text{rad}}_{\omega,\boldsymbol{k},t}\,d\omega\,d^3\boldsymbol{k};\tag{17.19}$$

$$A_i^{(a)\,\text{rad}} = \frac{e_a^2}{2\pi}\int\left(\frac{k_i}{k^2}B^{\parallel}((\boldsymbol{k}\cdot\boldsymbol{v})\cdot\boldsymbol{k})\right.$$

$$\left.+\frac{(\boldsymbol{k}\cdot\boldsymbol{v})\,[[\boldsymbol{k}\wedge\boldsymbol{v}]\wedge\boldsymbol{k}]_i}{k^2}B^{\perp}((\boldsymbol{k}\cdot\boldsymbol{v})\cdot\boldsymbol{k})\right)d^3\boldsymbol{k}.\tag{17.20}$$

As in § 14, the spectral function of the electric field strengths for the radiation region

$$(\delta E_i\delta E_j)^{\text{rad}}_{\omega,\boldsymbol{k},t} = \frac{k_ik_j}{k^2}(\delta\boldsymbol{E}^{\parallel}\cdot\delta\boldsymbol{E}^{\parallel})^{\text{rad}}_{\omega,\boldsymbol{k},t}$$

$$+\frac{1}{2}\left(\delta_{ij}-\frac{k_ik_j}{k^2}\right)(\delta\boldsymbol{E}^{\perp}\cdot\delta\boldsymbol{E}^{\perp})^{\text{rad}}_{\omega,\boldsymbol{k},t}\tag{17.21}$$

consists of two parts, the first being determined by the longitudinal electric field, and the other by the transverse electric field.

Having regard only to two roots of the equations

$$\text{Re}\,\varepsilon^{\parallel}(\omega,\boldsymbol{k}) = 0,\quad \omega^2\,\text{Re}\,\varepsilon^{\perp}(\omega,\boldsymbol{k})-c^2k^2 = 0\tag{17.22}$$

we have:

$$(\delta\boldsymbol{E}^{\parallel}\cdot\delta\boldsymbol{E}^{\parallel})^{\text{rad}}_{\omega,\boldsymbol{k}} = 2\pi\frac{\delta(\omega-\omega_{\boldsymbol{k}})+\delta(\omega+\omega_{\boldsymbol{k}})}{2}(\delta\boldsymbol{E}^{\parallel}\cdot\delta\boldsymbol{E}^{\parallel})^{\text{rad}}_{\boldsymbol{k},t};\tag{17.23}$$

$$(\delta\boldsymbol{E}^{\perp}\cdot\delta\boldsymbol{E}^{\perp})^{\text{rad}}_{\omega,\boldsymbol{k}} = 2\pi\frac{\delta(\omega-\omega_{\boldsymbol{k}})+\delta(\omega+\omega_{\boldsymbol{k}})}{2}(\delta\boldsymbol{E}^{\perp}\cdot\delta\boldsymbol{E}^{\perp})^{\text{rad}}_{\boldsymbol{k},t}\tag{17.24}$$

The diffusion can therefore be expressed in terms of the spatial spectral functions of the longitudinal and transverse fields.

The function $B^{\parallel}$ $(\omega, \boldsymbol{k})$ in (17.20) is given by (17.3), and the function $B^{\perp}$ $(\omega, \boldsymbol{k})$ by the analogous formula

$$B^{\perp}(\omega,\boldsymbol{k}) = \text{sign}\frac{\partial\varepsilon^{\perp}}{\partial\omega}\,\delta(\omega^2\varepsilon^{\perp}(\omega,\boldsymbol{k})-c^2k^2).\tag{17.25}$$

If just two roots of each equation of (17.22), are taken into account, the function $B^{\parallel}(\omega, \boldsymbol{k})$ is given by (17.10), whilst

$$B^{\perp}(\omega, \boldsymbol{k}) = \frac{\delta(\omega-\omega_{\boldsymbol{k}})+\delta(\omega+\omega_{\boldsymbol{k}})}{2\omega}; \quad \omega_{\boldsymbol{k}}^2 = \omega_{\mathrm{L}}^2+c^2k^2. \tag{17.26}$$

The spectral function of the magnetic field strength is found by the expression

$$(\delta B_i \delta B_j)_{\omega, \boldsymbol{k}, t} = \frac{c^2k^2}{\omega^2}(\delta E_i^{\perp}\delta E_j^{\perp})_{\omega, \boldsymbol{k}}. \tag{17.27}$$

If formula (17.24) is used, then (17.27) yields the following expression for the spatial spectral function $(\delta B_i \delta B_j)_{\boldsymbol{k}, t}$:

$$(\delta B_i \delta B_j)_{\boldsymbol{k}, t} = \frac{c^2k^2}{\omega_{\mathrm{L}}^2+c^2k^2}(\delta E_i^{\perp}\delta E_j^{\perp})_{\boldsymbol{k}, t}. \tag{17.28}$$

To obtain a closed set of equations, it is further necessary to use the equations for the spectral functions of the field strengths as well as the equations for f_a.

The equation for $(\delta \boldsymbol{E}^{\parallel}\cdot\delta \boldsymbol{E}^{\parallel})_{\omega, \boldsymbol{k}, t}$ and that for $(\delta \boldsymbol{E}^{\parallel}\cdot\delta \boldsymbol{E}^{\parallel})_{\boldsymbol{k}, t}$ coincide with (16.28) and (17.12) respectively.

No equations can be written for $(\delta \boldsymbol{E}^{\perp}\cdot\delta \boldsymbol{E}^{\perp})^{\mathrm{rad}}_{\omega, \boldsymbol{k}, t}$ since unless an external field is present, in the approximation under consideration in the radiation region the transverse waves do not interact with the charged particles of the plasma. This is because the phase velocities of the transverse waves are greater than the speed of light.

So in the second term of (17.19) one can leave only the term $\partial(\delta \boldsymbol{E}^{\parallel}\cdot\delta \boldsymbol{E}^{\parallel})_{\omega, \boldsymbol{k}, t}/\partial t$.

In the equilibrium case the solution of the relativistic set of equations is determined by the formula (13.48) and the expressions

$$(\delta \boldsymbol{E}^{\parallel}\cdot\delta \boldsymbol{E}^{\parallel})_{\boldsymbol{k}, t} = 4\pi\varkappa T; \quad (\delta \boldsymbol{E}^{\perp}\cdot\delta \boldsymbol{E}^{\perp})_{\boldsymbol{k}, t} = 8\pi\varkappa T. \tag{17.29}$$

In the same way a closed set of equations can be formed for the f_a and $(\delta E_i \delta E_j)_{\omega, \boldsymbol{k}, t}$ when the plasma is in a constant magnetic field and allowing for slight spatial inhomogeneity of the plasma.

The set of equations for f_a and $(\delta \boldsymbol{E}\cdot\delta \boldsymbol{E})_{\omega, \boldsymbol{k}, t}$ enables weak turbulence in a plasma to be described.

The plasma is said to be turbulent when the intensity of the excitation in the plasma, as characterized by the function $(\delta\boldsymbol{E}\cdot\delta\boldsymbol{E})_{\omega,\,\boldsymbol{k}}$, is greater than at statistical equilibrium.

In the approximation under consideration the turbulence may be due to the initial conditions, or to kinetic instability when the damping decrement $\gamma_a(\omega_{\boldsymbol{k}}, \boldsymbol{k})$ of some component of the plasma becomes negative†.

As a second-moment approximation one can describe the turbulent states, the development of which is confined to the variation of the distribution functions f_a. Otherwise in the equations for f_a and $(\delta\boldsymbol{E}\cdot\delta\boldsymbol{E})_{\omega,\,\boldsymbol{k},\,t}$ one must have regard to the non-linear terms in $(\delta\boldsymbol{E}\cdot\delta\boldsymbol{E})_{\omega,\,\boldsymbol{k},\,t}$, i.e. the second-moment approximation is not sufficient (see § 18).

Two different approches are open to us.

One can solve the equations for the higher correlation functions g_{abc}, g_{abcd}, ..., or for the corresponding higher moments, as is done by several authors [Silin, 1964; Kadomtsev and Petiashvilli, 1963; Iordanskii and Kulikovskii, 1964a, 1964b. Kovrizhnykh and Tsytovich, 1964; and Gorbunov, Pustovalov and Silin, 1964].

Alternatively, the higher moments can be taken into account by the method considered in §§ 14–16. This can produce the result without solving complicated equations for the single-time correlation functions.

Instead of the approximate equations (5.31) for the random deviations δN_a and $\delta\boldsymbol{E}$ one needs to use the exact equation (5.22, 23). Additional terms then appear in eqns. (16.2, 4). On the right-hand side of (16.2)

$$-\frac{ie_a}{\omega-(\boldsymbol{k}\cdot\boldsymbol{v})+i\Delta}\left(\frac{\partial}{\partial\boldsymbol{p}}\cdot\delta\boldsymbol{I}^a(\omega,\boldsymbol{k},\boldsymbol{p})\right), \tag{17.30}$$

and on the right-hand side of (16.4)

$$-\sum_a\frac{4\pi e_a^2\boldsymbol{k}}{k^2}\int\frac{1}{\omega-(\boldsymbol{k}\cdot\boldsymbol{v})+i\Delta}\left(\frac{\partial}{\partial\boldsymbol{p}}\cdot\delta\boldsymbol{I}^a(\omega,\boldsymbol{k},\boldsymbol{p})\right)d^3\boldsymbol{p}. \tag{17.31}$$

† Leontovich (1963); Vedenov, Velikhov and Sagdeyev (1961); Vedenov and Velikhov (1963); Vedenov (1962); Drummond and Pines (1961); Shapiro (1963) and Karpman (1964).

In these expressions

$$\delta \boldsymbol{I}^a(\Omega, \boldsymbol{p}) = \int_0^\infty d\tau \int d^3q e^{-\Delta\tau + i(\omega\tau - (\boldsymbol{k}\cdot\boldsymbol{q}))}$$

$$[\delta N_a(\boldsymbol{q}, \boldsymbol{p}, t+\tau)\, \delta \boldsymbol{E}(\boldsymbol{q}, t+\tau) - \overline{\delta N_a(\boldsymbol{q}, \boldsymbol{p}, t+\tau)\, \delta \boldsymbol{E}(\boldsymbol{q}, t+\tau)}]$$

$$= \frac{1}{(2\pi)^4} \int d\Omega' [\delta N_a(\Omega', \boldsymbol{p})\, \delta \boldsymbol{E}^*(\Omega' - \Omega)$$

$$- \overline{\delta N_a(\Omega', \boldsymbol{p})\, \delta \boldsymbol{E}^*(\Omega' - \Omega)}], \qquad (17.32)$$

where $\Omega = \omega, \boldsymbol{k}$.

By allowing for these extra terms in the equations for $(\delta \boldsymbol{E} \cdot \delta \boldsymbol{E})_{\omega, \boldsymbol{k}, t}$ and $(\delta N_a \delta \boldsymbol{E})_{\omega, \boldsymbol{k}, t}$ new terms appear containing the function $(\delta \boldsymbol{I}^a \cdot \delta \boldsymbol{E})_{\omega, \boldsymbol{k}, t}$. By virtue of (17.32) this function is the third moment in δN_a and $\delta \boldsymbol{E}$. Thus the equations for the second moments are no longer closed.

Assuming that the higher moments are small, the method of successive approximations can be used. All the higher approximations are then expressed in terms of the first, as in §§ 14–17. The higher moments are taken into account in § 18.

18. "Quasilinear Approximation" for a Set of Equations with a Self-consistent Field. Allowing for Higher Moments

In § 17 in the second-moment approximation a set of equations was found for the functions $f_a(\boldsymbol{p}, t)$ and $(\delta \boldsymbol{E} \cdot \delta \boldsymbol{E})_{\omega, \boldsymbol{k}, t}$ which may serve for describing weakly non-equilibrium turbulent processes in a spatially homogeneous plasma.

As we have seen, in a spatially homogeneous plasma in the absence of external fields the average strengths of the electric and magnetic fields are zero. Consequently, the self-consistent (average) field drops out of the equations for the functions f_a and so the variation of the f_a with time in a spatially homogeneous plasma is completely determined by the correlations of the random deviations δN_a, $\delta \boldsymbol{E}$ and $\delta \boldsymbol{B}$.

In Chapter 3 the other extreme case was considered when the average fields are large and so the correlations could be neglected. Here Vlasov's set of self-consistent equations was used – a closed set of equations for the first moments of the random functions N_a, $\boldsymbol{E}$ and $\boldsymbol{B}$.

In the present section we shall show that a complex set of self-consistent field equations can under certain conditions be simplified for smoothed distribution functions and slowly varying complex amplitudes of electric field strength. Such a approximation is said to be "quasilinear" [Vedenov, Velikhov and Sagdeyev, 1961; Vedenov and Velikhov, 1963; Vedenov, 1962; Drummond and Pines, 1961; Shapiro, 1963; and Karpman, 1964.]

We shall also show how the equations of § 17 are affected by the higher moments.

In considering the self-consistent field equations, as previously in §§ 10, 11, 16 and 17 two regions are distinguishable, viz. the short-wave and long-wave regions. The former is analogous to the collision region, and the latter to the radiation region. In the self-consistent field approximation the short-wave excitations quickly decay and so in most cases they are of no interest. Here we shall consider only the long-wave spectral region.

In this region the plasma waves decay weakly. Hence, right from the start we assume that the functions f_a, $\boldsymbol{E}$ and $\boldsymbol{B}$, as functions of coordinates and time, depend on the fast and slow variables, i.e. for instance,

$$f_a = f_a(\mu t, \mu \boldsymbol{q}, t, \boldsymbol{q}, \boldsymbol{p}), \tag{18.1}$$

whilst for the fields we use formulae (2.95).

As elsewhere†, we split the functions f_a, $\boldsymbol{E}$ and $\boldsymbol{B}$ into "background" and "pulsations" (i. e. slow and quick variations):

$$\bar{f}_a = f_a(\mu t, \mu \boldsymbol{q}, \boldsymbol{p}) + F_a(\mu t, \mu \boldsymbol{q}, t, \boldsymbol{q}, \boldsymbol{p}); \tag{18.2}$$
$$\boldsymbol{E} = \boldsymbol{E} + \boldsymbol{E}_1; \quad \boldsymbol{B} = \boldsymbol{B} + \boldsymbol{B}_1.$$

The method of division depends on the type of problem. Here it is assumed that

$$\bar{f}_a = \frac{1}{TV} \int dt \int d^3\boldsymbol{q} f_a(\mu t, \mu \boldsymbol{q}, t, \boldsymbol{q}, \boldsymbol{p}). \tag{18.3}$$

† Vedenov, Velikhov and Sagdeyev (1961); Vedenov and Velikhov (1963); Vedenov (1962); Drummond and Pines (1961); Shapiro (1963) and Karpman (1964).

The T and V are selected such that

$$T\frac{\partial \bar{f}_a}{\partial \mu t} \ll \bar{f}_a; \quad V^{1/3}\left|\frac{\partial \bar{f}_a}{\partial \mu \boldsymbol{q}}\right| \ll \bar{f}_a \quad \text{and so on} \tag{18.4}$$

We confine ourselves to the case when $\overline{\boldsymbol{E}} = \overline{\boldsymbol{B}} = 0$. Then

$$\boldsymbol{E}_1 = \boldsymbol{E}; \quad \boldsymbol{B}_1 = \boldsymbol{B}. \tag{18.5}$$

From (6.8), after averaging over the fast variables, our equation for the smoothed distribution function is

$$\frac{\partial \bar{f}_a}{\partial t} + \left(\boldsymbol{v}\cdot\frac{\partial \bar{f}_a}{\partial \boldsymbol{q}}\right) = -\frac{e_a}{TV}\left(\frac{\partial}{\partial \boldsymbol{p}}\cdot\int F_a(\mu t, \mu \boldsymbol{q}, t, \boldsymbol{q}, \boldsymbol{p}) \times \mathscr{E}(\mu t, \mu \boldsymbol{q}, t, \boldsymbol{q})\right) dt\, d^3\boldsymbol{q} \equiv S_a. \tag{18.6}$$

As in § 2, the functions F_a, $\boldsymbol{E}$ and $\boldsymbol{B}$ are expanded as Fourier integrals in the fast variables, e.g.

$$F_a = \frac{1}{(2\pi)^4}\int F_a(\mu t, \mu \boldsymbol{q}, \omega, \boldsymbol{k})\, e^{-i(\omega t - (\boldsymbol{k}\cdot\boldsymbol{q}))}\, d\omega\, d^3\boldsymbol{k}; \tag{18.7}$$

for $\boldsymbol{E}$ and $\boldsymbol{B}$ we use the formulae (2.96, 97).

By these expansions the right-hand side of (18.6) becomes

$$S_a = -\frac{e_a}{(2\pi)^4 TV}\left(\frac{\partial}{\partial \boldsymbol{p}}\cdot\int \operatorname{Re} F_a(\mu t, \mu \boldsymbol{q}, \omega, \boldsymbol{k}, \boldsymbol{p}) \times \mathscr{E}^*(\mu t, \mu \boldsymbol{q}, \omega, \boldsymbol{k})\right) d\omega\, d^3\boldsymbol{k}. \tag{18.8}$$

Here we put

$$\mathscr{E} = \boldsymbol{E} + \frac{1}{c}\,[\boldsymbol{v}\wedge\boldsymbol{B}]. \tag{18.9}$$

If the function $\bar{f}_a$ is isotropic as regards $\boldsymbol{p}$, i.e. depends only on $|\boldsymbol{p}|$, in (18.8), the term containing the magnetic field drops out and so in place of $\mathscr{E}$ we have $\boldsymbol{E}$.

To obtain the equation for F_a, it is necessary to subtract (18.6) from (6.8). We then get

$$\frac{\partial F_a}{\partial t} + \left(\boldsymbol{v}\cdot\frac{\partial F_a}{\partial \boldsymbol{q}}\right) + e_a\left(\mathscr{E}\cdot\frac{\partial \bar{f}_a}{\partial \boldsymbol{p}}\right) = -e_a\left(\frac{\partial}{\partial \boldsymbol{p}}\cdot\left[F_a\mathscr{E} - \frac{1}{TV}\int F_a\mathscr{E}\, d^3\boldsymbol{q}\, dt. \tag{18.10}\right.\right.$$

The equations for $\boldsymbol{E}$ and $\boldsymbol{B}$ coincide with (6.9–12) by setting F_a for f_a. The resulting set of equations for $\bar{f}_a$, F_a, $\boldsymbol{E}$ and $\boldsymbol{B}$ is equivalent to the set of self-consistent field equations (6.8–12). For the sake of simplicity we expand the Fourier components of the functions F_a, $\boldsymbol{E}$ and $\boldsymbol{B}$ as series in the small parameter μ

$$F_a = \sum_{l=0}^{\infty} \mu^l F_a^{(l)}, \quad \boldsymbol{E} = \sum_{l=0}^{\infty} \mu^l \boldsymbol{E}^{(l)}, \quad \boldsymbol{B} = \sum_{l=0}^{\infty} \mu^{(l)} \boldsymbol{B}^{(l)}. \tag{18.11}$$

This presupposes that the functions $F_a^{(0)}$, $\boldsymbol{E}^{(0)}$ and $\boldsymbol{B}^{(0)}$ in the zero approximation are not in the general case small. We thus allow for $F_a \sim \bar{f}_a$ but the energy of the electromagnetic field is of the same order as the kinetic energy.

The terms of order μ are the first non-vanishing non-linear terms and also they are proportional to the number of resonant particles, e.g. the imaginary part of the dielectric constant tensor ε_{ij}.

An expression for ε_{ij} is obtainable, as usual, from linearized equations for F_a, $\boldsymbol{E}$ and $\boldsymbol{B}$. It becomes the same as (14.69) if we substitute $\bar{f}_a(\mu t, \mu \boldsymbol{q}, \boldsymbol{p})$ for f_a. So now the tensor ε_{ij} depends on the slow coordinates and time through the function $\bar{f}_a$.

Knowing the tensor ε_{ij}, one can immediately write the Maxwell equations in the zero approximation in μ, i.e. the equations for $\boldsymbol{E}^{(0)}$ and $\boldsymbol{B}^{(0)}$. Naturally, they coincide with (2.102, 103). From them it follows that in the zero approximation the strengths $\boldsymbol{E}^{(0)}$ and $\boldsymbol{B}^{(0)}$, as functions of ω, $\boldsymbol{k}$, are non-zero only for values of ω, $\boldsymbol{k}$ which satisfy the dispersion equation.

From (2.103) it follows that

$$\boldsymbol{B}^{(0)} = \frac{c}{\omega}[\boldsymbol{k} \wedge \boldsymbol{E}^{(0)}] = \frac{c}{\omega}[\boldsymbol{k} \wedge \boldsymbol{e}] E^{(0)}. \tag{18.12}$$

Here $\boldsymbol{e}$ is a unit vector in the $\boldsymbol{E}^{(0)}$ direction. Using this relation, the zero approximation equation can be written as

$$[\boldsymbol{k} \wedge [\boldsymbol{k} \wedge \boldsymbol{E}^{(0)}]]_i + \frac{\omega^2}{c^2} \varepsilon'_{ij} E_j^{(0)} = 0. \tag{18.13}$$

Substituting (18.12) into (18.9), we get

$$\mathscr{E}^{(0)} = \left(\boldsymbol{e} + \frac{1}{\omega} \wedge [\boldsymbol{v} \wedge [\boldsymbol{k} \wedge \boldsymbol{e}]]\right) E^{(0)}. \tag{18.14}$$

From (18.10) for the steady state in the linear approximation it follows that

$$F_a = -\frac{ie_a}{\omega-(\boldsymbol{k}\cdot\boldsymbol{v})}\left(\mathcal{E}^{(0)}\cdot\frac{\partial \bar{f}_a}{\partial \boldsymbol{p}}\right). \tag{18.15}$$

We use the expression

$$\frac{1}{\omega-(\boldsymbol{k}\cdot\boldsymbol{v})} = P\frac{1}{\omega-(\boldsymbol{k}\cdot\boldsymbol{v})} - i\pi\delta\left(\omega-(\boldsymbol{k}\cdot\boldsymbol{v})\right)$$

but remark that the term containing $\delta(\omega-(\boldsymbol{k}\cdot\boldsymbol{v}))$ is proportional to the number of resonant particles and so should relate to the first approximation. The resulting expression for F_a in the zero approximation in μ is

$$F_a^{(0)} = -ie_a P\frac{1}{\omega-(\boldsymbol{k}\cdot\boldsymbol{v})}\left(\mathcal{E}^{(0)}\cdot\frac{\partial \bar{f}_a}{\partial \boldsymbol{p}}\right). \tag{18.16}$$

Consider now the corresponding expression for the first approximation. We represent the function $F_a^{(1)}$ as two parts (linear and non-linear):

$$F_a^{(1)} = F_a^{\mathrm{l}} + F_a^{\mathrm{nl}}. \tag{18.17}$$

Using the method of §§ 2 and 16, the expression for the linear part F_a^{l} is

$$F_a^{\mathrm{l}} = -ie_a P\frac{1}{\omega-(\boldsymbol{k}\cdot\boldsymbol{v})}\left(\mathcal{E}^{(1)}\cdot\frac{\partial \bar{f}_a}{\partial \boldsymbol{p}}\right) - \pi e_a\delta\left(\omega-(\boldsymbol{k}\cdot\boldsymbol{v})\right)$$
$$\times\left(\mathcal{E}^{(0)}\cdot\frac{\partial \bar{f}_a}{\partial \boldsymbol{p}}\right) + e_a\left\{\frac{\partial}{\partial\omega}P\frac{1}{\omega-(\boldsymbol{k}\cdot\boldsymbol{v})}\cdot\frac{\partial}{\partial t}\right.$$
$$\left.-\left(\frac{\partial}{\partial \boldsymbol{k}}\cdot P\frac{1}{\omega-(\boldsymbol{k}\cdot\boldsymbol{v})}\cdot\frac{\partial}{\partial \boldsymbol{q}}\right)\right\}\left(\mathcal{E}^{(0)}\cdot\frac{\partial \bar{f}_a}{\partial \boldsymbol{p}}\right). \tag{18.18}$$

Here

$$\mathcal{E}^{(0)} = \left(\boldsymbol{e}+\frac{1}{\omega}[\boldsymbol{v}\wedge[\boldsymbol{k}\wedge\boldsymbol{e}]]\right)E^{(0)}, \quad \text{and so on.} \tag{18.19}$$

In (18.18) all the terms are of order μ. In this same approximation we find from (18.10) that

$$F_a^{\mathrm{nl}} = -\frac{ie_a}{(2\pi)^4}\cdot\frac{1}{\omega-(\boldsymbol{k}\cdot\boldsymbol{v})}\cdot\frac{\partial}{\partial p_j}\int d\omega'\,d\omega''\,d^3\boldsymbol{k}'\,d^3\boldsymbol{k}''$$
$$\times\,\delta(\omega-\omega'-\omega'')\,\delta(\boldsymbol{k}-\boldsymbol{k}'-\boldsymbol{k}'')\,F_a^{(0)}(\omega'',\boldsymbol{k}'')\,\mathcal{E}_j^{(0)}(\omega',\boldsymbol{k}'). \tag{18.20}$$

We substitute here expression (18.16). In this case we omit the principal value sign since in the non-linear terms the substractions may apply to the non-resonant region and so their contribution may be substantial. As a result we get

$$F_a^{\text{nl}} = -\frac{e_a^2}{(2\pi)^4}\int d\omega'\,d\omega''\,d^3\boldsymbol{k}'\,d^3\boldsymbol{k}''\,\delta(\omega-\omega'-\omega'')\,\delta(\boldsymbol{k}-\boldsymbol{k}'-\boldsymbol{k}'')$$

$$\times\frac{\mathscr{E}_j^{(0)}(\omega',\boldsymbol{k}')}{\omega-(\boldsymbol{k}\cdot\boldsymbol{v})}\cdot\frac{\partial}{\partial p_j}\cdot\frac{\mathscr{E}_k^{(0)}(\omega'',\boldsymbol{k}'')}{\omega''-(\boldsymbol{k}''\cdot\boldsymbol{v})}\cdot\frac{\partial\bar{f}_a}{\partial p_k}. \tag{18.21}$$

In this expression integration is only carried out over those values of ω', $\boldsymbol{k}'$ and ω'', $\boldsymbol{k}''$ which satisfy the dispersion equation since, according to (18.13), the functions $\boldsymbol{E}^{(0)}(\omega', \boldsymbol{k}')$ and $\boldsymbol{E}^{(0)}(\omega'', \boldsymbol{k}'')$ are non-zero only for these values.

Consider two possibilities.

(1) Suppose that the arguments ω and $\boldsymbol{k}$ of the non-linear function F_a^{nl} do not satisfy the dispersion equation. In this case the non-linear term (18.21) in the first approximation in μ has no effect on the variation of the functions $\boldsymbol{E}^{(0)}(\omega, \boldsymbol{k})$ and $\boldsymbol{B}^{(0)}$ since these are non-zero only for values of ω and $\boldsymbol{k}$ which satisfy the dispersion equation.

(2) If, however, the values of ω and $\boldsymbol{k}$ do satisfy the dispersion equation, it follows from (18.21) that sets of three waves exist, the frequencies and wave numbers of which satisfy the relations

$$\omega_1 = \omega_2+\omega_3; \qquad \boldsymbol{k}_1 = \boldsymbol{k}_2+\boldsymbol{k}_3. \tag{18.22}$$

In this case, even in the first approximation, the non-linear term of (18.21) affects the variation of $\boldsymbol{E}^{(0)}(\omega, \boldsymbol{k})$ and $\boldsymbol{B}^{(0)}$.

If the conditions (18.22) can never be satisfied, one has to consider the following expression for the non-linear term—obtained by eliminating the function F_a from the right-hand side of (18.10) twice—

$$F_a^{\text{nl}} = \frac{ie_a^3}{(2\pi)^8}\int d\Omega'\,d\Omega''\,d\Omega'''\,\delta(\Omega-\Omega'-\Omega''-\Omega''')$$

$$\times\frac{\mathscr{E}_j^{(0)}(\Omega')}{\omega-(\boldsymbol{k}\cdot\boldsymbol{v})}\cdot\frac{\partial}{\partial p_j}\cdot\frac{\mathscr{E}_k^{(0)}(\Omega'')}{\omega''+\omega'''-(\boldsymbol{k}''+\boldsymbol{k}'''\cdot\boldsymbol{v})}\cdot\frac{\partial}{\partial p_k}$$

$$\times\frac{\mathscr{E}_l^{(0)}(\Omega''')}{\omega'''-(\boldsymbol{k}'''\cdot\boldsymbol{v})}\cdot\frac{\partial\bar{f}_a}{\partial p_l}. \tag{18.23}$$

Here

$$d\Omega = d\omega\, d^3\boldsymbol{k}, \qquad \Omega = (\omega, \boldsymbol{k}). \tag{18.24}$$

The function F_a^{nl}, as defined by this expression, even in the first approximation in μ, affects the variation of the functions $E_i^{(0)}(\omega, \boldsymbol{k})$ if the plasma's dispersive properties permit the existence of at least one set of four waves, the frequencies and wave numbers of which are connected by the relations

$$\omega = \omega_1+\omega_2+\omega_3; \qquad \boldsymbol{k} = \boldsymbol{k}_1+\boldsymbol{k}_2+\boldsymbol{k}_3. \tag{18.25}$$

Following the terminology of Akhmanov and Khokhlov (1964), we shall say that the term (18.21) describes three-wave interaction, and the term (18.23) four-wave interaction.

To form the equations of the first approximation in μ for the functions $\boldsymbol{E}^{(0)}$ and $\boldsymbol{B}^{(0)}$, we begin, as in § 2 also, by writing the expressions for the electric-induction vector, but now in the form

$$\boldsymbol{D} = \boldsymbol{D}^{(0)}+\boldsymbol{D}^{\text{l}}+\boldsymbol{D}^{\text{nl}}. \tag{18.26}$$

Using the expressions (18.16, 21, 18, 23), we obtain

$$D_i^{(0)} = \varepsilon'_{ij}E_j^{(0)}, \tag{18.27}$$

$$D_i^{\text{l}} = \varepsilon'_{ij}E_j^{(1)}+i\varepsilon''_{ij}E_j^{(0)}+i\frac{\partial}{\partial t}\left(\frac{\partial \varepsilon'_{ij}}{\partial\omega}E_j^{(0)}\right) - i\left(\frac{\partial}{\partial \boldsymbol{q}}\cdot\left(\frac{\partial\varepsilon'_{ij}}{\partial \boldsymbol{k}}E_j^{(0)}\right)\right). \tag{18.28}$$

Here and also in (18.31, 33), it is important that f_a is a function of μt, $\mu\boldsymbol{q}$, and $|\boldsymbol{p}|$. These expressions differ from (2.99) in that the tensor ε_{ij} now depends on the slow variables μt and $\mu\boldsymbol{q}$. The expression for $\boldsymbol{D}^{\text{nl}}$ coincides with (2.100). For the tensors χ_{ijk} and θ_{ijkl}, by means of (18.21, 23), we get the following expressions:

$$\chi_{ijk}(\Omega, \Omega')e'_je''_k = i\sum_a \frac{4\pi e_a^3 n_a}{\omega}\int \frac{v_iA'_j}{\omega-(\boldsymbol{k}\cdot\boldsymbol{v})} \times\frac{\partial}{\partial p_j}\frac{A''_k}{\omega''-(\boldsymbol{k}''\cdot\boldsymbol{v})}\cdot\frac{\partial \bar{f}_a}{\partial p_k}\,d^3\boldsymbol{p}; \tag{18.29}$$

$$\Theta_{ijkl}(\Omega, \Omega''+\Omega''', \Omega''')e'_j e''_k e'''_l$$
$$= \sum_a \frac{4\pi e_a^4 n_a}{\omega} \int \frac{v_i A'_j}{\omega-(\boldsymbol{k}\cdot\boldsymbol{v})}$$
$$\times \frac{\partial}{\partial p_j} \frac{A''_k}{\omega''+\omega'''-(\boldsymbol{k}''+\boldsymbol{k}'''\cdot\boldsymbol{v})}$$
$$\times \frac{\partial}{\partial p_k} \frac{A'''_l}{\omega'''-(\boldsymbol{k}'''\cdot\boldsymbol{v})} \cdot \frac{\partial \bar{f}_a}{\partial p_l}\, d^3\boldsymbol{p}. \tag{18.30}$$

Here $\boldsymbol{A}=\boldsymbol{e}+(1/\omega)[\boldsymbol{v}\wedge[\boldsymbol{k}\wedge\boldsymbol{e}]]$, and $\boldsymbol{e}', \boldsymbol{e}'', \boldsymbol{e}'''$ are unit vectors determining the polarization of the waves with $\Omega', \Omega'', \Omega'''$.

Using these expressions we find the Fourier components of the time and space derivatives of the induction vector

$$\left(\frac{\partial D_i}{\partial t}\right)^{\mathrm{l}} = -i\omega\varepsilon'_{ij}E_j^{(1)}+\omega\varepsilon''_{ij}E_j^{(0)}+\frac{\partial}{\partial t}\left(\frac{\partial\omega\varepsilon'_{ij}}{\partial\omega}E_j^{(0)}\right)$$
$$-\left(\frac{\partial}{\partial\boldsymbol{q}}\cdot\left(\frac{\partial\omega\varepsilon'_{ij}}{\partial\boldsymbol{k}}E_j^{(0)}\right)\right), \tag{18.31}$$
$$\left(\frac{\partial\boldsymbol{D}}{\partial t}\right)^{\mathrm{n}} = -i\omega\boldsymbol{D}^{\mathrm{nl}}, \tag{18.32}$$

$$\operatorname{div}\boldsymbol{D}^{\mathrm{l}} = ik_i\varepsilon'_{ij}E_j^{(1)}-k_i\varepsilon''_{ij}E_j^{(0)}-\frac{\partial}{\partial t}\left(\frac{\partial k_i\varepsilon'_{ij}}{\partial\omega}E_j^{(0)}\right)$$
$$+\left(\frac{\partial}{\partial\boldsymbol{q}}\cdot\left(\frac{\partial k_i\varepsilon'_{ij}}{\partial\boldsymbol{k}}E_j^{(0)}\right)\right), \tag{18.33}$$
$$\operatorname{div}\boldsymbol{D}^{\mathrm{nl}} = i(\boldsymbol{k}\cdot\boldsymbol{D}^{\mathrm{nl}}). \tag{18.34}$$

In the first approximation, equations are obtained for the functions $\boldsymbol{E}^{(1)}$ and $\boldsymbol{B}^{(1)}$ which coincide with (2.102, 103), and so they drop out from the equations for $\boldsymbol{E}^{(0)}$ and $\boldsymbol{B}^{(0)}$. Thus the equations of the first approximation for $\boldsymbol{E}^{(0)}$ and $\boldsymbol{B}^{(0)}$ are

$$\operatorname{curl}\boldsymbol{B}^{(0)} = \frac{1}{c}\left(\frac{\partial\boldsymbol{D}}{\partial t}\right)^{\mathrm{l}}_{\omega,\,\boldsymbol{k}} - i\frac{\omega}{c}\boldsymbol{D}^{\mathrm{nl}}, \tag{18.35}$$

$$\operatorname{curl}\boldsymbol{E}^{(0)} = -\frac{1}{c}\cdot\frac{\partial\boldsymbol{B}^{(0)}}{\partial t}, \tag{18.36}$$

$$\operatorname{div}\boldsymbol{B}^{(0)} = 0,\ \operatorname{div}\boldsymbol{D}^{\mathrm{l}}_{\omega,\,\boldsymbol{k}}+i(\boldsymbol{k}\cdot\boldsymbol{D}^{\mathrm{nl}}) = 0. \tag{18.37}$$

Unlike the corresponding eqns. (2.107–109), these are not closed equations because the expressions for the tensors ε_{ij}, χ_{ijk} and Θ_{ijkl} contain the unknown functions $\bar{f}_a(\mu t, \mu \boldsymbol{q}, \boldsymbol{p})$. The equations for these functions in turn contain the functions $\boldsymbol{E}^{(0)}$ and $\boldsymbol{B}^{(0)}$.

By means of the zero approximation equations the function $\boldsymbol{B}^{(0)}$ can be eliminated from (18.37). Having done this, the following equation is obtained:

$$\frac{\partial}{\partial t}\left(\frac{\partial \omega^2 \varepsilon'_{ij}}{\partial \omega} E_j^{(0)}\right) - \left(\frac{\partial}{\partial \boldsymbol{q}} \cdot \frac{\partial \omega^2 \varepsilon'_{ij}}{\partial \boldsymbol{k}} E_j^{(0)}\right) - c^2([\boldsymbol{k} \wedge \operatorname{curl} \boldsymbol{E}^{(0)}] + \operatorname{curl}[\boldsymbol{k} \wedge \boldsymbol{E}^{(0)}])_i = -\omega^2 \varepsilon''_{ij} E_j^{(0)} + i\omega^2 D_i^{\text{nl}}. \tag{18.38}$$

If in the first approximation one can neglect the variation of the direction of polarization of the waves, from eqn. (18.38) one can obtain an equation for the scalar function $(\boldsymbol{e} \cdot \boldsymbol{E}) = E$. To do this we find the scalar product of eqn. (18.38) with the unit vector $\boldsymbol{e}$, and use the vectorial identity

$$(\boldsymbol{e} \cdot \{[\boldsymbol{k} \wedge \operatorname{curl} \boldsymbol{E}] + \operatorname{curl}[\boldsymbol{k} \wedge \boldsymbol{E}]\}) = 2((\boldsymbol{k} \cdot \boldsymbol{e}) \operatorname{grad}(\boldsymbol{E} \cdot \boldsymbol{e}) - (\boldsymbol{k} \cdot \operatorname{grad})\, \boldsymbol{E})$$

and also the notation (2.116, 118) for the group-velocity vector and the damping decrement. The resulting equation is

$$\frac{\partial E^{(0)}}{\partial t} + \left(\boldsymbol{v}_{\text{gr}} \cdot \frac{\partial E^{(0)}}{\partial \boldsymbol{q}}\right) = -\gamma E^{(0)} + \left[i\omega^2 (\boldsymbol{e} \cdot \boldsymbol{D}^{\text{nl}}) - \left(\frac{\partial^2}{\partial t\, \partial \omega} \omega^2 e_i \varepsilon'_{ij} e_j - \frac{\partial^2}{(\partial \boldsymbol{q} \cdot \partial \boldsymbol{k})} \omega^2 e_i \varepsilon'_{ij} e_j\right) E^{(0)}\right] \Big/ \frac{\partial}{\partial \omega} \omega^2 e_i \varepsilon'_{ij} e_j. \tag{18.39}$$

To close the set of equations for $\bar{f}_a$ and $\boldsymbol{E}^{(0)}$, one needs to express the right-hand sides of (18.6) in terms of $\boldsymbol{E}^{(0)}$. Using expressions (18.16, 18, 21 and 23), we obtain

$$S_a = S_a^{\text{l}} + S_a^{\text{nl}}, \tag{18.40}$$

$$S_a^1 = \pi \frac{e_a^2}{(2\pi)^4 TV}$$

$$\times \frac{\partial}{\partial p_i} \int \delta(\omega - (\boldsymbol{k}\cdot\boldsymbol{v}) \mathscr{E}_j^{(0)}(\omega, \boldsymbol{k}) \mathscr{E}_j^{(0)*}(\omega, \boldsymbol{k}) \frac{\partial \bar{f}_a}{\partial p_j} d\omega\, d^3\boldsymbol{k}$$

$$-\frac{e_a^2}{(2\pi)^4 TV} \cdot \frac{\partial}{\partial p_i} \int \left[\frac{\partial}{\partial \omega} P \frac{1}{\omega - (\boldsymbol{k}\cdot\boldsymbol{v})} \cdot \frac{\partial}{\partial t} \right.$$

$$\left. - \left(\frac{\partial}{\partial \boldsymbol{k}} P \frac{1}{\omega - (\boldsymbol{k}\cdot\boldsymbol{v})} \cdot \frac{\partial}{\partial \boldsymbol{q}} \right) \right]$$

$$\times \mathscr{E}_j^{(0)}(\omega, \boldsymbol{k}) \mathscr{E}_i^{(0)*}(\omega, \boldsymbol{k}) \frac{\partial \bar{f}_a}{\partial p_j} d\omega\, d^3\boldsymbol{k}. \tag{18.41}$$

The operators $\partial/\partial t$ and $\partial/\partial \boldsymbol{q}$ do not act on $\mathscr{E}_i^{(0)*}$

$$S_a^{\text{nl}} = \frac{e_a^3}{(2\pi)^8 TV} \int d\Omega\, d\Omega'\, d\Omega''\, \delta(\Omega - \Omega' - \Omega'') \operatorname{Re} \mathscr{E}_i^{(0)*}(\Omega) \frac{\partial}{\partial p_i}$$

$$\times \frac{\mathscr{E}_j^{(0)}(\Omega')}{\omega - (\boldsymbol{k}\cdot\boldsymbol{v})} \cdot \frac{\partial}{\partial p_j} \cdot \frac{\mathscr{E}_k^{(0)}(\Omega'')}{\omega'' - (\boldsymbol{k}''\cdot\boldsymbol{v})} \cdot \frac{\partial f_a^0}{\partial p_k} + \frac{e_a^4}{(2\pi)^{12} TV}$$

$$\times \int d\Omega\, d\Omega'\, d\Omega''\, d\Omega'''\, \delta(\Omega - \Omega' - \Omega'' - \Omega''') \operatorname{Re}(-i) \mathscr{E}_i^{(0)*}(\Omega)$$

$$\times \frac{\partial}{\partial p_i} \frac{\mathscr{E}_j^{(0)}(\Omega')}{\omega - (\boldsymbol{k}\cdot\boldsymbol{v})} \cdot \frac{\partial}{\partial p_j} \cdot \frac{\mathscr{E}_k^{(0)}(\Omega'')}{\omega'' + \omega''' - (\boldsymbol{k}'' + \boldsymbol{k}'''\cdot\boldsymbol{v})}$$

$$\times \frac{\partial}{\partial p_k} \frac{\mathscr{E}_l^{(0)}(\Omega''')}{\omega''' - (\boldsymbol{k}'''\cdot\boldsymbol{v})} \cdot \frac{\partial \bar{f}_a}{\partial p_l}. \tag{18.42}$$

These equations form a closed set for the smoothed distribution functions and the slowly varying Fourier components of the field strength.

We will consider two cases.

(1) Coherent interaction of waves. From the structure of the non-linear terms it follows that, for instance, in the case of three-wave interaction one can satisfy the Maxwell equations of the first approximation if the functions $\boldsymbol{E}^{(0)}(\mu t, \mu \boldsymbol{q}, \omega, \boldsymbol{k})$ and $\boldsymbol{B}^{(0)}$ are of the form

$$\boldsymbol{E}^{(0)} = (2\pi)^4 \sum_{1 \leq \alpha \leq 3} \boldsymbol{E}_\alpha \delta(\omega - \omega_\alpha)\, \delta(\boldsymbol{k} - \boldsymbol{k}_\alpha),$$

$$\boldsymbol{B}^{(0)} = \frac{c}{\omega} [\boldsymbol{k} \wedge \boldsymbol{E}^{(0)}], \tag{18.43}$$

where ω_1, ω_2, ω_3 and $\boldsymbol{k}_1$, $\boldsymbol{k}_2$, $\boldsymbol{k}_3$ are connected by the relations (18.22). The equations of the first approximation for the functions $\boldsymbol{E}_\alpha$ and $\boldsymbol{B}_\alpha$ are the same in form as eqns. (18.35) or (18.38). The expression for the non-linear induction vector in the case of three-wave interaction is

$$(\boldsymbol{e}^{(\alpha)}\cdot\boldsymbol{D}^{\mathrm{nl}}) = \left(e_i^{(\alpha)}\chi_{ijk}(\Omega_\alpha,\Omega_\beta)\,e_j^{(\gamma)}e_k^{(\beta)} + e_i^{(\alpha)}\chi_{ijk}(\Omega_\alpha,\Omega_\gamma)\,e_j^{(\beta)}e_k^{(\gamma)}\right)E_\gamma^{(0)}E_\beta^{(0)}. \tag{18.44}$$

In this approximation the expression (18.41) becomes:

$$S_a^1 = \sum_{1\le\alpha\le 3}\left\{\pi e_a^2\frac{\partial}{\partial p_i}\delta(\omega_\alpha-(\boldsymbol{k}_\alpha\cdot\boldsymbol{v}))\,\mathscr{E}_{(\alpha)i}\mathscr{E}^*_{(\alpha)j}\frac{\partial\bar{f}_a}{\partial p_j} - e_a^2\frac{\partial}{\partial p_i}\left[\frac{\partial}{\partial\omega_\alpha}P\frac{1}{\omega_\alpha-(\boldsymbol{k}_\alpha\cdot\boldsymbol{v})}\cdot\frac{\partial}{\partial t}-\left(\frac{\partial}{\partial\boldsymbol{k}_\alpha}P\frac{1}{\omega_\alpha-(\boldsymbol{k}_\alpha\cdot\boldsymbol{v})}\cdot\frac{\partial}{\partial\boldsymbol{q}}\right)\right]\mathscr{E}_{(\alpha)i}\mathscr{E}^*_{(\alpha)j}\frac{\partial\bar{f}_a}{\partial p_j}\right.. \tag{18.45}$$

Here it is taken into account that $(2\pi)^4\,\delta(\omega-\omega_\alpha)\,\delta(\boldsymbol{k}-\boldsymbol{k}_\alpha)/TV=1$. The three-wave part of (18.42) is similarly transformed.

Thus, in this case, we get a closed set of equations for the distribution functions f_a and also three complex amplitudes $\boldsymbol{E}_\alpha$ of waves, the frequencies and wave vectors of which are linked by the relations (18.22).

In the case of four-wave interaction, instead of (18.43), we use the following expression

$$\boldsymbol{E}^{(0)}(\mu t,\mu\boldsymbol{q},\omega,\boldsymbol{k}) = (2\pi)^4\sum_{1\le\alpha\le 4}\delta(\omega-\omega_\alpha)\,\delta(\boldsymbol{k}-\boldsymbol{k}_\alpha)\boldsymbol{E}_\alpha, \tag{18.46}$$

in which the frequencies and wave vectors are coupled by the relations (18.25). In this case we get a closed set of equations for f_a and four complex amplitudes.

These equations describe the process in a plasma with regard to the phases of the waves, i.e. they describe coherent interaction of waves.

If the tensors ε_{ij}, χ_{ijk} and Θ_{ijkl} can be regarded as constant, we get the closed set of electrodynamic equations for complex amplitudes, considered by Akhmanov and Khokhlov (1964).

In the same way one can obtain equations which describe the interaction of many waves.

(2) Further simplification of our equations is possible by changing to a hydrodynamic approximation. The equations obtained thus are much simpler in solving stationary problems when the $\overline{f^a}$ and $\boldsymbol{E}_\alpha$ are independent of time, or otherwise depend only on time.

Note that the division into fast and slow motion is not a universally applicable distinction. It is essential, in particular, that the dispersion equation, which contains the real part of the tensor ε_{ij}, should have real roots. This stipulation is not satisfied, for instance, in a beam of charged particles in a plasma when hydrodynamic instability occurs. The method of dividing into "background" and "pulsation" has to be altered if hydrodynamic instability is to be taken into account.

In deriving the equations of the quasilinear approximation, it is assumed† that the phases of the plasma waves are random and that they are correlated for a much shorter time than the relaxation time for the functions $\overline{f_a}$, $\boldsymbol{E}_\alpha$ and the wave amplitudes. But any presumption of phase randomness essentially goes beyond the self-consistent field approximation to which Vlasov's equations are applicable. In this case one should use the method of describing non-equilibrium processes in a plasma developed in §§ 16, 17.

In these sections the kinetic equations were formed with regard to the radiation of plasma waves. Only the second moments of the random functions δN_a, $\delta \boldsymbol{E}$ and $\delta \boldsymbol{B}$ were considered.

This second-moment approximation is suitable when the deviations from equilibrium are small. With a large deviation from equilibrium it is necessary to take higher moments into account.

So as not to over-complicate the problem, consider the case of a spatially homogeneous plasma. The higher moments can then be taken into account by the method explained at the end of § 17. If, however, we confine ourselves to the higher moments for the region of low-wave excitations (the radiation region), the required results are obtainable more simply.

† Vedenov, Velikhov and Sagdeyev (1961; Vedenov and Velikhov (1963); Vedenov (1962); Drummond and Pines (1961); Shapiro (1963) and Karpman (1964).

We return to eqn. (16.28). The right-hand side contains two terms of the same order for states close to equilibrium. In this case the higher moments $\overline{\delta E_i\,\delta E_j\,\delta E_k}$; $\overline{\delta E_i\,\delta E_j\,\delta E_k\,\delta E_l}$; . . . , are small and so can be neglected. If, however, the state is far from equilibrium, the rôle of the second term, which is independent of the field strength, is small and it too can be neglected, but one has to take the higher correlations of the fields into account.

For this one can use (18.39) as the equation for the field's random deviation δE. In the spatially homogeneous case we obtain the following equation for δE (see footnote on p. 197):

$$\frac{\partial \delta E}{\partial t} = -\gamma' \delta E + \frac{i\omega^2(\boldsymbol{e}\cdot\delta\boldsymbol{D}^{\mathrm{nl}})}{\dfrac{\partial\omega^2 e_i \varepsilon'_{ij} e_j}{\partial\omega}},$$

$$\gamma' = \gamma + \frac{\partial}{\partial t}\ln\frac{\partial\omega^2 e_i\varepsilon'_{ij}e_j}{\partial\omega}. \tag{18.47}$$

The expression for $\delta\boldsymbol{D}^{\mathrm{nl}}$ is obtained from (2.100)

$$\delta D_i^{\mathrm{nl}}(\mu t, \Omega) = \frac{1}{(2\pi)^4}\int d\Omega'\,d\Omega''\,\delta(\Omega-\Omega'-\Omega'')\,\chi_{ijk}(\Omega,\Omega'')$$
$$\times\delta(\delta E_j(\Omega')\,\delta E_k(\Omega''))+\frac{1}{(2\pi)^8}\int d\Omega'\,d\Omega''\,d\Omega'''$$
$$\times\delta(\Omega-\Omega'-\Omega''-\Omega''')\cdot\Theta_{ijkl}(\Omega,\Omega''+\Omega''',\Omega''')$$
$$\times\delta(\delta E_j(\Omega')\,\delta E_k(\Omega'')\,\delta E_l(\Omega''')). \tag{18.48}$$

Using (18.47) the equation for the spectral function $(\delta E_i \delta E_j)_{\omega,\boldsymbol{k},t}$ is

$$\frac{\partial}{\partial t}(\delta E_i\delta E_j)_{\omega,\boldsymbol{k},t} = -2\gamma'(\delta E_i\delta E_j)_{\omega,\boldsymbol{k},t}$$
$$-2\omega^2 e_i e_k\,\mathrm{Im}\,(\delta D_k\delta E_j)_{\omega,\boldsymbol{k},t}/\partial(\omega^2 e_i\varepsilon'_{ij}e_j)/\partial\omega. \tag{18.49}$$

Consider now the case of three-wave interaction. Only the first term remains in (18.48), and the threefold correlation $\overline{\delta E_i\delta E_j\delta E_k}$ comes into (18.49).

By means of (18.47) we write down the equation for the threefold correlation. It contains the fourfold correlation $\overline{\delta E_i\delta E_j\delta E_k\delta E_l}$. Within the context of three-wave interaction this function can be expressed in terms of double correlations. We then get a set of equations for the functions $\overline{\delta E_i \delta E_j}$ and $\overline{\delta E_i \delta E_j \delta E_k}$. If the tensors ε_{ij} and χ_{ijk} are constant, it is a closed set. But if they vary owing to variation with time of the functions $f_a(\mu t, \boldsymbol{p})$, in order to close the set it is necessary to use the corresponding equations for the functions f_a.

For four-wave interaction the right-hand side of (18.49) contains the fourfold correlation $\overline{\delta E_i \delta E_j \delta E_k \delta E_l}$. A special case of four-wave interaction is two-wave interaction. In this case the fourfold correlation can be expressed in terms of double correlations. If ε_{ij} and Θ_{ijkl} are constant, a closed set of equations is obtained for the double correlations. If ε_{ij} and Θ_{ijkl} are variable, these equations are closed by means of the equations for the f_a.

If it is impossible to represent four-wave interaction as two-wave interaction, one has to write the equations for the fourfold correlations. They contain the correlations of six values of the electric field strength. Within the context of four-wave interactions such correlations can be expressed in terms of double correlations. For constant functions f_a we get a closed set of equations for the functions of double and fourfold correlations.

The equations for the functions f_a and for the field correlations become much simpler if, for instance, for three-wave interactions the random functions $\delta \boldsymbol{E}$ can be represented as (18.43), i.e.

$$\delta \boldsymbol{E}(\mu t, \omega, \boldsymbol{k}) = (2\pi)^4 \sum_{1 \leq \alpha \leq 3} \boldsymbol{E}_\alpha(\mu t)\, \delta(\omega - \omega_\alpha)\, \delta(\boldsymbol{k} - \boldsymbol{k}_\alpha). \tag{18.50}$$

$$\Omega_1 \neq \Omega_2 \neq \Omega_3$$

The quantities ω_α and $\boldsymbol{k}_\alpha$ satisfy the conditions (18.22). In this expression the functions $\boldsymbol{E}_\alpha$ themselves are random functions. It is important for the $\boldsymbol{E}_\alpha$ to be real functions if the phases of the waves are quickly varying random functions. We make this assumption here, although it is not essential to do so.

Considering that

$$\frac{1}{(2\pi)^4} \int (\delta \boldsymbol{E} \cdot \delta \boldsymbol{E})_{\omega, \boldsymbol{k}, t}\, d\omega\, d^3\boldsymbol{k} = \sum_{1 \leq \alpha \leq 3} \overline{E_\alpha^2},$$

from (18.49) the equation for the function $\overline{E_\alpha^2}$ is

$$\frac{\partial \overline{E_\alpha^2}}{\partial t} = -2\gamma'_\alpha \overline{E_\alpha^2} - 2F_{\alpha\beta\gamma}\overline{E_\alpha E_\beta E_\gamma}. \tag{18.51}$$

Here

$$F_{\alpha\beta\gamma} = \frac{\omega_\alpha^2}{\dfrac{\partial}{\partial \omega_\alpha}\left(\omega_\alpha^2 e_i^{(\alpha)} \varepsilon'_{ij} e_j^{(\alpha)}\right)} \operatorname{Im}\left(e_i^{(\alpha)}\chi_{ijk}(\Omega_\alpha, \Omega_\beta)\, e_j^{(\gamma)} e_k^{(\beta)}\right.$$
$$\left. + e_i^{(\alpha)}\chi_{ijk}(\Omega_\alpha, \Omega_\gamma)\, e_j^{(\beta)} e_k^{(\gamma)}\right).$$

Summation is not carried out over twice-recurring Greek suffixes.

We write down the equation for the function $\overline{E_\alpha E_\beta E_\gamma}$. Considering that

$$\overline{E_\alpha E_\alpha E_\beta E_\beta} = \overline{E_\alpha^2}\,\overline{E_\beta^2} \quad \text{if} \quad \Omega_\alpha \neq \Omega_\beta,$$

we obtain the equation

$$\frac{\partial}{\partial t}\overline{E_\alpha E_\beta E_\gamma} = -(\gamma'_\alpha + \gamma'_\beta + \gamma'_\gamma)\,\overline{E_\alpha E_\beta E_\gamma}$$
$$-F_{\alpha\beta\gamma}\overline{E_\beta^2}\,\overline{E_\gamma^2} - F_{\beta\gamma\alpha}\overline{E_\gamma^2}\,\overline{E_\alpha^2} - F_{\gamma\alpha\beta}\overline{E_\alpha^2}\,\overline{E_\beta^2}. \tag{18.52}$$

If the tensors ε_{ij} and χ_{ijk} depend on time, we also require the equations for the functions f_a. In the spatially homogeneous case these may be written as

$$\frac{\partial f_a}{\partial t} = S_a^{\text{coll}} + S_a^{\text{rad}}. \tag{18.53}$$

Here S_a^{coll} is the collision integral, as defined in § 11. The term S_a^{rad} describes the variation of the functions f_a due to the radiation of plasma waves, defined in § 17 for states near to equilibrium. If the deviations from equilibrium are considerable, it is necessary to take the interaction of waves into account. For three-wave interaction

$$S_a^{\text{rad}} = S_a^{\text{l}} + S_a^{\text{nl}}, \tag{18.54}$$

where

$$S_a^{\text{l}} = \sum_{1 \le \alpha \le 3} e_a^2 \frac{\partial}{\partial p_i}\left[\pi\delta(\omega_\alpha - (\boldsymbol{k}_\alpha \cdot \boldsymbol{v}))\right.$$
$$\left. - \frac{\partial}{\partial \omega_\alpha} P \frac{1}{\omega_\alpha - (\boldsymbol{k}_\alpha \cdot \boldsymbol{v})} \frac{\partial}{\partial t}\right] A_i^{(\alpha)} A_j^{(\alpha)} \overline{E_\alpha^2} \frac{\partial f_a}{\partial p_j}, \tag{18.55}$$

$$S_a^{\rm nl} = e_a^3 \sum_{1 \le \alpha \le 3} A_i^{(\alpha)} \frac{\partial}{\partial p_i} \operatorname{Re} \left[\frac{A_j^{(\beta)}}{\omega_\alpha - (\boldsymbol{k}_\alpha \cdot \boldsymbol{v})} \cdot \frac{\partial}{\partial p_j} \right.$$
$$\times \frac{A_k^{(\gamma)}}{\omega_\gamma - (\boldsymbol{k}_\gamma \cdot \boldsymbol{v})} + \left. \frac{A_j^{(\gamma)}}{\omega_\alpha - (\boldsymbol{k}_\alpha \cdot \boldsymbol{v})} \cdot \frac{\partial}{\partial p_j} \cdot \frac{A_k^{(\beta)}}{\omega_\beta - (\boldsymbol{k}_\beta \cdot \boldsymbol{v})} \right]$$
$$\times \frac{\partial f_a}{\partial p_k} \overline{E_\alpha E_\beta E_\gamma}. \tag{18.56}$$

Here

$$\boldsymbol{A} = \boldsymbol{e} + \frac{1}{\omega} [\boldsymbol{v} \wedge [\boldsymbol{k} \wedge \boldsymbol{e}]].$$

We have thus formed a closed set of equations for the distribution functions f_a and the moments $\overline{E_\alpha^2}$ and $\overline{E_\alpha E_\beta E_\gamma}$ of the electric field strength. By means of these equations one can describe the turbulent state with regard to third moments. From the resulting equations the conditions can be established for which a stationary or quasistationary state will exist in a plasma.

If four-wave interaction is allowed for, in the same way we obtain a closed set of equations for the functions f_a, the second $\overline{E_\alpha^2}$ and the fourth moments of the electric field strength. This process can be continued. The number of moments of the field strength that one needs to use, depends on the number of interacting waves.

Further terms appear in the equations if in the expansion as a Fourier integral one takes into account the dependence of the frequency and wave vector on the slow coordinates and time. For a Coulomb plasma in the spatially homogeneous case they are introduced in § 16. A more general case is elaborated in a paper by Klimontovich (1964).

Finally, the foregoing exposition is an illustration of only one of the problems in non-linear theory. The present state of this problem and also the applications of quasilinear theory are treated more comprehensively in the papers by Leontovich (1963), Silin (1964), Kadomtsev and Petviashvili (1963), Iordanskii and Kulikovskii (1964a, 1946b), Kovrizhnykh and Tsytovich (1964), Gorbunov, Pustovalov and Silin (1964), Vedenov, Velikhov and Sagdeyev (1961), Vedenov and Velikhov (1963), Vedenov (1962), Drummond and Pines (1961), Shapiro (1963), Karpman (1964) and Klimontovich (1965a).

19. Quasilinear Approximation Taking "Collisions" into Account

The results of §§ 16–18 can be generalized so as to take into account simultaneously the self-consistent field and also the correlations which determine the dissipative processes. To show up the main features of the problem, we at once make some simplifying assumptions.

(1) The plasma is a Coulomb plasma.

(2) The dissipative processes are determined in the main by the short-wave spectral region—the "collision" region, where $|\boldsymbol{k}| > 1/r_d$. Hence we can neglect the polarization effect in evaluating the correlation functions, i.e. we can confine ourselves to the approximation which in a homogeneous plasma leads to Landau's collision integral.

We write down the initial equations which hold good under these conditions.

The equations for the functions f_a, allowing for the average field, are (5.21). For the function $S_a(\boldsymbol{q}, \boldsymbol{p}, t)$ it is convenient to use (5.18) since by neglecting the polarization no difficulties arise in solving the equations for the correlation functions.

The equations for the correlation functions follow from eqns. (5.35) if we discard the last two terms on the left-hand side which take into account the polarization. Thus the initial set of equations can be written as

$$\frac{\partial f_a}{\partial t} + \left(\boldsymbol{v} \cdot \frac{\partial f_a}{\partial \boldsymbol{q}}\right) + e_a \left(\boldsymbol{E}(\boldsymbol{q}, t) \cdot \frac{\partial f_a}{\partial \boldsymbol{p}}\right) = S_a(\boldsymbol{q}, \boldsymbol{p}, t) \quad (19.1)$$

$$S_a = \sum_b n_b \int \left(\frac{\partial}{\partial \boldsymbol{q}} \cdot \frac{e_a e_b}{|\boldsymbol{q}-\boldsymbol{q}'|} \frac{\partial}{\partial \boldsymbol{p}}\right) g_{ab}(\boldsymbol{q}, \boldsymbol{q}', \boldsymbol{p}, \boldsymbol{p}')\, d^3q'\, d^3p' \quad (19.2)$$

$$\operatorname{div} \boldsymbol{E} = 4\pi \sum_a e_a n_a \int f_a\, d^3p \quad (19.3)$$

$$\left[\frac{\partial}{\partial t} + \left(\boldsymbol{v} \cdot \frac{\partial}{\partial \boldsymbol{q}}\right) + \left(\boldsymbol{v}' \cdot \frac{\partial}{\partial \boldsymbol{q}'}\right) + e_a \left(\boldsymbol{E}(\boldsymbol{q}, t) \cdot \frac{\partial}{\partial \boldsymbol{p}}\right) + e_b \left(\boldsymbol{E}(\boldsymbol{q}', t) \cdot \frac{\partial}{\partial \boldsymbol{p}'}\right)\right] g_{ab} = \left(\frac{\partial}{\partial \boldsymbol{q}} \cdot \frac{e_a e_b}{|\boldsymbol{q}-\boldsymbol{q}'|} \times \left\{\frac{\partial f_a}{\partial \boldsymbol{p}} f_b - \frac{\partial f_b}{\partial \boldsymbol{p}'} f_a\right\}\right). \quad (19.4)$$

In Silin's papers [1960, 1962b] these equations are fundamental to the kinetic theory of quickly varying processes, i.e. the theory in which the effects due to the correlations as well as to the self-consistent field are taken into account simultaneously.

Consider now some supplementary assumptions.

We shall assume that the average electric field is a high-frequency field, i.e. the following condition is satisfied

$$\omega \gg 1/\tau_r . \tag{19.5}$$

Using this condition we divide the functions f_a and g_{ab} into their fast and slow parts

$$f_a = f_a^{(0)} + f_a^{(1)}; \quad g_{ab} = g_{ab}^{(0)} + g_{ab}^{(1)} \tag{19.6}$$

The functions $f_a^{(0)}$ and $g_{ab}^{(0)}$ are obtained from f_a and g_{ab} by averaging over a time interval $T \sim 1/\Delta$ such that

$$\frac{2\pi}{\omega} \ll T \ll \tau_r . \tag{19.7}$$

We impose the following restriction on the value of the average field:

$$\frac{eE}{mv_T\Delta} \ll 1. \tag{19.8}$$

On this condition

$$f_a^{(1)} \ll f_a^{(0)}; \quad g_{ab}^{(1)} \ll g_{ab}^{(0)} . \tag{19.9}$$

By making these assumptions eqns. (19.1, 4) yield the following equations for the functions $f_a^{(0)}$ and $f_a^{(1)}$:

$$\frac{\partial f_a^{(0)}}{\partial t} + \left(\boldsymbol{v} \cdot \frac{\partial f_a^{(0)}}{\partial \boldsymbol{q}} \right) = -e_a \left(\frac{\partial}{\partial \boldsymbol{p}} \cdot \overline{\boldsymbol{E} f_a^{(1)}} \right)^{(0)} + S_a^{(0)} \tag{19.10}$$

$$\frac{\partial f_a^{(1)}}{\partial t} + \left(\boldsymbol{v} \cdot \frac{\partial f_a^{(1)}}{\partial \boldsymbol{q}} \right) = -e_a \left(\boldsymbol{E} \cdot \frac{\partial f_a^{(0)}}{\partial \boldsymbol{p}} \right) + S_a^{(1)} . \tag{19.11}$$

The bar together with the superscript (0) indicates the slow component.

We introduce new variables $\boldsymbol{q} - \boldsymbol{q}' = \boldsymbol{r}$, $\boldsymbol{q} = \boldsymbol{R}$ in the equations for the functions $g_{ab}^{(0)}$ and $g_{ab}^{(1)}$.

Consider the last simplifying assumption. The average field is defined as

$$\boldsymbol{E}(\boldsymbol{R}, t) = \boldsymbol{Re}\ \mathbf{E}(\omega, \boldsymbol{K}, \mu t)\, e^{-i\omega t + i(\boldsymbol{K} \cdot \boldsymbol{R})} . \tag{19.12}$$

Thus the average field is a plane wave with slowly varying amplitude. The wavelength $2\pi/K \gg r_d$, i.e. it is much greater than the correlation radius. Hence in the equations for the functions $g_{ab}^{(0)}$ and $g_{ab}^{(1)}$ one can expand as a series in powers of $(\boldsymbol{r}\cdot\partial/\partial\boldsymbol{R})$.

In the zeroth approximation in this parameter having regard to (19.8) we get from (19.4) the following equations for the functions $g_{ab}^{(0)}$ and $g_{ab}^{(1)}$:

$$\left(\frac{\partial}{\partial t}+\left(\boldsymbol{v}-\boldsymbol{v}'\cdot\frac{\partial}{\partial \boldsymbol{r}}\right)\right)g_{ab}^{(0)}=\left(\frac{\partial}{\partial \boldsymbol{r}}\cdot\frac{e_a e_b}{|\boldsymbol{r}|}\left\{\frac{\partial f_a^{(0)}}{\partial \boldsymbol{p}}f_b^{(0)}\right.\right.$$
$$\left.\left.-\frac{\partial f_b^{(0)}}{\partial \boldsymbol{p}'}f_a^{(0)}\right\}\right)-\Delta g_a^{(0)} \tag{19.13}$$

$$\left(\frac{\partial}{\partial t}+\left(\boldsymbol{v}\cdot\frac{\partial}{\partial \boldsymbol{R}}\right)+\left(\boldsymbol{v}-\boldsymbol{v}'\cdot\frac{\partial}{\partial \boldsymbol{r}}\right)\right)g_{ab}^{(1)}$$
$$=-\left[\left(e_a\boldsymbol{E}(\boldsymbol{R},t)\cdot\frac{\partial}{\partial \boldsymbol{p}}\right)+\left(e_b\boldsymbol{E}(\boldsymbol{R},t)\cdot\frac{\partial}{\partial \boldsymbol{p}'}\right)\right]g_{ab}^{(0)}$$
$$+\left(\frac{\partial}{\partial \boldsymbol{r}}\cdot\frac{e_a e_b}{|\boldsymbol{r}|}\left\{\frac{\partial f_a}{\partial \boldsymbol{p}}f_b-\frac{\partial f_b}{\partial \boldsymbol{p}'}f_a\right\}^{(1)}\right)-\Delta g_{ab}^{(1)}. \tag{19.14}$$

The superscript (1) of $\{\}^{(1)}$ indicates the fast time component. The supplementary terms $-\Delta g_{ab}^{(0)}$, $-\Delta g_{ab}^{(1)}$ in these equations as a rough approximation take into account the rôle of the higher correlations which are missing in the initial equations. The quantity $\Delta \sim 1/T$ satisfies the condition (19.7).

Given these restrictions, $f_a^{(0)} = f_a^{(0)}(\boldsymbol{p}, \mu t)$, i.e. the distribution function does not depend on the coordinates and is a slowly varying time function.

The solution of eqn. (19.13) can be written as follows

$$g_{ab}^{(0)}(\boldsymbol{k},\boldsymbol{p},\boldsymbol{p}')=\left(\frac{4\pi e_a e_b \boldsymbol{k}}{k^2[(\boldsymbol{k}\cdot\boldsymbol{v}-\boldsymbol{v}')-i\Delta]}\cdot\left\{\frac{\partial f_a^{(0)}}{\partial \boldsymbol{p}}f_b^{(0)}\right.\right.$$
$$\left.\left.-\frac{\partial f_b^{(0)}}{\partial \boldsymbol{p}'}f_a^{(0)}\right\}\right). \tag{19.15}$$

Here $g_{ab}^{(0)}(\boldsymbol{k},\boldsymbol{p},\boldsymbol{p}')$ is the Fourier component with respect to $\boldsymbol{r}$ of the function $g_{ab}^{(0)}(\boldsymbol{r},\boldsymbol{p},\boldsymbol{p}')$.

For solving eqn. (19.14) we use the first approximation for the function $f_a^{(1)}$:

$$f_a^{(1)} = -\operatorname{Re}\frac{ie_a}{\omega-(\boldsymbol{K}\cdot\boldsymbol{v})+i\nu_a}\left(\boldsymbol{E}(\omega,\boldsymbol{K},\mu t)\cdot\frac{\partial f_a^{(0)}}{\partial\boldsymbol{p}}\right)e^{-i\omega t+i(\boldsymbol{K}\cdot\boldsymbol{R})}. \tag{19.16}$$

The quantity ν_a is not the same as Δ. It will be determined below.

The expression (19.16) follows from (19.11) provided that the dissipative terms due to the "collisions" and Landau damping have a higher order of smallness.

By the use of (19.12) the function $g_{ab}^{(1)}$ becomes

$$g_{ab}^{(1)}(\boldsymbol{R},\boldsymbol{r},\boldsymbol{p},\boldsymbol{p}',t) = \operatorname{Re} g_{ab}^{(1)}(\omega,\boldsymbol{K},\boldsymbol{r},\boldsymbol{p},\boldsymbol{p}')\,e^{-i\omega t+i(\boldsymbol{K}\cdot\boldsymbol{R})}. \tag{19.17}$$

After simple transformations, and using (19.16), we get for the expression for the Fourier component in $\boldsymbol{r}$ of the function $g_{ab}(\omega, \boldsymbol{K}, \boldsymbol{r}, \boldsymbol{p}, \boldsymbol{p}')$

$$g_{ab}^{(1)}(\omega,\boldsymbol{K},\boldsymbol{k},\boldsymbol{p},\boldsymbol{p}') = \frac{i}{\omega-(\boldsymbol{K}\cdot\boldsymbol{v})-\boldsymbol{k}(\boldsymbol{v}-\boldsymbol{v}')+i\Delta}$$
$$\times\left\{-\left(1-\frac{(\boldsymbol{k}\cdot\boldsymbol{v}-\boldsymbol{v}')-i\Delta}{\omega-(\boldsymbol{K}\cdot\boldsymbol{v})+i\nu_a}\right)\cdot\left(e_a\left(\boldsymbol{E}\cdot\frac{\partial}{\partial\boldsymbol{p}}\right)+e_b\left(\boldsymbol{E}\cdot\frac{\partial}{\partial\boldsymbol{p}'}\right)\right)g_{ab}^{(0)}\right.$$
$$\left.+\frac{(\boldsymbol{k}\cdot\boldsymbol{E})}{\omega-(\boldsymbol{K}\cdot\boldsymbol{v})+i\nu_a}\left(\frac{e_a}{m_a}-\frac{e_b}{m_b}\right)g_{ab}^{(0)}\right\} \tag{19.18}$$

Consider now the expressions for the collision integrals $S_a^{(0)}(p,\mu t)$ and $S_a^{(1)}(\boldsymbol{R}, t, \boldsymbol{p}, \mu t)$.

Into the integral in (19.2) we substitute the variables $\boldsymbol{q}-\boldsymbol{q}' = \boldsymbol{r}$ and $\boldsymbol{q} = \boldsymbol{R}$, and then expand the integrand as a Fourier integral in $\boldsymbol{r}$. As a result we get

$$S_a(\boldsymbol{R},\boldsymbol{p},t) = \frac{1}{(2\pi)^3}\sum_b 4\pi e_a e_b n_b\left(\frac{\partial}{\partial\boldsymbol{p}}\cdot\int\frac{\boldsymbol{k}}{k^2}\operatorname{Im} g_{ab}\right)d^3\boldsymbol{k}. \tag{19.19}$$

To find $S_a^{(0)}$ it is necessary to substitute (19.15) into (19.19). We then obtain

$$S_a^{(0)} = \sum_b 2e_a^2 e_b^2 n_b\frac{\partial}{\partial p_i}\int\frac{k_i k_j\delta((\boldsymbol{k}\cdot\boldsymbol{v})-(\boldsymbol{k}\cdot\boldsymbol{v}'))}{k^4}$$
$$\times\left\{\frac{\partial f_a^{(0)}}{\partial p_j}f_b^{(0)}-\frac{\partial f_b^{(0)}}{\partial p_j'}f_a^{(0)}\right\}d^3\boldsymbol{k}\,d^3\boldsymbol{p}'. \tag{19.20}$$

In accord with our earlier assumption the integration over $\boldsymbol{k}$ in (19.20) is restricted by the condition $|\boldsymbol{k}| > 1/r_d$.

Naturally, the collision integral $S_a^{(0)}$ coincides with Landau's collision integral (see (11.4) and (11.28)).

To find the function $S_a^{(1)}(\boldsymbol{R}, \boldsymbol{p}, t)$ we represent it in accordance with (19.17) as

$$S_a^{(1)}(\boldsymbol{R}, \boldsymbol{p}, t) = \text{Re}\; S_a^{(1)}(\omega, \boldsymbol{K}, \boldsymbol{p})\, e^{-i(\omega t - (\boldsymbol{K}\cdot\boldsymbol{R}))} \tag{19.21}$$

From (19.19, 21) it follows that

$$S_a^{(1)}(\omega, \boldsymbol{K}, \boldsymbol{p}) = \sum_b \frac{4\pi e_a e_b}{(2\pi)^3} \left(\frac{\partial}{\partial \boldsymbol{p}} \cdot \int \frac{\boldsymbol{k}}{k^2} \right.$$
$$\left. \times \frac{g_{ab}^{(1)}(\omega, \boldsymbol{K}, \boldsymbol{k}, \boldsymbol{p}, \boldsymbol{p}') - g_{ab}^{(1)}(\omega, \boldsymbol{K}, -\boldsymbol{k}, \boldsymbol{p}, \boldsymbol{p}')}{2i} \right) d^3\boldsymbol{p}\, d^3\boldsymbol{k}\,. \tag{19.22}$$

Substituting (19.18) into (19.22) we find the expression for $S_a^{(1)}(\omega, \boldsymbol{K}, \boldsymbol{p})$.

We return to eqn. (19.11) for the fast part of the distribution function. By taking the correlations into account in this equation we are able to describe the dissipative processes in the fast motions. For a characterization of the dissipation an apt concept is the frequency of "collisions" (the collision rate). Putting ν_a for this rate, we determine it from the equation

$$\nu_a f_a^{(1)} + S_a^{(1)} = 0 \quad \text{or} \quad \nu_a = -\frac{S_a^{(1)} f_a^{(1)*}}{|f_a^{(1)}|^2} \tag{19.23}$$

The functions $S_a^{(1)}$ and $f_a^{(1)}$ are expressed in terms of the function $f_a^{(0)}$, so that

$$\nu_a = \nu_a(\omega, \boldsymbol{K}, \boldsymbol{p}, f_a^{(0)})$$

Here there is no explicit dependence on the field strength since the functions $S_a^{(1)}$ and $f_a^{(1)}$ are proportional to the field strength. The dependence on $\boldsymbol{E}$ enters implicitly via the functions $f_a^{(0)}$.

Using the definition of ν_a, the stationary solution of (19.11) is

$$f_a^{(1)}(\omega, \boldsymbol{K}, \boldsymbol{p}) = -\frac{ie_a}{\omega - (\boldsymbol{K}\cdot\boldsymbol{v}) + i\nu_a} \left(\boldsymbol{E}(\omega, \boldsymbol{K}) \cdot \frac{\partial f_a^{(0)}}{\partial \boldsymbol{p}} \right) \tag{19.24}$$

When considering the slow variation with time of $\boldsymbol{E}$ and $f_a^{(0)}$, additional terms appear in (19.24).

To form the equation for the field strength $\boldsymbol{E}(\omega, \boldsymbol{K}, \mu t)$, we substitute (19.24) in Poisson's equation. Using the expression for the dielectric constant

$$\varepsilon = \varepsilon' + i\varepsilon'' = 1 + \sum_a \frac{4\pi e_a^2 n_a}{K^2} \int \frac{\left(\boldsymbol{K} \cdot \frac{\partial f_a^{(0)}}{\partial \boldsymbol{p}}\right)}{\omega - (\boldsymbol{K} \cdot \boldsymbol{v}) + i\nu_a} d^3\boldsymbol{p} \tag{19.25}$$

we obtain the equation

$$\frac{\partial \boldsymbol{E}(\omega, \boldsymbol{K}, \mu t)}{\partial \mu t} = -\gamma_{\text{eff}} \boldsymbol{E} \tag{19.26}$$

Here

$$\gamma_{\text{eff}} = \varepsilon'' \bigg/ \frac{\partial \varepsilon'}{\partial \omega} + \gamma_{\text{non-stat}} \tag{19.27}$$

is the effective damping decrement; $\gamma_{\text{non-stat}}$ represents the contribution from non-stationary processes.

By means of (19.24) we can eliminate the function $f_a^{(1)}$ from eqn. (19.10). We then get a closed set of equations for the functions $f_a^{(0)}$ and $\boldsymbol{E}$

$$\frac{\partial f_a^{(0)}}{\partial \mu t} = \frac{\partial}{\partial p_i} \frac{K_i K_j}{K^2} \left\{ \frac{\frac{1}{2}\nu_a e_a^2 |\boldsymbol{E}|^2}{\omega - (\boldsymbol{K} \cdot \boldsymbol{v})^2 + \nu_a^2} + D_{\text{non-stat}} \right\} \frac{\partial f_a^{(0)}}{\partial p_j} + S_a^{(0)} \tag{19.28}$$

$$\frac{\partial^2 |\boldsymbol{E}|^2}{\partial \mu t} = -2\gamma_{\text{eff}} |\boldsymbol{E}|^2. \tag{19.29}$$

Here $D_{\text{non-stat}}$ represents the contribution from the non-stationary processes.

The set of eqns. (19.28, 29) should also include the expression (19.23) which associates the collision rate ν_a with the distribution functions $f_a^{(0)}$.

Equations (19.28, 29) differ from the corresponding equations of §§ 16–18 in that instead of Δ they contain the rate ν_a which itself depends on the type of distribution functions $f_a^{(0)}$. So eqns. (19.28, 29) more completely take into account the dissipative processes. In particular, they take into account the collisions as well as Landau damping.

These equations may be used to form model equations which can be rigorously solved. For instance, one can thereby investigate the distribution function's dependence on a given field, the field distribution for a given source in momentum space and so on.

Our restrictions are not fundamental and in a similar fashion more general results can be obtained; for instance, the transverse field, polarization, wave interaction, ..., can be taken into account.

Klimontovich and Logvinov (1966) have considered examples of solutions of eqns. (19.28, 29) for the stationary case. In particular, they found the stationary field distribution in a plasma perturbed by an electron beam.

20. Approximation of "Free" and "Bound" Charges for a Plasma. Self-consistent Equations for Second Distribution Functions

In the foregoing sections in deriving the kinetic equations of a plasma it has been assumed that the conditions are such that the correlation functions are small. Thus in the zeroth approximation a set of self-consistent equations is obtained for the first distribution functions and average fields. Such an approximation may be called the "free charge" approximation since in this case the correlations are zero. In the next approximation the correlations are taken into account, but it is assumed that they are small, i.e. only slight deviations from the "free" charge approximation are taken into account.

Naturally, this approach is quite unsuitable when, for instance, for a partially ionized hydrogen plasma one must take into account the "bound" states of the charged particles as well as their "free" states. With bound states the correlations between the pairs of particles forming the atoms are large, so the requisite approximation for taking them into account may be called the "bound" charge approximation.

Consider a two-component plasma.

For forming the kinetic equations taking bound states into account, the equations for the microscopic phase densities are convenient initial equations

$$N_{ab}(\boldsymbol{q}_a, \boldsymbol{q}_b, \boldsymbol{p}_a, \boldsymbol{p}_b, t) = \sum_{1 \leq i \leq N} \delta(\boldsymbol{q}_a - \boldsymbol{q}_{ai}(t))\, \delta(\boldsymbol{q}_b - \boldsymbol{q}_{bi}(t)) \times \delta(\boldsymbol{p}_a - \boldsymbol{p}_{ai}(t))\, \delta(\boldsymbol{p}_b - \boldsymbol{p}_{bi}(t)). \tag{20.1}$$

Here a is the subscript for ions, b represents electrons, the $\boldsymbol{q}_{ai}$ and $\boldsymbol{p}_{ai}$ are variables of an ion with number i, and $\boldsymbol{q}_{bi}$, $\boldsymbol{p}_{bi}$ are variables of an electron with number i.

The function N_{ab} determines at the instant t the virtual number of electron–ion pairs in which the electrons have the coordinates and momenta $\boldsymbol{q}_b$, $\boldsymbol{p}_b$, and the ions $\boldsymbol{q}_a$, $\boldsymbol{p}_a$.

In the Coulomb approximation the equation for the function N_{ab} is

$$\left(\frac{\partial}{\partial t} + \left(\boldsymbol{v}_a \cdot \frac{\partial}{\partial \boldsymbol{q}_a}\right) + \left(\boldsymbol{v}_b \cdot \frac{\partial}{\partial \boldsymbol{q}_b}\right) - \left(\frac{\partial \varphi_{ab}}{\partial \boldsymbol{q}_a} \cdot \frac{\partial}{\partial \boldsymbol{p}_a}\right) - \left(\frac{\partial \varphi_{ab}}{\partial \boldsymbol{q}_b} \cdot \frac{\partial}{\partial \boldsymbol{p}_b}\right)\right) N_{ab} + e_a \left(\boldsymbol{E}^{\mathrm{M}}(\boldsymbol{q}_a, t) \cdot \frac{\partial N_{ab}}{\partial \boldsymbol{p}_a}\right) + e_b \left(\boldsymbol{E}^{\mathrm{M}}(\boldsymbol{q}_b, t) \cdot \frac{\partial N_{ab}}{\partial \boldsymbol{p}_b}\right) = 0. \tag{20.2}$$

Here φ_{ab} is the potential energy of a pair.

The equation for the field can be written as

$$\operatorname{div} \boldsymbol{E}^{\mathrm{M}}(\boldsymbol{q}, t) = 4\pi \int (e_a \delta(\boldsymbol{q} - \boldsymbol{q}_a) + e_b \delta(\boldsymbol{q} - \boldsymbol{q}_b)) \times N_{ab}\, d^3\boldsymbol{q}_a\, d^3\boldsymbol{q}_b\, d^3\boldsymbol{p}_a\, d^3\boldsymbol{p}_b. \tag{20.3}$$

Our earlier microscopic equations (4.20, 21) for the functions N_a and $\boldsymbol{E}^{\mathrm{M}}$, which hold for a Coulomb plasma, follow from (20.2, 3). In this case it must be taken into account that

$$N_b = \int N_{ab}\, d^3\boldsymbol{q}_a\, d^3\boldsymbol{p}_a, \quad N_a = \int N_{ab}\, d^3\boldsymbol{q}_b\, d^3\boldsymbol{p}_b,$$

where N_b and N_a are six-dimensional phase densities for the electrons and ions, respectively.

In the "bound" charge approximation it is convenient to use the variables

$$\boldsymbol{R} = \frac{m_a \boldsymbol{q}_a + m_b \boldsymbol{q}_b}{m_a + m_b}, \quad \boldsymbol{r} = \boldsymbol{q}_a - \boldsymbol{q}_b,$$

$$\boldsymbol{\Pi} \equiv (m_a + m_b)\boldsymbol{V} = \boldsymbol{p}_a + \boldsymbol{p}_b; \; \boldsymbol{p} \equiv \mu \boldsymbol{v} = \frac{m_b \boldsymbol{p}_a - m_a \boldsymbol{p}_b}{m_a + m_b};$$

$$\mu = \frac{m_a m_b}{m_a + m_b}. \tag{20.4}$$

For the function $N_{ab}(\boldsymbol{R}, \boldsymbol{\Pi}, \boldsymbol{r}, \boldsymbol{p}, t)$, eqn. (20.2) yields the equation

$$\frac{\partial N_{ab}}{\partial t} + \left(\boldsymbol{V} \cdot \frac{\partial N_{ab}}{\partial \boldsymbol{R}}\right) + \left(\boldsymbol{v} \cdot \frac{\partial N_{ab}}{\partial \boldsymbol{r}}\right) - \left(\frac{\partial \varphi}{\partial \boldsymbol{r}}(|\boldsymbol{r}|) \cdot \frac{\partial N_{ab}}{\partial \boldsymbol{p}}\right)$$
$$+ \left(\mathscr{E}^{(+)}(\boldsymbol{R}, \boldsymbol{r}) \cdot \frac{\partial N_{ab}}{\partial \boldsymbol{\Pi}}\right) + \left(\mathscr{E}^{(-)}(\boldsymbol{R}, \boldsymbol{r}) \cdot \frac{\partial N_{ab}}{\partial \boldsymbol{p}}\right) = 0. \tag{20.5}$$

Here

$$\mathscr{E}^{(+)}(\boldsymbol{R}, \boldsymbol{r}) = e_a \boldsymbol{E}^{\mathrm{M}}\left(\boldsymbol{R} + \frac{m_b}{m_a + m_b}\boldsymbol{r}\right)$$
$$+ e_b \boldsymbol{E}^{\mathrm{M}}\left(\boldsymbol{R} - \frac{m_a}{m_a + m_b}\boldsymbol{r}\right),$$

$$\mathscr{E}^{(-)}(\boldsymbol{R}, \boldsymbol{r}) = \frac{e_a m_b}{m_a + m_b}\boldsymbol{E}^{\mathrm{M}}\left(\boldsymbol{R} + \frac{m_b}{m_a + m_b}\boldsymbol{r}\right)$$
$$+ \frac{e_b m_a}{m_a + m_b}\boldsymbol{E}^{\mathrm{M}}\left(\boldsymbol{R} - \frac{m_a}{m_a + m_b}\boldsymbol{r}\right), \tag{20.6}$$

$$\operatorname{div} \boldsymbol{E}^{\mathrm{M}} = 4\pi \int \left[e_a \delta\left(\boldsymbol{q} - \left(\boldsymbol{R} + \frac{m_b}{m_a + m_b}\boldsymbol{r}\right)\right)\right.$$
$$\left. + e_b \delta\left(\boldsymbol{q} - \left(\boldsymbol{R} - \frac{m_a}{m_a + m_b}\boldsymbol{r}\right)\right)\right]$$
$$\cdot N_{ab}(\boldsymbol{R}, \boldsymbol{\Pi}, \boldsymbol{r}, \boldsymbol{p}', t)\, d^3\boldsymbol{R}\, d^3\boldsymbol{\Pi}\, d^3\boldsymbol{r}\, d^3\boldsymbol{p}. \tag{20.7}$$

The sets (4.20, 21), (20.2, 3) and (20.5–7) of microscopic equations are equivalent. The superiority of some particular form becomes apparent after averaging on changing to the approximate equations for the lowest moments.

The first moments approximation for (4.20, 21) leads to Vlasov's equations and so corresponds to complete neglect of the correlations. The same approximation for (20.5–7) leads to a closed set of self-consistent equations for the second distribution functions $f_{ab} = \bar{N}_{ab}/n$ and the average field. In this approximation the correlation between the particles in the pair is taken into account, but that between particles of different pairs is neglected.

If the function $f_{ab}(\boldsymbol{R}, \boldsymbol{\Pi}, \boldsymbol{r}, \boldsymbol{p}, t)$, as a function of $\boldsymbol{R}$, varies little over distances of the order of the correlation radius, one can expand as a series in $(\boldsymbol{r}\cdot\partial/\partial\boldsymbol{R})$. In the dipole approximation the set of equations for the functions f_{ab} and $\boldsymbol{E}$ is

$$\frac{\partial f_{ab}}{\partial t} + \left(\boldsymbol{V}\cdot\frac{\partial f_{ab}}{\partial \boldsymbol{R}}\right) + \left(\boldsymbol{v}\cdot\frac{\partial f_{ab}}{\partial \boldsymbol{r}}\right) - \left(\frac{\partial \varphi_{ab}}{\partial \boldsymbol{r}}\cdot\frac{\partial f_{ab}}{\partial \boldsymbol{p}}\right)$$
$$+ e_a\left(\boldsymbol{r}\cdot\frac{\partial}{\partial \boldsymbol{R}}\right)\left(\boldsymbol{E}\cdot\frac{\partial f_{ab}}{\partial \boldsymbol{\Pi}}\right) + e_a\left(\boldsymbol{E}(\boldsymbol{R}, t)\cdot\frac{\partial f_{ab}}{\partial \boldsymbol{p}}\right) = 0. \tag{20.8}$$

$$\operatorname{div} \boldsymbol{E}(\boldsymbol{R}, t) = -4\pi e_a n\left(\frac{\partial}{\partial \boldsymbol{R}}\cdot\int \boldsymbol{r} f_{ab}\right) d^3\boldsymbol{\Pi}\, d^3\boldsymbol{r}\, d^3\boldsymbol{p}$$
$$= -4\pi \operatorname{div} \boldsymbol{P}(\boldsymbol{R}, t). \tag{20.9}$$

Here $\boldsymbol{P}(\boldsymbol{R}, t)$ is the polarization vector.

In the quantum case, instead of (20.1), we use the function

$$N_{ab} = \frac{1}{(2\pi)^6}\int \varrho\left(\boldsymbol{R} + \frac{1}{2}\hbar\boldsymbol{\theta}, \boldsymbol{r} + \frac{1}{2}\hbar\boldsymbol{\tau},\right.$$
$$\left.\boldsymbol{R} - \frac{1}{2}\hbar\boldsymbol{\theta}, \boldsymbol{r} - \frac{1}{2}\hbar\boldsymbol{\tau}\right) e^{-i(\boldsymbol{\theta}\cdot\boldsymbol{\Pi}) - i(\boldsymbol{\tau}\cdot\boldsymbol{p})}\, d^3\boldsymbol{\theta}\, d^3\boldsymbol{\tau}. \tag{20.10}$$

Here ϱ is the density matrix operator.

If the spectrum corresponding to the relative motion of the particles in the pairs is discrete, instead of (20.10) we use the function

$$N_{ab}(\boldsymbol{R}, \boldsymbol{\Pi}, \boldsymbol{r}, \boldsymbol{p}, t) = \sum_{nm} N_{nm}^{(ab)}(\boldsymbol{R}, \boldsymbol{\Pi}, t) f_{nm}(\boldsymbol{r}, \boldsymbol{p}), \tag{20.11}$$

where

$$N_{nm}(\boldsymbol{R}, \boldsymbol{\Pi}, t) = \frac{1}{(2\pi)^3} \int \varrho_{nm} \left(\boldsymbol{R} + \frac{1}{2}\hbar\boldsymbol{\theta}, \boldsymbol{R} - \frac{1}{2}\hbar\boldsymbol{\theta}\right)$$

$$\times e^{-(\boldsymbol{\theta}\cdot\boldsymbol{\Pi})}\, d^3\boldsymbol{\theta},$$

$$f_{nm}(\boldsymbol{r}, \boldsymbol{p}) = \frac{1}{(2\pi)^3} \int \psi_m^* \left(\boldsymbol{r} - \frac{1}{2}\hbar\boldsymbol{\tau}\right)$$

$$\times \psi_n \left(\boldsymbol{r} + \frac{1}{2}\hbar\boldsymbol{\tau}\right) e^{-i(\boldsymbol{\tau}\cdot\boldsymbol{p})}\, d^3\boldsymbol{\tau}$$

and the ψ_n are eigenfunctions of the operator $\hat{H} = \hat{\boldsymbol{p}}^2/2\mu + \phi(|\boldsymbol{r}|)$.

The equation for the function $N_{nm}^{(ab)}(\boldsymbol{R}, \boldsymbol{\Pi}, t)$ is

$$\frac{\partial N_{nm}^{(ab)}}{\partial t} + \left(\boldsymbol{V} \cdot \frac{\partial N_{nm}^{(ab)}}{\partial \boldsymbol{R}}\right) = \frac{1}{i\hbar}(E_n - E_m) N_{nm}^{(ab)}$$

$$+ \frac{e_a}{i\hbar(2\pi)^3} \int \sum_k \left(U_{nk}^{(-)}\left(\boldsymbol{R} + \frac{1}{2}\hbar\boldsymbol{\theta}\right) N_{km}^{(ab)}(\boldsymbol{R}, \boldsymbol{\Pi}') \right.$$

$$\left. - N_{nk}^{(ab)}(\boldsymbol{R}, \boldsymbol{\Pi}')\, U_{km}^{(-)}\left(\boldsymbol{R} - \frac{1}{2}\hbar\boldsymbol{\theta}\right)\right) e^{i(\boldsymbol{\theta}\cdot\boldsymbol{\Pi} - \boldsymbol{\Pi}')}\, d^3\boldsymbol{\theta}\, d^3\boldsymbol{\Pi}' \tag{20.12}$$

where

$$U_{nm}^{(-)}(\boldsymbol{R}) = \int \psi_n^*(\boldsymbol{r})\, U^{(-)}(\boldsymbol{R}, \boldsymbol{r})\, \psi_m(\boldsymbol{r})\, d^3\boldsymbol{r}$$

$$U^{(-)}(\boldsymbol{R}, \boldsymbol{r}) = U^{\mathrm{M}}\left(\boldsymbol{R} + \frac{m_b}{m_a + m_b}\boldsymbol{r}\right) - U^{\mathrm{M}}\left(\boldsymbol{R} - \frac{m_a}{m_a + m_b}\boldsymbol{r}\right).$$

The equation for the field $\boldsymbol{E}^{\mathrm{M}} = -\partial U^{\mathrm{M}}/\partial \boldsymbol{R}$ is the same as before.

If the motion as regards $\boldsymbol{R}$ and $\boldsymbol{\Pi}$ can be deemed to be classical and we use the dipole approximation, eqn. (20.12) simplifies to

$$\frac{\partial N_{nm}^{(ab)}}{\partial t} + \left(\boldsymbol{V} \cdot \frac{\partial N_{nm}^{(ab)}}{\partial \boldsymbol{R}}\right) = \frac{1}{i\hbar}(E_n - E_m) N_{nm}^{(ab)}$$

$$- \frac{e_a}{i\hbar} \sum_k \left(\left(\boldsymbol{r}_{nk} N_{km}^{(ab)}(\boldsymbol{R}, \boldsymbol{\Pi}) - N_{nk}^{(ab)} \boldsymbol{r}_{km}\right) \cdot \boldsymbol{E}(\boldsymbol{R}, t)\right)$$

$$-\frac{e_a}{2}\sum_k\left[\left(\frac{\partial}{\partial \boldsymbol{R}}(\boldsymbol{r}_{nk}\cdot\boldsymbol{E}(\boldsymbol{R},t))\cdot\frac{\partial N_{km}^{(ab)}}{\partial \boldsymbol{\Pi}}\right)\right.$$

$$\left.-\left(\frac{\partial N_{nk}}{\partial \boldsymbol{\Pi}}\cdot\frac{\partial}{\partial \boldsymbol{R}}(\boldsymbol{r}_{km}\cdot\boldsymbol{E}(\boldsymbol{R},t))\right)\right]. \tag{20.13}$$

For taking the transverse field into account, in place of (20.3), the complete set of Lorentz equations is used. The microscopic current in this case is given by the expression

$$\boldsymbol{j}^{\mathrm{M}}(\boldsymbol{q},t)=\int(e_a\boldsymbol{v}_a\delta(\boldsymbol{q}-\boldsymbol{q}_a)+e_b\boldsymbol{v}_b\delta(\boldsymbol{q}-\boldsymbol{q}_b))$$

$$\times N_{ab}d^3\boldsymbol{q}_a\,d^3\boldsymbol{q}_b\,d^3\boldsymbol{p}_a\,d^3\boldsymbol{p}_b. \tag{20.14}$$

The methods propounded in the foregoing sections can be used also for the set of microscopic equations for the functions N_{ab} and $\boldsymbol{E}^{\mathrm{M}}$. More general kinetic equations are then obtained for the field function and the distribution function $N_{nm}^{(ab)}(\boldsymbol{R},\boldsymbol{\Pi},t)$. For instance, with a zero average field we get the kinetic equation $\overline{N}_{nm}^{(ab)}=\delta_{nm}\overline{N}_{nn}(\boldsymbol{\Pi},\mu t)$. The equilibrium solution of this equation is a Maxwell distribution in $\boldsymbol{\Pi}$ and a Boltzmann distribution in E_n.

With a rapidly varying field we get equations corresponding to those in § 19, but taking transitions between levels into account.

For simultaneously taking into account "bound" as well as "free" charges, the initial equations are the microscopic equations in a mixed discrete-continuous representation.

To do this we use as the starting set of equations a coupled set of the equations for four density matrix operators and the equations for the microscopic field strengths. One of the density matrices describes free states, a second one bound states, and two density matrices describe transitions between free and bound states. To obtain the kinetic equations one could also in this general case use the methods considered in the preceding sections.

Chapter VI

Hydrodynamic Description of Processes in a Plasma

21. Hydrodynamic Equations for a Heavily Ionized Plasma Neglecting Wave Radiation

In the present section the kinetic equations for functions f_a, formed in § 11, are used to derive the hydrodynamic equations.†

Consider a heavily ionized plasma. In the equations for the f_a the collisions between charged and neutral particles can be neglected and therefore one may confine oneself to collisions in between charged particles. Only elastic collisions are considered in which the colliding particles retain their kinetic energy.

The hydrodynamic or gas-dynamic functions could be determined by means of the functions $f_a(\boldsymbol{q}, \boldsymbol{p}, t)$, but it is more convenient to use the distribution functions

$$F_a(\boldsymbol{q}, \boldsymbol{p}, t) = n_a f_a(\boldsymbol{q}, \boldsymbol{p}, t). \tag{21.1}$$

The normalization condition for these functions is

$$\int F_a(\boldsymbol{q}, \boldsymbol{p}, t)\, d^3\boldsymbol{p}\, d^3\boldsymbol{q} = N_a, \tag{21.2}$$

where N_a is the total number of particles of component a.

Definition of the quantities in the hydrodynamic equations: The density of the particles of component a is

$$\varrho_a(\boldsymbol{q}, t) = \int F_a(\boldsymbol{q}, \boldsymbol{p}, t)\, d^3\boldsymbol{p}, \tag{21.3}$$

$$\varrho(\boldsymbol{q}, t) = \sum_a \varrho_a(\boldsymbol{q}, t). \tag{21.4}$$

† See Leontovich (1963), Braginskii (1958), Herdan and Liley (1960), Gr ad (1949), Klimontovich and Ebeling (1962) and Zhdanov (1962).

The average velocity of component a is

$$\boldsymbol{U}_a(\boldsymbol{q}, t) = \frac{1}{\varrho_a}\int \boldsymbol{v} F_a(\boldsymbol{q}, \boldsymbol{p}, t)\, d^3\boldsymbol{p}, \tag{21.5}$$

the momentum density of component a is

$$m_a \varrho_a \boldsymbol{U}_a, \tag{21.6}$$

the plasma momentum density is

$$\sum_a m_a \varrho_a \boldsymbol{U}_a. \tag{21.7}$$

The deviation of the particle velocity from the average velocity of component a is

$$\delta\boldsymbol{v}_a = \boldsymbol{v} - \boldsymbol{U}_a; \quad \int \delta\boldsymbol{v}_a F_a\, d^3\boldsymbol{p} = 0. \tag{21.8}$$

The subscript a of $\delta\boldsymbol{v}$ is omitted whenever practicable.

The kinetic-energy density of component a, not connected with the motion of this component as a whole, is

$$\varepsilon_a(\boldsymbol{q}, t) = \int \frac{p^2}{2m_a} F_a\, d^3\boldsymbol{p} - \frac{m_a U_a^2}{2} = \int \frac{m_a(\delta\boldsymbol{v})^2}{2} F_a\, d^3\boldsymbol{p}, \tag{21.9}$$

$$\varepsilon(\boldsymbol{q}, t) = \sum_a \varepsilon_a(\boldsymbol{q}, t). \tag{21.10}$$

$$\varrho_a \varkappa T_a = \frac{2}{3}\varepsilon_a(\boldsymbol{q}, t) = m_a \int \frac{(\delta\boldsymbol{v})^2}{3} F_a\, d^3\boldsymbol{p}. \tag{21.11}$$

The latter relation defines the temperature T_a of component a.

$$p_a(\boldsymbol{q}, t) = \varrho_a(\boldsymbol{q}, t)\varkappa T_a(\boldsymbol{q}, t); \quad p = \sum_a p_a, \tag{21.12}$$

where p_a stands for partial pressure and p for the total pressure. The internal stress tensor is

$$P_{ij}^a = m_a \int \delta v_i^a \delta v_j^a F_a\, d^3\boldsymbol{p}; \quad P_{ii}^a = 3p_a; \quad P_{ij} = \sum_a P_{ij}^a. \tag{21.13}$$

$$p_{ij}^a = P_{ij}^a - \delta_{ij} p_a; \quad p_{ij} = \sum_a p_{ij}^a; \quad p_{ii}^a = 0 \tag{21.14}$$

the "viscous" stress tensor is

$$S_{ijk}^a = m_a \int \delta v_i^a \delta v_j^a \delta v_k^a F_a\, d^3\boldsymbol{p}. \tag{21.15}$$

The contraction of this tensor determines the thermal flux vector

$$S_k^a = S_{iik}^a = m_a \int \delta v_k^a (\delta \boldsymbol{v}^a)^2 F_a \, d^3\boldsymbol{p}, \quad S_k = \sum_a S_k^a. \tag{21.16}$$

Similarly, one can define still more complex functions which are moments of velocities of higher order.

All the foregoing functions are functions of the coordinates $\boldsymbol{q}$ and time t. We shall say that they are *hydrodynamic functions*.

Thus, by using the functions $F_a(\boldsymbol{q}, \boldsymbol{p}, t)$, one can construct an infinite number of hydrodynamic functions.

We show that the kinetic equations for the functions $f_a(\boldsymbol{q}, \boldsymbol{p}, t)$ can be replaced by an infinite set of equations for the simpler hydrodynamic functions $\varrho_a, \boldsymbol{U}_a, T_a, p_{ij}^a, \ldots$.

Accordingly, we expand the distribution function $F_a(\boldsymbol{q}, \boldsymbol{p}, t)$, as a function of $\boldsymbol{p}$, into a series in three-dimensional Hermite–Chebyshev polynomials. As the independent variables we take the components of the dimensionless relative velocity vector

$$\boldsymbol{\xi}_a = \frac{\delta \boldsymbol{v}_a}{\sqrt{\left(\frac{\varkappa T_a}{m_a}\right)}}. \tag{21.17}$$

In some formulae we shall omit the subscript a of $\boldsymbol{\xi}$ and $\delta\boldsymbol{v}$.

We write $H_{i_1, \ldots, i_n}^{(n)}(\xi)$ for the nth degree Hermite–Chebyshev polynomial of the three independent variables ξ_1, ξ_2 and ξ_3. The subscripts $i_1, i_2, \ldots, i_n$ assume value 1, 2, 3. The nth degree polynomial is a tensor of nth rank.

The Hermite–Chebyshev polynomials are defined as follows:

$$H_{i_1 \ldots i_n}^{(n)}(\boldsymbol{\xi}) = (-1)^n e^{\frac{\xi^2}{2}} \frac{\partial^n}{\partial \xi_{i_1} \ldots \partial \xi_{i_n}} e^{-\frac{\xi^2}{2}}. \tag{21.18}$$

From this formula, in particular, we find that

$$\begin{aligned} &H^{(0)} = 1; \quad H_i^{(1)} = \xi_i; \quad H_{ij}^{(2)} = \xi_i \xi_j - \delta_{ij}; \\ &H_{ijk}^{(3)} = \xi_i \xi_j \xi_k - \delta_{ij}\xi_k - \delta_{jk}\xi_i - \delta_{ki}\xi_j. \end{aligned} \tag{21.19}$$

The orthononormality condition of Hermite–Chebyshev polynomials of three variables can be written as

$$\frac{1}{(2\pi)^{3/2}}\int e^{-\frac{\xi^2}{2}} H^{(n)}_{i_1,\dots i_n}(\boldsymbol{\xi}) H^{(m)}_{j_1,\dots j_m}(\boldsymbol{\xi})\, d^3\boldsymbol{\xi}$$

$$= \delta_{nm}\delta_{i_1\dots i_n, j_1,\dots j_n}. \tag{21.20}$$

Here $\delta_{n,m}$ is the ordinary Kronecker symbol, and

$$\delta_{i_1,\dots,i_n,j_1,\dots,j_n} = \begin{cases} 1, \text{ if the set } i_1,\dots,i_n \text{ can be obtained by permutation of the set } j_1,\dots,j_n;\ 0, \text{ if no such permutation is possible.}\end{cases}$$

The condition (21.20) implies that polynomials of different degrees are orthogonal.

We write the expansion of the distribution functions $F_a = n_a f_a$ into Hermite–Chebyshev polynomials as

$$F_a(\boldsymbol{q}, \boldsymbol{p}, t) = \frac{\varrho_a}{(2\pi m_a \varkappa T_a)^{3/2}} e^{-\frac{\xi_a^2}{2}} \sum_{n=0}^{\infty} \sum_{i_1,\dots,i_n} \frac{1}{n!}$$

$$\times a^{(n)a}_{i_1,\dots,i_n}(\boldsymbol{q}, t)\, H^{(n)}_{i_1,\dots,i_n}(\boldsymbol{\xi}_a). \tag{21.21}$$

The vector $\boldsymbol{\xi}$ is given by (21.17).

By the use of (21.20), we obtain from (21.21) an expression for the coefficients of the expansion

$$a^{(n)a}_{i_1,\dots,i_n}(\boldsymbol{q}, t) = \frac{1}{\varrho_a}\int F_a(\boldsymbol{q}, \boldsymbol{p}, t)\, H^{(n)}_{i_1,\dots,i_n}(\boldsymbol{\xi})\, d^3\boldsymbol{p}. \tag{21.22}$$

This formula enables us to establish the connexion between these coefficients $a^{(n)a}_{i_1,\dots,i_n}$ and the foregoing hydrodynamic functions.

Setting $n = 0, 1, 2, 3$ in the formula (21.22) and then using the expressions (21.3–16), we get

$$a^{(0)a} = 1; \tag{21.23}$$

$$a^{(1)a}_i = 0; \tag{21.24}$$

$$a^{(2)a}_{ij} = \frac{(P^a_{ij} - \delta_{ij} p^a)}{p^a} = \frac{p^a_{ij}}{p^a}; \tag{21.25}$$

$$a^{(3)a}_{ijk} = \frac{S^a_{ijk}}{p_a\sqrt{\left(\frac{\theta_a}{m_a}\right)}} \tag{21.26}$$

Here and throughout we put $\theta_a = \varkappa T_a$ to simplify the notation.

If we substitute the expansion (21.21) into the kinetic equation and use condition (21.20), we get a set of differential equations for the functions $a^{(n)a}_{i_1,\ldots,i_n}$.

This set is an infinite chain of coupled equations insofar as coefficients of higher order enter into the equation for the coefficient $a^{(n)a}_{i_1,\ldots,i_n}$.

Thus the solution of the set of kinetic equations for the functions f_a boils down to the solution of an infinite chain of equations for the hydrodynamic functions ϱ_a, $\boldsymbol{U}_a$, T_a, p^a_{ij}, S^a_{ijk}, ..., which depend only on the coordinates and time. Such a set is, naturally, just as complicated as the initial equations for the distribution functions.

To break the chain of equations and thereby obtain a closed set for a finite number of hydrodynamic functions, one needs to confine oneself to a coarser description than that obtainable by using the kinetic equations.

In the derivation of the kinetic equations in § 11 it was shown that they can be used for describing the processes for which the distribution functions notably vary during the "free path time"

$$\tau_r \sim \frac{1}{\omega_L \varepsilon} \gg \frac{1}{\omega_L}$$

and over a distance of the order of the "mean free path"

$$\lambda_r \sim \frac{r_d}{\varepsilon} \gg r_d.$$

Thus the main restriction on the functions $f_a(\boldsymbol{q}, \boldsymbol{p}, t)$ is that they vary little during time of the order of the natural-oscillation period and over distances of the order of the Debye radius.

If the characteristic time T is much greater than the relaxation time τ_r, and the characteristic distance L is much greater than λ_r, further "coarsening" of the description of the processes in a plasma becomes possible.

In fact, provided that

$$T \gg \tau_r, \quad L \gg \lambda_r \tag{21.27}$$

the processes for which the distribution functions and hydrodynamic functions vary little during the relaxation time τ_r over the mean free path λ_r can be isolated.

So we introduce the small parameter

$$\mu \sim \lambda_r \frac{\left|\dfrac{\partial A}{\partial \boldsymbol{q}}\right|}{A(\boldsymbol{q}, t)}, \tag{21.28}$$

where $A(\boldsymbol{q}, t)$ is an arbitrary hydrodynamic function.

If the characteristic time interval is

$$T \sim \frac{L}{v_T},$$

where v_T is the average thermal velocity, the parameter μ characterizes the slowness of the variation of the hydrodynamic functions in time.

By virtue of the smallness of μ, a closed set of equations can be found for the functions ϱ_a, $\boldsymbol{U}^a$, T_a, i.e. the hydrodynamic equations.

The changeover to hydrodynamic equations may be made by the Chapman–Enskog method [Braginskii, 1958; Herdan and Liley, 1960; Grad, 1949; Bogolyubov, 1962].

Another method of forming the hydrodynamic equations has been propounded by Grad (1949).

According to him, the state of each component of a plasma is determined by its density ϱ_a, average velocity $\boldsymbol{U}_a$, temperature T_a, the viscous stress tensor p_{ij}^a and the thermal flux vector $\boldsymbol{S}^a$. Since the tensor p_{ij}^a is symmetric and the sum of its diagonal terms is zero, it is defined by five hydrodynamic functions.

Thus the state of each component is determined by defining thirteen hydrodynamic functions. All the other hydrodynamic functions are expressed in terms of these thirteen.

For example, the tensor S_{ijk}^a is

$$S_{ijk}^a = \frac{1}{5}(\delta_{ij}S_k + \delta_{ik}S_j + \delta_{kj}S_i); \quad S_{iik} = S_k. \tag{21.29}$$

Comparing this with (21.26),

$$a_{ijk}^{(3)a} = \frac{1}{5p_a\sqrt{\left(\frac{\theta_a}{m_a}\right)}}(\delta_{ij}S_k+\delta_{ik}S_j+\delta_{kj}S_i). \tag{21.30}$$

Thus the first four coefficients of the expansion (21.21) are determined in this approximation by the formulae (21.23–25, 30), and the others are assumed to be zero, i.e.

$$a_{i_1,\ldots,i_n}^{(n)}(\boldsymbol{q}, t) = 0, \quad n \geqslant 4. \tag{21.31}$$

Using the formulae (21.30, 19),

$$\frac{1}{3!}a_{ijk}^{(3)a}H_{ijk}^{(3)} = \frac{1}{10p_a\sqrt{\left(\frac{\theta_a}{m_a}\right)}}\xi_k(\xi^2-5)\,S_k^a. \tag{21.32}$$

Having regard to (21.31, 32), from (21.21) in the "thirteen-moment approximation" the expression for the function F_a is:

$$F_a(\boldsymbol{q}, \boldsymbol{p}, t) = \frac{p_a}{(2\pi m_a \varkappa T_a)^{3/2}}\exp\left(-\frac{m_a(\delta v_a)^2}{2\theta_a}\right)$$
$$\times\left\{1+\frac{m_a\delta v_i^a \delta v_j^a}{2p_a\theta_a}p_{ij}^a+\frac{m_a\delta v_i^a}{2p_a\theta_a}\left(\frac{m_a(\delta v_a)^2}{5\theta_a}-1\right)S_i^a\right\}. \tag{21.33}$$

The part played by the terms discarded in the expansion (21.21) can only be assessed qualitatively (see Grad, 1949), which is the method's main drawback.

We use the kinetic equations (11.46) to find the equations for the functions ϱ_a, $\boldsymbol{U}_a$, T_a (or p_a), p_{ij}^a and $\boldsymbol{S}^a$. Here we multiply (11.46) by $n_a\varphi_a(\boldsymbol{p})$ and then integrate over $\boldsymbol{p}$.

We introduce the notation

$$I_a\{n_a\varphi_a(\boldsymbol{p})\} = n_a\int \varphi_a(\boldsymbol{p})\,S_a(\boldsymbol{q}, \boldsymbol{p}, t)\,d^3\boldsymbol{p}. \tag{21.34}$$

Putting successively $\varphi_a = 1$, $\boldsymbol{p}$ and $p^2/2m_a$, the balance equations for the number of particles, the momentum density and the kinetic energy density are:

$$\frac{\partial \varrho_a}{\partial t}+\left(\frac{\partial}{\partial \boldsymbol{q}}\cdot \varrho_a \boldsymbol{U}_a\right)=0; \tag{21.35}$$

$$\frac{\partial m_a \varrho_a U_i^a}{\partial t}+\frac{\partial m_a \varrho_a U_i^a U_j^a}{\partial q_j}=-\frac{\partial p_a}{\partial q_i}-\frac{\partial p_{ij}^a}{\partial q_j}$$
$$+q_a E_i+\frac{1}{c}\,[\boldsymbol{j}_a\wedge \boldsymbol{B}]_i+I_a\{n_a p_i\}; \tag{21.36}$$

$$\frac{\partial}{\partial t}\left\{\varrho_a\frac{m_a U_a^2}{2}+\frac{3}{2}\,\varrho_a\theta_a\right\}=-\frac{\partial}{\partial q_k}\left\{U_k^a\frac{m_a \boldsymbol{U}_a^2}{2}\right.$$
$$\left.+p_{ik}^a U_i^a+\frac{5}{2}\,p^a U_k^a+\frac{1}{2}\,S_k^a\right\}=(\boldsymbol{j}\cdot\boldsymbol{E})+I_a\left\{n_a\frac{p^2}{2m_a}\right\}; \tag{21.37}$$

here q_a and $\boldsymbol{j}_a$ are the charge density and current density of component a.

Equations (21.36, 37) contain four, as yet, unknown functions:

$$p_{ij}^a,\ S_k^a,\ I_a\{n_a\boldsymbol{p}\},\ I_a\left\{\frac{n_a p^2}{2m_a}\right\}.$$

The latter two functions enter into the balance equations of the momentum and of the energy of the individual components.

In the equations of the momentum and energy of all the plasma, obtained from (21.36, 37) by summation over a, the collision integrals are discarded since by virtue of the laws of the conservation of the momentum and energy of charged particles (see eqns. (11.13, 14))

$$\sum_a I_a\{n_a\boldsymbol{p}\}=0,\quad \sum_a I_a\left\{\frac{n_a p^2}{2m_a}\right\}=0. \tag{21.38}$$

Using (21.35, 36) we eliminate from (21.37) the translational kinetic energy of component a as a whole. We thus obtain the following equation for the temperature θ_a:

$$\frac{\partial\theta_a}{\partial t}+U_k^a\frac{\partial\theta_a}{\partial q_k}+\frac{2}{3}\,\theta_a\frac{\partial U_k^a}{\partial q_k}+\frac{2}{3}\,\frac{p_{ik}^a}{\varrho_a}\cdot\frac{\partial U_k^a}{\partial q_i}$$
$$+\frac{1}{3\varrho_a}\cdot\frac{\partial S_k^a}{\partial q_k}=\frac{1}{3\varrho_a}\,I_a\{n_a m_a(\delta\boldsymbol{v}_a)^2\}. \tag{21.39}$$

In forming this equation it is taken into account that

$$I_a\{n_a m_a \boldsymbol{v}^2\} - 2I_a\{n_a m_a(\boldsymbol{U}_a \cdot \boldsymbol{v})\} = I_a\{n_a m_a(\delta v_a)^2\},$$

since $I_a\{n_a m_a\} = 0$ by virtue of the law of the conservation of the number of particles of each component.

Consider now the equations for the stress tensor P^a_{ij} and the vector $\boldsymbol{S}^a$.

We multiply eqn. (11.46) by $n_a m_a v_i v_j$ and then integrate over $\boldsymbol{p}$. As a result we obtain an equation describing the variation with time of the function

$$m_a \varrho_a U^a_i U^a_j + P^a_{ij}.$$

Using eqns. (21.35, 36) to eliminate from this equation the derivative $\partial(m_a \varrho_a U^a_i U^a_j)/\partial t$, the equation for the tensor P^a_{ij} is

$$\frac{\partial}{\partial t} P^a_{ij} + P^a_{ik} \frac{\partial U^a_j}{\partial q_k} + P^a_{jk} \frac{\partial U^a_i}{\partial q_k} + \frac{\partial (P^a_{ij} U^a_k)}{\partial q_k} + \frac{\partial S^a_{ijk}}{\partial q_k}$$
$$= I_a\{n_a m_a \delta v^a_i \delta v^a_j\}. \tag{21.40}$$

We avail ourselves of the smallness of parameter μ, as defined by (21.28).

We make the assumption (justified by the result) that

$$p^a_{ij},\ S^a_j \sim \mu. \tag{21.41}$$

Hence (21.21) in the zeroth approximation in μ yields the following expression for the functions F_a:

$$F^0_a = \frac{\varrho_a}{(2\pi m_a \varkappa T_a)^{3/2}} \exp\left(-\frac{m(\delta v_a)^2}{2\theta_a}\right). \tag{21.42}$$

Thus, in the zeroth approximation, the functions F_a are Maxwell distributions in which the functions ϱ_a, $\boldsymbol{U}_a$ and θ_a depend on the coordinates and time (local Maxwell distributions).

From (21.13–16) we have in the zeroth approximation in μ

$$p^a_{ij} = 0, \quad S^a_i = 0. \tag{21.43}$$

Therefore in the first approximation in μ the terms in (21.36, 37, 39) containing the functions p^a_{ij} and S^a_i, can be discarded. Equation (21.39) then becomes

$$\frac{\partial \theta_a}{\partial t} + U^a_k \frac{\partial \theta_a}{\partial q_k} + \frac{2}{3}\theta_a \frac{\partial U^a_k}{\partial q_k} = \frac{1}{3\varrho_a} I_a\{m_a n_a (\delta v_a)^2\}. \tag{21.44}$$

We write out eqn. (21.40) in the same approximation. Considering that $P_{ij}^a = \delta_{ij} p^a$ owing to (21.43), we obtain

$$\left(\frac{\partial p_a}{\partial t} + \frac{\partial}{\partial q_k}(p_a U_k^a) + \frac{2}{3} p_a \frac{\partial U_k^a}{\partial q_k}\right) \delta_{ij}$$
$$+ p_a \left(\frac{\partial U_i^a}{\partial q_j} + \frac{\partial U_j^a}{\partial q_i} - \frac{2}{3}\delta_{ij}\frac{\partial U_k^a}{\partial q_k}\right) = I_a\{n_a m_a \delta v_i^a \delta v_j^a\}. \tag{21.45}$$

Using the equation of state $p_a = \varrho_a \theta_a$ and also the equation of continuity, the first term in (21.45) becomes

$$\varrho_a \left(\frac{\partial \theta_a}{\partial t} + U_k \frac{\partial \theta_a}{\partial q_k} + \frac{2}{3}\theta_a \frac{\partial U_k^a}{\partial q_k}\right)\delta_{ij}.$$

Subtracting from (21.45) eqn. (21.44), multiplied by $\varrho_a \delta_{ij}$, we get the equation

$$p_a \left(\frac{\partial U_i^a}{\partial q_j} + \frac{\partial U_j^a}{\partial q_i} - \frac{2}{3}\delta_{ij}\frac{\partial U_k^a}{\partial q_k}\right)$$
$$= I_a \left\{n_a m_a \left(\delta v_i^a \delta v_j^a - \frac{1}{3}\delta_{ij}(\delta v_a)^2\right)\right\}. \tag{21.46}$$

Similarly, we transform the equation for the thermal flux vector $\boldsymbol{S}^a$. We multiply the kinetic equation (11.46) by $n_a m_a v_k v^2$ and then integrate over $\boldsymbol{p}$. By means of (21.35, 36) we eliminate the time derivatives of the functions ϱ_a and U_i^a. Leaving the first-order terms in μ, we get the equation

$$5\frac{p_a}{m_a} \cdot \frac{\partial \theta_a}{\partial q_k} = I_a\{n_a m_a \delta v_k^a (\delta v_a)^2 - 5\theta_a \delta v_k^a\}. \tag{21.47}$$

Substituting the expression (21.33) into the right-hand sides of (21.46, 47), the viscous stress tensor p_{ij}^a and thermal flux vector $\boldsymbol{S}^a$ can be expressed in terms of the functions ϱ_a, $\boldsymbol{U}_a$ and θ_a, and thus expressions can be found for p_{ij}^a and $\boldsymbol{S}^a$ in the first approximation in μ.

Using the resulting expressions for p_{ij}^a and $\boldsymbol{S}^a$, we can find a closed set of equations for ϱ_a, $\boldsymbol{U}_a$ and θ_a—the set of hydrodynamic equations.

For this purpose we substitute the expression (21.33) for the distribution function F_a into the collision integrals $I_a\{\ldots\}$ on the right-hand sides of (21.36, 37, 39, 46 and 47) and then carry out integration over the impulses $\boldsymbol{p}$ and $\boldsymbol{p}'$.

We take the collision integral in the kinetic equation (11.46) in Landau's approximation when the tensor Q_{ij}^{ab} is determined by (11.28) or (11.40). The collision integral is thus taken for a homogeneous plasma, i.e. the second term of (11.56) is neglected. The part played by this term will be elucidated below.

Substituting the right-hand side of (11.4) into (21.34) and then integrating by parts, we obtain

$$I_a\{n_a\varphi_a(\boldsymbol{p})\} = -\sum_b n_a n_b \int \frac{\partial \varphi_a}{\partial p_\alpha} Q_{\alpha\beta}^{ab} \left\{ \frac{\partial f_a}{\partial p_\beta} f_b - \frac{\partial f_b}{\partial p'_\beta} f_a \right\} d^3\boldsymbol{p}\, d^3\boldsymbol{p}'. \tag{21.48}$$

If this expression is summed over a and then symmetrised, it coincides with (11.13). Here the subscripts α and β take the place of the i and j over which the summation is carried out.

For the tensor Q_{ij}^{ab} we use (11.28) or (11.40).

To show how the integrals (21.48) are evaluated, let us consider the collision integral on the right-hand side of (21.36).

We substitute into (21.48) $\varphi_a = p_i$ and also the expression (11.28) for $Q_{\alpha\beta}^{ab}$. Considering that $\partial p_i/\partial p_\alpha = \delta_{i\alpha}$, we have

$$I_a\{n_a p_i\} = -2\sum_b e_a^2 e_a^2 \int \frac{k_i k_\beta}{k^4}\, \delta((\boldsymbol{k}\cdot\boldsymbol{v})-(\boldsymbol{k}\cdot\boldsymbol{v}')) \times \left\{ \frac{\partial F_a}{\partial p_\beta} F_b - \frac{\partial F_b}{\partial p'_\beta} F_a \right\} d^3\boldsymbol{k}\, d^3\boldsymbol{p}\, d^3\boldsymbol{p}', \tag{21.49}$$

bearing in mind that $F_a = n_a f_a$.

We integrate firstly over the momenta. The direction of the vector $\boldsymbol{k}$ is taken $\| x$. In (21.49) the functions F_a and F_b will then be differentiated only with respect to p_x and p'_x and so it is convenient to integrate first over p_z, p_y, p'_z, p'_y. In this case the following functions appear

$$F_a(p_x) = \int F_a(\boldsymbol{p})\, dp_y\, dp_z; \quad F_b(p'_x) = \int F_b(\boldsymbol{p}')\, dp'_y\, dp'_z.$$

To determine them, it is necessary to integrate the expressions (21.33) over p_y and p_z.

From (21.33) we get

$$F_a(p_x) = \frac{\varrho_a}{(2\pi m_a\theta_a)^{1/2}} e^{-\frac{m_a(\delta v_a)^2}{2\theta_a}} \left\{1+\frac{m_a \delta v_x^a}{10 p_a\theta_a}\right.$$
$$\left.\times\left(\frac{m_a(\delta v_x^a)^2}{\theta_a}-3\right)\right\}. \tag{21.50}$$

We substitute this result into formula (21.49) and differentiate with respect to p_x and p_x', and then, using the property of the function $\delta(kv_x - kv_x') = \delta(v_x - v_x')/k$, we integrate over p_x.

The resulting expression (omitting the subscript x of v and U) is:

$$I_a\{n_a p_i\} = \sum_b \frac{e_a^2 e_b^2 \varrho_a \varrho_b}{\pi} \sqrt{\left(\frac{m_a m_b}{\theta_a\theta_b}\right)} \int dv\, d^3\boldsymbol{k}\, \frac{k_x^2}{k^5}$$
$$\times e^{\frac{m_a(\delta v_a)^2}{2\theta_a}-\frac{m_b(\delta v_b)^2}{2\theta_b}} \left\{\left(\frac{\delta v_i^a}{\theta_a}-\frac{\delta v_i^b}{\theta_b}\right)-\frac{3}{10p_a\theta_a}\right.$$
$$\left.\times\left(\frac{m(\delta v_a)^2}{\theta_a}-1\right)S_i^a+\frac{3}{10p_b\theta_b}\left(\frac{m_b(\delta v_b)^2}{\theta_b}-1\right)S_i^b\right\}, \tag{21.51}$$

where $\delta v_a = v - U_x^a$ and $\delta v_b = v - U_x^b$.

The calculations are now continued on the assumption that the plasma consists of two components, viz. electrons and ions. The suffixes a and b in this case can only be 1 or 2. The index 1 is used for electrons, and 2 for ions.

It is considered that the electron mass is much less than the ion mass, i.e. $m_1 \ll m_2$.

We assume that the relative velocity of the electrons and ions is small compared with the thermal velocity of the ions, i.e.

$$U_1 - U_2 \ll \sqrt{\left(\frac{\theta_1}{m_1}\right)}. \tag{21.52}$$

Moreover,

$$\theta_1 - \theta_2 \ll \theta_1, \theta_2, \tag{21.53}$$

and so we can neglect the terms

$$\frac{(\theta_1-\theta_2)}{\theta_1} S_i^a; \quad \frac{(\theta_1-\theta_2)}{\theta_1} p_{ij}^a; \quad \left(\frac{U_1}{\theta_1}-\frac{U_2}{\theta_2}\right) S_i^a;$$
$$\left(\frac{U_1}{\theta_1}-\frac{U_2}{\theta_2}\right) p_{ij}^a \tag{21.54}$$

We introduce into the integral the variable of integration $\delta v_2 \equiv y$ in lieu of v. Considering that $\delta v_1 = \delta v_2 - (U_1 - U_2)_x$, we obtain

$$\delta v_1^2 = \delta v_2^2 - 2\delta v_2 (U_1 - U_2)_x + (U_1 - U_2)_x^2$$
$$\approx \delta v_2^2 - 2\delta v_2 (U_1 - U_2)_x. \tag{21.55}$$

We substitute this expression into (21.51) and then, considering that $m_1 \ll m_2$, and also having regard to (21.52–54), for $a = 1$ we get

$$I_1\{n_1 p_i\} = -\frac{e_1^2 e_2^2 \varrho_1 \varrho_2}{\pi} \sqrt{\left(\frac{m_1 m_2}{\theta_1 \theta_2}\right)} \int d^3\boldsymbol{k}\, dy\, e^{-\frac{m_2 y^2}{2\theta^2}} \frac{k_x^2}{k^5}$$
$$\times \left\{ \frac{(U_1 - U_2)_i}{\theta_1} + \frac{3}{10 p_1 \theta_1} \left(\frac{m_1 y^2}{\theta_1} - 1 \right) S_i^1 \right\}.$$

In this expression we integrate over y and $\boldsymbol{k}$, allowing for the fact that in Landau's approximation the integration over the magnitude of vector k is to be within the limits

$$\frac{1}{r_d} < k < \frac{1}{r_{\min}}. \tag{21.56}$$

We then get

$$I_1\{n_1 m_1 \boldsymbol{v}\} = -\frac{\varrho_1 m_1}{t_{1,2}} (\boldsymbol{U}_1 - \boldsymbol{U}_2) + \frac{3 m_1}{10 \theta_1} \mathbf{S}^1. \tag{21.57}$$

Here

$$t_{ab} = \frac{3\sqrt{(m_a)}\, \theta_a^{3/2}}{4\sqrt{(2\pi)}\, \varrho_b e_a^2 e_b^2 \ln \dfrac{r_d}{r_{\min}}}. \tag{21.58}$$

It is readily verifiable that the collision integral in the equation of motion of the ions is

$$I_2\{n_2 m_2 \boldsymbol{v}\} = -I_1\{n_1 m_1 \boldsymbol{v}\}. \tag{21.59}$$

This relation is in accord with the law of the conservation of the total momentum of the electrons and ions.

Expressions can be found in the same way for the collision integrals in eqns. (21.39, 46 and 47).

The integrals in the equations for θ_1 and θ_2 can be written in the form

$$I_1\{m_1 n_1(\delta v_1)^2\} = -6\varrho_1 \frac{m_1}{m_2} \cdot \frac{1}{t_{12}} (\theta_1 - \theta_2),$$

$$I_2\{m_2 n_2(\delta v_2)^2\} = -I_1\{m_1 n_1(\delta v_1)^2\}. \tag{21.60}$$

The latter relation is in accord with the law of the conservation of the total kinetic energy of the electrons and ions.

The collision integrals in eqns. (21.46, 47) on the conditions (21.52–54) are linear functions of the tensor p^a_{ij} and the vector $\boldsymbol{S}^a$ respectively. By these equations one can therefore express the functions p^a_{ij} and S^a_i in terms of the functions ϱ_a, $\boldsymbol{U}^a$ and θ_a and also the derivatives of these functions with respect to the co-ordinates.

By evaluating the integral on the right-hand side of (21.46), for the tensor p^a_{ij} of the electrons and ions we have:

$$p^1_{ij} = -\frac{5p_1}{6} \cdot \frac{\sqrt{(2)}\, t_{11} t_{12}}{t_{12} + \sqrt{(2)}\, t_{11}} \left(\frac{\partial U^1_i}{\partial q_j} + \frac{\partial U^1_j}{\partial q_i} - \frac{2}{3} \delta_{ij} \frac{\partial U^1_k}{\partial q_k} \right); \tag{21.61}$$

$$p^2_{ij} = -\frac{5p_2}{6} \sqrt{(2)}\, t_{22} \left(\frac{\partial U^2_i}{\partial q_j} + \frac{\partial U^2_j}{\partial q_i} - \frac{2}{3} \delta_{ij} \frac{\partial U^2_k}{\partial q_k} \right). \tag{21.62}$$

Evaluating the integral on the right-hand side of (21.47), for the thermal flux vector S^a of each component we get

$$\boldsymbol{S}^1 = -\frac{p_1}{m_1} \cdot \frac{25\sqrt{(2)}\, t_{11} t_{12}}{8 t_{12} + 13\sqrt{(2)}\, t_{11}} \cdot \frac{\partial \theta_1}{\partial \boldsymbol{q}}$$

$$+ (\boldsymbol{U}^1 - \boldsymbol{U}^2)\, \varrho_1 \theta_1 \frac{15\sqrt{(2)}\, t_{11}}{8 t_{12} + 13\sqrt{(2)}\, t_{11}}; \tag{21.63}$$

$$\boldsymbol{S}^2 = -\frac{p_2 25\sqrt{(2)}\, t_{22}}{m_2} \cdot \frac{\partial \theta_2}{\partial \boldsymbol{q}}. \tag{21.64}$$

The expressions (21.61–64) determine the coefficients of "viscosity" and thermal conductivity of the electrons and ions.

Note that the thermal flux vector in an electron–ion plasma is determined not only by the temperature gradient, but depends also on the relative velocity of the electrons and ions.

In turn the friction coefficient in the equations of motion (21.36) which is given by the expressions (21.57–59), is determined not only by the relative velocity, but also by the temperature gradient, in the presence of which the so-called thermoforce arises.

If we substitute the expressions (21.57, 59–64) into eqns. (21.36, 39) we obtain a set of hydrodynamic equations for a two-component electron–ion plasma. The electric and magnetic field strengths enter into eqns. (21.36) and so eqns. (21.35, 36 and 39) for the functions ϱ_a, $\boldsymbol{U}_a$ and θ_a must be solved simultaneously with the Maxwell equations.

Under certain conditions this set can be simplified as a set of equations in magnetohydrodynamics (see § 3). This is possible for sufficiently slow processes when the inertia of the electrons is negligible, but provided there is sufficient homogeneity so that the space charge is negligible. Under these conditions a plasma can be regarded as a single-component conducting medium.

In forming the hydrodynamic equations use was made of the kinetic equations in Landau's approximation.

These equations can be bettered in two respects:

(1) the more precise expression (11.4, 5) can be used for the collision integral;

(2) the collision integral (11.56) in which the plasma's spatial inhomogeneity is taken into account can be used.

In the hydrodynamic equations this permits corrections to the equation of state, equation of energy and so on, owing to the interaction of charged particles.

For instance, if the conditions (21.52, 53) are fulfilled, the expression for the pressure of component a is

$$p_a = \varrho_a \left[\theta_a - \frac{e_a^2}{6r_d} \right].$$

The second term in this expression determines a correction to the equation of state of an ideal gas. This correction is small since the quantity

$$\frac{e^2}{r_d \theta} \sim \left(\frac{r_{av}}{r_d} \right)^3 = \varepsilon \ll 1.$$

The corrections to the other thermodynamic functions are of the same order.

If the more precise kinetic equation (11.4, 5) is used, one can have regard to kinetic coefficients of waves having relaxation times much less than the first distribution functions (see Leontovich, 1963; Gorbunov and Silin, 1964; Akhiezer, Daneliya and Tsinzadze, 1964). If waves having relaxation times comparable with the relaxation times of the particle distribution functions are excited in a plasma, to form the hydrodynamic equations it is necessary to use the set of equations for the particle distribution function and the spectral function of the field. It is to this that the next section is devoted.

22. Taking Plasma Wave Radiation into Account in the Hydrodynamic Equations†

To discover the changes in the hydrodynamic equations when plasma wave radiation is taken into account, consider the case of a homogeneous and isotropic plasma.

As the initial equations we use the set (17.4) and (16.28) for the functions f_a and $(\delta \boldsymbol{E} \cdot \delta \boldsymbol{E})_{\omega, \boldsymbol{k}}$, or the simpler set (17.4), (16.37) and (17.12).

As in § 21, we represent the function f_a as a series in Hermite polynomials. In the isotropic case when the functions f_a depend only on the absolute value of the momentum, only terms with even polynomials remain in the expansion (21.21).

We consider the simplest approximation when the first term alone remains in (21.21). Considering that in the isotropic case the average velocities $\boldsymbol{U}_a$ are zero, we obtain the expression

$$f_a(\boldsymbol{p}, t) = (2\pi m_a \varkappa T_a)^{-3/2} \exp\left(-\frac{p^2}{2m_a \varkappa T_a}\right). \qquad (22.1)$$

We thus assume that the functions f_a are Maxwell distribution functions with a different temperature for each component of the plasma.

† Klimontovich (1963).

In this approximation the hydrodynamic equations of § 21, neglecting the radiation, are

$$\frac{\partial \varrho_a}{\partial t} = 0, \quad \frac{\partial \boldsymbol{U}_a}{\partial t} = 0; \quad \frac{\partial (T_a - T_b)}{\partial t} = -\alpha_{ab}(T_a - T_b). \tag{22.2}$$

These equations imply that in the absence of radiation only heat transfer takes place, leading to an equalization of the temperatures of the charged particles of the different components of the plasma. If the temperatures of the components are identical, all the hydrodynamic functions in this approximation are constant.

Corresponding equations will be obtained when the radiation is considered. Consider the simplest case when the temperatures of the components are identical, i.e. $T_a = T_b$.

We shall show that when the radiation is taken into account, the temperature of the particles can vary owing to heat exchange with the radiation.

We multiply equation (17.4) by $n_a p^2/2m_a$, integrate over $\boldsymbol{p}$ and then sum over a. Using the definition of the particle temperature

$$n_a \int \frac{p^2}{2m_a} f_a \, d^3\boldsymbol{p} = \varrho_a \frac{3}{2} \varkappa T_a,$$

after integration by parts we obtain the equation

$$\frac{3}{2} \varrho \frac{\partial \varkappa T}{\partial t} = -\sum_a \int \left\{ v_i D^a_{ij} \frac{\partial f_a}{\partial p_j} + v_i A^a_i f_a \right\} d^3\boldsymbol{p};$$

$$\varrho = \sum_a \varrho_a. \tag{22.3}$$

According to (17.5, 6) the coefficients D^a_{ij} and A^a_i each consist of two parts which relate respectively to the collision region and the radiation region.

From (11.13) it follows that collisions in a homogeneous plasma do not alter the total kinetic energy of charged particles and so in (22.3) one only needs to take into account the contribution from the radiation region.

Consider the first term on the right-hand side of (22.3). We substitute into it the expressions (17.7) and (22.1). Using the expressions for the real and imaginary parts of $\varepsilon(\omega, \boldsymbol{k})$:

$$\varepsilon'(\omega, \boldsymbol{k}) = 1+\sum_a \frac{4\pi e_a^2 n_a}{k^2} P \int \frac{\left(\boldsymbol{k}\cdot\frac{\partial f_a}{\partial \boldsymbol{p}}\right)}{\omega-(\boldsymbol{k}\cdot\boldsymbol{v})} d^3\boldsymbol{p};$$

$$\varepsilon'' = -\sum_a \frac{4\pi^2 e_a^2 n_a}{k^2} \int \delta(\omega-(\boldsymbol{k}\cdot\boldsymbol{v})) \left(\boldsymbol{k}\cdot\frac{\partial f_a}{\partial \boldsymbol{p}}\right) d^3\boldsymbol{p},$$

we obtain for the first term on the right-hand side of (22.3)

$$\frac{1}{64\pi^5}\int \Big\{\omega\varepsilon''(\omega, \boldsymbol{k})(\delta\boldsymbol{E}\cdot\delta\boldsymbol{E})^{\mathrm{rad}}_{\omega,\boldsymbol{k},t} + \frac{1}{2}\frac{\partial}{\partial\omega}[\omega(\varepsilon'(\omega, \boldsymbol{k})-1)]\frac{\partial}{\partial t}(\delta\boldsymbol{E}\cdot\delta\boldsymbol{E})_{\omega,\boldsymbol{k},t}\Big\}\, d\omega\, d^3\boldsymbol{k}; \tag{22.4}$$

in the second term it is taken into account that

$$\sum_a \frac{4\pi e_a^2 n_a}{k^2}\int (\boldsymbol{k}\cdot\boldsymbol{v})\frac{\partial}{\partial\omega}\left(P\frac{1}{\omega-(\boldsymbol{k}\cdot\boldsymbol{v})}\right)\left(\boldsymbol{k}\cdot\frac{\partial f_a}{\partial \boldsymbol{p}}\right) d^3\boldsymbol{p} = \frac{\partial}{\partial\omega}[\omega(\varepsilon'(\omega, \boldsymbol{k})-1)].$$

We transform the second term on the right-hand side of (22.3). We substitute into it the expressions (17.8) and (22.1) and then use the formula (17.3) and, after a simple transformation, we obtain the expression

$$-\sum_a \frac{ne_a^2}{2\pi}\int \frac{(\boldsymbol{k}\cdot\boldsymbol{v})}{k^2}\delta(\omega-(\boldsymbol{k}\cdot\boldsymbol{v}))\,\mathrm{sign}\frac{\partial\varepsilon'}{\partial\omega}\,\delta(\varepsilon'(\omega, \boldsymbol{k})) \times f_a\, d^3\boldsymbol{p}\, d\omega\, d^3\boldsymbol{k}.$$

Using the definition of $\varepsilon''(\omega, \boldsymbol{k})$, we write this expression as

$$-\frac{\varkappa T}{8\pi^3}\int \varepsilon''(\omega, \boldsymbol{k})\,\mathrm{sign}\frac{\partial\varepsilon'}{\partial\omega}\,\delta(\varepsilon'(\omega, \boldsymbol{k}))\, d\omega\, d^3\boldsymbol{k}. \tag{22.5}$$

The sum of the expressions (22.4, 5) determines the right-hand side of (22.3). To simplify it, consider eqn. (16.28). We substitute into it the expressions (22.1) and then, using the definition of

$\varepsilon''(\omega, \boldsymbol{k})$, this equation becomes

$$\frac{\partial}{\partial t}(\delta \boldsymbol{E}\cdot\delta \boldsymbol{E})^{\text{rad}}_{\omega, \boldsymbol{k}, t} = -2\gamma(\omega, \boldsymbol{k})(\delta \boldsymbol{E}\cdot\delta \boldsymbol{E})^{\text{rad}}_{\omega, \boldsymbol{k}, t} + 16\pi^2 \frac{\delta(\varepsilon'(\omega, \boldsymbol{k}))}{\omega\left|\frac{\partial \varepsilon'}{\partial \omega}\right|}\varepsilon''(\omega, \boldsymbol{k})\varkappa T.$$

The last term can be transformed by using the definition of the damping decrement (16.22).

We thus get the following equation for the spectral function

$$\frac{\partial}{\partial t}(\delta \boldsymbol{E}\cdot\delta \boldsymbol{E})^{\text{rad}}_{\omega, \boldsymbol{k}, t} = -2\gamma(\omega, \boldsymbol{k})\left\{(\delta \boldsymbol{E}\cdot\delta \boldsymbol{E})_{\omega, \boldsymbol{k}, t} - \frac{8\pi^2}{\omega}\operatorname{sign}\frac{\partial \varepsilon'}{\partial \omega}\delta(\varepsilon'(\omega, \boldsymbol{k}))\varkappa T.\right\}. \tag{22.6}$$

This equation in the equilibrium case yields an expression for the spectral function which coincides with (17.15).

We now transform the right-hand side of (22.3), which is determined by the sum of the expressions (22.4, 5).

We add together the expressions (22.4, 5) and then eliminate the time derivative $\partial(\delta \boldsymbol{E}\cdot\delta \boldsymbol{E})_{\omega, \boldsymbol{k}, t}/\partial t$ by means of (22.6).

The resulting equation for the particle temperature T is

$$\frac{3}{2}\varrho\frac{\partial \varkappa T}{\partial t} = \frac{1}{8\pi^3}\int \gamma(\omega, \boldsymbol{k})\left\{\frac{(\delta \boldsymbol{E}\cdot\delta \boldsymbol{E})_{\omega, \boldsymbol{k}}}{8\pi^2} - \frac{1}{\omega}\operatorname{sign}\frac{\partial \varepsilon'}{\partial \omega}\delta(\varepsilon'(\omega, \boldsymbol{k}))\varkappa T\right\} d\omega\, d^3\boldsymbol{k}. \tag{22.7}$$

Equations (22.6, 7) form a closed set for the functions T and $(\delta \boldsymbol{E}\cdot\delta \boldsymbol{E})^{\text{rad}}_{\omega, \boldsymbol{k}, t}$. This set describes, in the hydrodynamic approximation, the energy exchange with the radiation and charged particles in a homogeneous and isotropic plasma.

So the law of the conservation of the total energy of the plasma is

$$\frac{3}{2}\varrho\varkappa T + \frac{1}{16\pi^4}\int \frac{(\delta \boldsymbol{E}\cdot\delta \boldsymbol{E})^{\text{rad}}_{\omega, \boldsymbol{k}}}{8\pi}\, d\omega\, d^3\boldsymbol{k}. \tag{22.8}$$

This expression is a special case of the more general expression (17.17).

In the equilibrium case the spectral function $(\delta\boldsymbol{E}\cdot\delta\boldsymbol{E})_{\omega,\boldsymbol{k}}$ is determined by the formula (17.15).

In the two-root approximation, instead of (22.6, 7), a simpler set of equations is obtained for T and $(\delta\boldsymbol{E}\cdot\delta\boldsymbol{E})^{\text{rad}}_{\boldsymbol{k},t}$.

Using the notation of (17.14) for the radiation temperature, this set becomes

$$\frac{3}{2}\varrho\frac{\partial\varkappa T}{\partial t} = \frac{1}{8\pi^3}\int \gamma(\omega_{\boldsymbol{k}},\boldsymbol{k})(T^{\text{rad}}_{\boldsymbol{k}}-T)\,d^3\boldsymbol{k}; \tag{22.9}$$

$$\frac{\partial T^{\text{rad}}_{\boldsymbol{k}}}{\partial t} = -2\gamma(\omega_{\boldsymbol{k}},\boldsymbol{k})(T^{\text{rad}}_{\boldsymbol{k}}-T). \tag{22.10}$$

Clearly, equilibrium is attained when the particle temperature is equal to the radiation temperature, i.e. $T = T^{\text{rad}}_{\boldsymbol{k}}$, and then the law of the conservation of energy can be written as

$$\frac{3}{2}\varrho\varkappa T+\frac{1}{8\pi^3}\int\frac{\varkappa T^{\text{rad}}_{\boldsymbol{k}}}{2}\,d^3\boldsymbol{k} = \text{const.} \tag{22.11}$$

In this example the plasma is stable in the sense that the damping decrement is constant for all values of T.

To describe the development of turbulence within the framework of the hydrodynamic equations, more terms need to be retained in the Hermite polynomial expansion.

Unless the growth of instability is confined to variation of the f_a, eqns. (16.28) and (17.4) must be supplemented by terms which have regard to higher moments. The right-hand sides of eqns. (22.9, 10) then contain supplementary terms which are non-linear in $T^{\text{rad}}_{\boldsymbol{k}}$. For this the equations of § 18 are used.

The foregoing hydrodynamic equations can easily be generalized to the case of a weakly inhomogeneous plasma.

23. Magnetohydrodynamic Equations for a Non-isothermic Plasma without "Collisions"

The hydrodynamic equations of §§ 21 and 22 are unsuitable if the dimensions of the system are less than the mean free path and if the characteristic times are less than the free path time.

In §§ 6–9 it was shown that under these conditions the processes in a plasma can be described by a set of self-consistent equations—the equations for the first moments.

The set of self-consistent equations is very complicated, so it is important to discover the conditions under which this set can be replaced by a set of simpler hydrodynamic equations.

In the present section we show how to describe the processes in a strongly non-isothermic plasma, when $T_e \gg T_i$, by hydrodynamic equations which differ in the dissipative terms from their conventional form (see Klimontovich and Silin, 1961; and Lovetskii and Rukhadze, 1962).

In a strongly non-isothermic plasma in many cases one can neglect the thermal motion of the ions, then in the absence of collisions for describing their motion one can use the equation of continuity

$$\frac{\partial \varrho}{\partial t} + \left(\frac{\partial}{\partial \boldsymbol{q}} \cdot \varrho \boldsymbol{U}\right) = 0 \tag{23.1}$$

and Newton's equation

$$m_i \varrho \left(\frac{\partial \boldsymbol{U}}{\partial t} + \left(\boldsymbol{U} \cdot \frac{\partial}{\partial \boldsymbol{q}}\right) \boldsymbol{U}\right) = q_i \left(\boldsymbol{E} + \frac{1}{c} [\boldsymbol{U} \wedge \boldsymbol{B}]\right), \tag{23.2}$$

where ϱ is density, q_i is the charge density of the ions, $\boldsymbol{U}$ is the velocity of the ions, and $\boldsymbol{E}$ and $\boldsymbol{B}$ the electric and magnetic field strengths. The suffix i of ϱ and $\boldsymbol{U}$ is omitted.

To describe the motion of electrons in a non-isothermic plasma, one may use the self-consistent field kinetic equation

$$\frac{\partial f_e}{\partial t} + \left(\boldsymbol{v} \cdot \frac{\partial f_e}{\partial \boldsymbol{q}}\right) + e\left(\left\{\boldsymbol{E} + \frac{1}{c} [\boldsymbol{v} \wedge \boldsymbol{B}]\right\} \cdot \frac{\partial f_e}{\partial \boldsymbol{p}}\right) = 0. \tag{23.3}$$

For frequencies ω which are low in comparison with the ion Larmor frequency (in the frame of reference linked with the ions), from the equation (23.2), neglecting terms of second order of smallness, we find that

$$\boldsymbol{E} = -\frac{1}{c} [\boldsymbol{U} \wedge \boldsymbol{B}]. \tag{23.4}$$

Substituting this expression for $\boldsymbol{E}$ into the field equation $c \text{ curl } \boldsymbol{E} = -\partial \boldsymbol{B}/\partial t$, we get

$$\frac{\partial \boldsymbol{B}}{\partial t} = \text{curl } [\boldsymbol{U} \wedge \boldsymbol{B}]. \tag{23.5}$$

Equation (23.5) is one of the set of magnetohydrodynamic equations for a plasma. Owing to neglecting the collisions the conductivity turns out to be infinite. The second equation is

$$\text{div } \boldsymbol{B} = 0. \tag{23.6}$$

If the ion plasma frequency is much greater than the particular frequency ω, the field equations in which the displacement current is negligible become

$$\boldsymbol{j} = \frac{c}{4\pi} \text{curl } \boldsymbol{B}, \quad q = 0, \tag{23.7}$$

where $\boldsymbol{j} = q_i \boldsymbol{U} + e \int \boldsymbol{v} f_e \, d^3\boldsymbol{p}$ is the current density, and $q = q_i + e \int f_e \, d^3\boldsymbol{p}$ is the charge density of the plasma.

To form a closed set of magnetohydrodynamic equations, it is necessary, using eqns. (23.3, 7), to define the electric field in terms of the electron characteristics and then eliminate it from eqn. (23.2).

We shall do this first neglecting dissipative processes. If the characteristic magnetohydrodynamic velocities are much less than the thermal velocities of the electrons $[V_{T_e} = \sqrt{(\varkappa T_e/m)}]$, then in deriving the hydrodynamic equation without dissipative terms in the kinetic equation (23.3) for the electrons, the term $\partial f_e/\partial t$ can be neglected. This implies that one is always able to establish a stationary distribution for the electrons.

We put $\varphi(\boldsymbol{q}, t)$ for the electric potential, and in terms of the electron drift velocity we try to satisfy (23.3) by a solution of the kind

$$f_e = F\left(e\varphi(\boldsymbol{q}, t) + \frac{1}{2} m_e (\boldsymbol{v} - \boldsymbol{U}_e)^2\right), \tag{23.8}$$

where F is an arbitrary function. As a special case, for instance, F may be a Maxwell–Boltzmann distribution.

It is required to find an expression for $\boldsymbol{E}$ as a function of q_e, T, $\boldsymbol{U}_e$ and $\boldsymbol{B}$, for which the expression (23.8) satisfies eqn. (23.3). Accordingly, we multiply eqn. (23.3) for $\partial f_e/\partial t = 0$ by v_i and then integrate over the momenta. As a result we obtain the transport equation for the density and momentum of electrons

$$m_e \frac{\partial}{\partial q_k} \int v_i v_k f_e \, d^3\boldsymbol{p} = q_e \left(E_i + \frac{e}{c} [\boldsymbol{U}_e \wedge \boldsymbol{B}]_i \right). \qquad (23.9)$$

Using the expression (23.8), we get

$$\int v_i v_k f_e \, d^3\boldsymbol{p} = \frac{q_e}{e} \left\{ U_i^e U_k^e + \delta_{ik} \frac{\varkappa T}{m} \right\}. \qquad (23.10)$$

Here

$$\frac{q_e}{e} = \int f_e \, d^3\boldsymbol{p}; \quad \frac{q_e}{e} \cdot \frac{\varkappa T}{m_e} = \frac{1}{3} \int (\boldsymbol{v} - \boldsymbol{U}_e)^2 f_e d^3\boldsymbol{p}.$$

Substituting the expression (23.10) into eqn. (23.9) and using the equation of continuity $\left(\frac{\partial}{\partial \boldsymbol{q}} \cdot \left(\frac{q_e}{e} \boldsymbol{U} \right) \right) = 0$, we get

$$m_e \left(\boldsymbol{U}_e \cdot \frac{\partial}{\partial \boldsymbol{q}} \right) \boldsymbol{U}_e + \frac{1}{q_e} \cdot \frac{\partial}{\partial \boldsymbol{q}} (q_e \varkappa T) = e \left(\boldsymbol{E} + \frac{1}{c} [\boldsymbol{U}_e \wedge \boldsymbol{B}] \right). \qquad (23.11)$$

Comparing eqns. (23.11) and (23.2), we see that in calculating the electric field strength $\boldsymbol{E}$, owing to the smallness of the mass ratio m_e/m_i, we can neglect the first term in (23.11). The required expression for E therefore is

$$e\boldsymbol{E} = \frac{1}{q_e} \cdot \frac{\partial}{\partial \boldsymbol{q}} (q_e \varkappa T) - \frac{e}{c} [\boldsymbol{U}_e \wedge \boldsymbol{B}]. \qquad (23.12)$$

Substituting this expression into eqn. (23.2) and considering that, in accordance with (23.7), $q_i \boldsymbol{U} + q_e \boldsymbol{U}_e = c \operatorname{curl} \boldsymbol{B}$ and $q_e = -q_i = -e_i \varrho$, the magnetohydrodynamic equation of motion neglecting dissipative processes is

$$\frac{\partial \boldsymbol{U}}{\partial t} + \left(\boldsymbol{U} \cdot \frac{\partial}{\partial \boldsymbol{q}} \right) \boldsymbol{U} = -\frac{v_s^2}{\varrho} \cdot \frac{\partial \varrho}{\partial \boldsymbol{q}} - \frac{1}{4\pi \varrho m_i} [\boldsymbol{B} \wedge \operatorname{curl} \boldsymbol{B}], \qquad (23.13)$$

where $v_s = \sqrt{(\varkappa T/m_i)}$ is the velocity of sound in a plasma and $T = \text{constant}$. Equations (23.1, 13, 5 and 6) are also a closed set of magnetohydrodynamic equations coinciding with the corresponding set of equations for an ideal fluid if the pressure is $p = m_i v_s^2 \varrho$.

To take into account the dissipative processes which take place in a plasma without collisions, we proceed as follows.

Assuming that the dissipative terms are small, for their determination one can use the solution of eqn. (23.3) for the distribution function f_e of the electrons in the linear approximation.

Such a solution was obtained in § 9.

Using the expression (9.68) for the electron current, we express $\boldsymbol{E}$ in terms of $\boldsymbol{j}_e$. We then get

$$e_i n_i \boldsymbol{E}(\boldsymbol{q}, t) = -m_i v_s^2 \frac{\partial \varrho_1}{\partial \boldsymbol{q}} + \frac{1}{c}[\boldsymbol{j}_e \wedge \boldsymbol{B}_0] + \boldsymbol{F}_{\text{diss}}. \tag{23.14}$$

Here $\varrho_1 = \int f_e' \, d^3\boldsymbol{p}$ is the non-equilibrium addition to the electron density, $\boldsymbol{B}_0$ is the external magnetic field, and $\boldsymbol{F}_{\text{diss}}$ is the "density" of the force due to the dissipative processes (see below):

$$\boldsymbol{F}_{\text{diss}} = m_i n_i v_s^2 \left\{ \left(\boldsymbol{b}_0 \left(\boldsymbol{b}_0 \cdot \frac{\partial}{\partial \boldsymbol{q}} \right) + \left[\boldsymbol{b}_0 \wedge \left[\boldsymbol{b}_0 \wedge \frac{\partial}{\partial \boldsymbol{q}} \right]\right] \right) \right.$$
$$\left. \times \left(\boldsymbol{b}_0 \cdot \frac{\partial}{\partial \boldsymbol{q}} \right) b_{0j} - \left[\boldsymbol{b}_0 \wedge \left[\boldsymbol{b}_0 \wedge \frac{\partial}{\partial \boldsymbol{q}} \right]\right] \frac{\partial}{\partial q_j} \right\}$$
$$\times \int d^3\boldsymbol{q}' Q(\boldsymbol{q} - \boldsymbol{q}') \, U_j(\boldsymbol{q}', t), \quad \boldsymbol{b}_0 = \boldsymbol{B}_0 / B_0. \tag{23.15}$$

In this expression

$$Q(\boldsymbol{r}) = \frac{1}{(2\pi)^3} \int \tau(\boldsymbol{k}) \, e^{i(\boldsymbol{k} \cdot \boldsymbol{r})} \, d^3\boldsymbol{k}, \quad \tau(\boldsymbol{k}) = \sqrt{\left(\frac{\pi m_e}{2\varkappa T} \right)} \frac{1}{|(\boldsymbol{b}_0 \cdot \boldsymbol{k})|}. \tag{23.16}$$

From the expressions (23.15, 16) it follows that the dissipative force is proportional to the square root of the mass ratio m_e/m_i.

The expression (23.14) without the term $\boldsymbol{F}_{\text{diss}}$ in the linear approximation coincides with (23.12) and therefore by using the linear approximation for calculating $\boldsymbol{F}_{\text{diss}}$, the expression (23.14) can be written as

$$q_i \boldsymbol{E} = -m_i v_s^2 \frac{\partial \varrho}{\partial \boldsymbol{q}} + \frac{1}{c}[\boldsymbol{j}_e \wedge \boldsymbol{B}] + \boldsymbol{F}_{\text{diss}}.$$

Substituting this expression into (23.2) and considering that

$$\boldsymbol{j} = \boldsymbol{j}_e + q_i \boldsymbol{U} = \frac{c}{4\pi} \operatorname{curl} \boldsymbol{B},$$

we get in lieu of (23.13) the equation

$$\frac{\partial \boldsymbol{U}}{\partial t} + \left(\boldsymbol{U} \cdot \frac{\partial}{\partial \boldsymbol{q}}\right) \boldsymbol{U} = -\frac{v_s^2}{\varrho} \cdot \frac{\partial \varrho}{\partial \boldsymbol{q}} - \frac{1}{4\pi \varrho m_i} [\boldsymbol{B} \wedge \operatorname{curl} \boldsymbol{B}]$$
$$+ \frac{1}{m_i n_i} \boldsymbol{F}_{\text{diss}}.$$

It is this equation and eqns. (22.1, 5 and 6) for a given temperature T_e which are the required set of magnetohydrodynamic equations for a plasma without collisions.

These equations differ from the conventional equations of magnetohydrodynamics (see § 3) in that now the dissipative force is of a different nature. The dissipation here is due to the absorption of magnetosonic waves by the electrons of the plasma. So the dissipative force $\boldsymbol{F}_{\text{diss}}$ is non-local, i.e. at the point $\boldsymbol{q}$ it is determined by the values of the velocity $\boldsymbol{U}(\boldsymbol{q}', t)$ in the domain of space as a whole, including the point $\boldsymbol{q}$.

For $\boldsymbol{B} = 0$, eqn. (23.16) simplifies to

$$\frac{\partial \boldsymbol{U}}{\partial t} + \left(\boldsymbol{U} \cdot \frac{\partial}{\partial \boldsymbol{q}}\right) \boldsymbol{U} = -\frac{v_s^2}{\varrho} \cdot \frac{\partial \varrho}{\partial \boldsymbol{q}}$$
$$+ v_s^2 \frac{\partial}{\partial \boldsymbol{q}} \int Q^\circ(\boldsymbol{q} - \boldsymbol{q}') \operatorname{div} \boldsymbol{U}(\boldsymbol{q}', t)\, d^3\boldsymbol{q}'. \tag{23.17}$$

The kernel Q° differs from Q (see 23.16) in the replacement of $1/|(\boldsymbol{k} \cdot \boldsymbol{b}_0|$ by $1/|\boldsymbol{k}|$.

This equation, together with the equation of continuity (23.1) for a given electron temperature, forms a closed set. The kernel Q, or Q° in the absence of the magnetic field, slowly decreases with increasing r. This is due to the fact that the integrand has singularities if $k = 0$, in connexion with the fact that in the case under consideration the characteristic dimensions of the spatial inhomogeneities are small compared with the mean free path.

For distances r comparable with, or greater than, the mean free path λ, in lieu of the expression for Q one can use the approximate expression

$$Q(r)=\frac{1}{(2\pi)^3}\int\frac{d^3\boldsymbol{k}}{\left[(\boldsymbol{k}\cdot\boldsymbol{b}_0)^2+\dfrac{\pi m\nu}{\varkappa T}\right]^{1/2}}e^{i(\boldsymbol{k}\cdot\boldsymbol{r})},\tag{23.18}$$

where ν is the collision frequency.

For the one-dimensional case when the Q depends on the coordinate x and on t, the kernel Q needs to be integrated over y and z. In this case, in lieu of the expression for Q, we get

$$Q(x)=\frac{1}{\pi\,|b_{0x}|}K_0\left(\frac{x}{l\,|b_{0x}|}\right),\quad l=\lambda\sqrt{\left(\frac{2}{\pi}\right)}.\tag{23.19}$$

In the absence of the magnetic field the $1/|b_{0x}|$ in this expression is to be replaced by unity. The K is a MacDonald function.

Let us consider the possibility of stationary shock waves existing in a plasma without collisions. We begin with the case $\boldsymbol{B}=0$.

It suffices to consider eqns. (23.1 and 17) in the one-dimensional case.

We introduce a frame of reference fixed to the surface of the shock discontinuity, and the x-direction is perpendicular to this surface. Using eqns. (23.1, 17) we find the continuity conditions of the flux of matter and the momentum flux on the surface of discontinuity. Putting $\varrho\boldsymbol{U}=\boldsymbol{j}_0$ and eliminating ϱ from these continuity conditions, the continuity condition of the momentum density flux is the integral equation

$$\left(U+\frac{v_s^2}{U}\right)j_0-\frac{a}{\pi}v_s\varrho_0\int_{-\infty}^{\infty}K_0\left(\frac{|x-x'|}{\lambda}\right)\times\frac{dU(x')}{dx'}\,dx'=Cj_0,\tag{23.20}$$

where

$$a=\sqrt{(\pi m v_s^2/2\varkappa T)}.$$

We introduce the constant U^- and then write C as $U^-+v_s^2/U^-$. Equation (23.20) then becomes

$$(U-U^-)+v_s^2\left(\frac{1}{U}-\frac{1}{U^-}\right)=\frac{a v_s\varrho_0}{\pi j_0}\int_{-\infty}^{\infty}K_0\left(\frac{|x-x'|}{\lambda}\right)\times\frac{dU(x')}{dx'}\,dx'.\tag{23.21}$$

Equation (23.21) is satisfied by definite constant values of the velocity U. To determine these constant values, eqn. (23.21) yields the equation

$$(U-U^{-})+v_{\mathrm{s}}^{2}\left(\frac{1}{U}-\frac{1}{U^{-}}\right)=0, \tag{23.22}$$

whence we get two constant values for U:

$$U=U^{-}, \quad U=\frac{v_{\mathrm{s}}^{2}}{U^{-}}\equiv U^{+}.$$

Both values are the same if $U^{-}=v_{\mathrm{s}}$.

To answer the question whether shock waves can exist in a plasma, one has to consider the possibility of a solution of eqn. (23.21) which for $x=\pm\infty$ gives U^{+} and U^{-} with $U^{+}\neq U^{-}$.

From (23.21) it follows that this solution exists whenever the transition from $x=+\infty$ to $x=-\infty$ is such that $U(x, t)$ varies little over distances of the order of the mean free path. In fact, in this case the dU/dx can be taken outside the integral and then the integral equation in the first approximation becomes the differential equation

$$U-U^{-}+v_{\mathrm{s}}^{2}\left(\frac{1}{U}-\frac{1}{U^{-}}\right)=a\lambda\frac{v_{\mathrm{s}}\varrho_{0}}{j_{0}}\cdot\frac{dU}{dx}. \tag{23.23}$$

This equation has a solution which is equal to U^{+} and U^{-} for $x=\pm\infty$, and then for the solution's stability it is necessary that $U^{-}>v_{\mathrm{s}}$ and $U^{+}<v_{\mathrm{s}}$: the width of the transitional region is determined by the mean free path. In our approximation this case is analogous to that considered in gas dynamics.

From (23.21) it follows that no stationary shock wave can exist in a plasma in which the transition from $x=-\infty$ to $x=+\infty$ is much greater than the mean free path, i.e. under conditions when the collisions can be neglected.

In fact, in this case, supposing that the transition from $x=-\infty$ to $x=+\infty$ takes place near x_0, eqn. (23.21) can be written approximately as follows:

$$U-U^{-}+v_{\mathrm{s}}^{2}\left(\frac{1}{U}-\frac{1}{U^{-}}\right)=(U^{-}-U^{+})\frac{av_{\mathrm{s}}\varrho_{0}}{j_{0}} \times K_{0}\left(\frac{|x-x_{0}|}{\lambda}\right). \tag{23.24}$$

Since the right-hand side is also non-zero for $x - x_0 \sim \lambda$, the assumption made in forming (23.24) is not justified.

Thus no stationary shock waves exist in a plasma with width much less than the mean free path.

Recapitulating, the conditions under which our magnetohydrodynamic conditions are valid, are:

(1) Mean free path infinitely large:

(2) Plasma highly non-isothermic. Zero ion thermal velocity.

(3) Notable variations of the functions ϱ, $\boldsymbol{U}$ and $\boldsymbol{B}$ take place over distances much greater than the Debye radius, the Larmor radius and the length c/ω_L.

In the paper by Lovetskii and Rukhadze (1962) the foregoing magnetohydrodynamic equations are supplemented by dissipative terms taking the ion collisions in the plasma into account.

24. Hydrodynamic Description of Charged Particle Motion in a Weakly Ionized Plasma

A plasma is deemed to be weakly ionized if the concentration of the charged particles is so low that the natural oscillation frequency ω_L of the plasma is less than the frequency ν_{an} of collisions between charged particles and neutral atoms:

$$\omega_L < \nu_{an}. \tag{24.1}$$

The subscript a refers to charged particles, and n to neutral atoms.

According to (11.42) the collision frequency of the charged particles in a rarefied plasma is much less than ω_L, so (24.1) implies that in a weakly ionized plasma the frequency ν_{ab} of collisions between charged particles and other charged particles is much less than ν_{an}, i.e.

$$\nu_{ab} < \nu_{an}. \tag{24.1a}$$

If these conditions are fulfilled, the time taken to establish the local Maxwell distribution for charged particles, which is of the order of $1/\nu_{an}$, may be less than that taken to establish the equilibrium or quasi (local) equilibrium of the correlation function g_{ab}. Hence, in a weakly ionized plasma (as in § 16) it is impossible to express the correlation functions in terms of first distribution functions and then obtain closed equations for the first distribution functions—the kinetic equations for the functions f_a.

For this reason, for deriving the hydrodynamic equations which describe the motion of charged particles in a weakly ionized plasma, one has to use, not kinetic equations, as in § 21, but a set of equations for the functions f_a and g_{ab}, or a corresponding set of equations for the moments and random functions N_a.

Here we give the hydrodynamic equations of the first approximation [see papers by Klimontovich and Ebeling (1963) and Falkenhagen and Ebeling (1963) for the derivation].

In forming the equations of the approximation in § 21 for the functions f_a we used the local Maxwell distribution (21.42):

$$n_a f_a(\boldsymbol{q}, \boldsymbol{p}, t) = \frac{\varrho_a(\boldsymbol{q}, t)}{(2\pi m\varkappa_a T)^{3/2}} e^{-\frac{(\boldsymbol{p}-m_a \boldsymbol{U}_a(\boldsymbol{q}, t))^2}{2m_a \varkappa T}}. \tag{24.2}$$

Unlike (21.42), here T is the neutral gas temperature and $\boldsymbol{U}_a$ is the average velocity of the charged components.

Suppose that the neutral gas temperature is constant and that the average velocity is zero. We assume also that in the first approximation the correlation functions $g_{ab}(\boldsymbol{q}, \boldsymbol{q}', \boldsymbol{p}, \boldsymbol{p}', t)$ can be written in the form

$$g_{ab} = \frac{\gamma_{ab}(\boldsymbol{q}, \boldsymbol{q}', t)}{(4\pi^2 m_a m_b (\varkappa T)^2)^{3/2}} e^{-\frac{(\boldsymbol{p}-m_a \overset{b}{\boldsymbol{W}}_a(\boldsymbol{q}, \boldsymbol{q}', t))^2}{2m_a \varkappa T} - \frac{(\boldsymbol{p}-m_b \overset{a}{\boldsymbol{W}}_b(\boldsymbol{q}, \boldsymbol{q}', t))^2}{2m_b \varkappa T}}; \tag{24.3}$$

$$\gamma_{ab}(\boldsymbol{q}, \boldsymbol{q}', t) = \int g_{ab}(\boldsymbol{q}, \boldsymbol{q}', \boldsymbol{p}, \boldsymbol{p}', t)\, d^3\boldsymbol{p}\, d^3\boldsymbol{p}'; \tag{24.4}$$

$$\boldsymbol{W}_a^b = \frac{1}{\gamma_{ab}} \int v g_{ab}\, d^3\boldsymbol{p}\, d^3\boldsymbol{p}';$$

$$\boldsymbol{W}_b^a = \frac{1}{\gamma_{ab}} \int v' g_{ab}\, d^3\boldsymbol{p}\, d^3\boldsymbol{p}'. \tag{24.5}$$

The function g_{ab} is thus determined by the following hydrodynamic functions: γ_{ab}—the spatial correlation function; and $\boldsymbol{W}_a^b$, $\boldsymbol{W}_b^a$—the correlation velocities.

By using the expressions (24.3, 4 and 5), the equations for f_a and g_{ab} provide equations for the functions ϱ_a, $\boldsymbol{U}_a$, γ_{ab} $\boldsymbol{W}_a^b$, and $\boldsymbol{W}_b^a$.

We write down first the equations for the functions ϱ_a and $\boldsymbol{U}_a$. For this we use eqn. (5.21) for f_a with the right-hand side in the form (5.18), supplemented by the term

$$e_a\left(\left\{\boldsymbol{E}+\frac{1}{c}\,[\boldsymbol{v}\wedge\boldsymbol{B}]\right\}\cdot\frac{\partial f_a}{\partial\boldsymbol{p}}\right),$$

which takes into account the action of the external fields $\boldsymbol{E}$ and $\boldsymbol{B}$, and also the term

$$\nu_{an}\left(\frac{\partial}{\partial\boldsymbol{p}}\cdot(\boldsymbol{v}f_a)\right),\tag{24.7}$$

which approximately takes into account the interaction with neutral atoms.

The equations for the functions ϱ_a and $\boldsymbol{U}_a$ are

$$\frac{\partial\varrho_a}{\partial t}+\left(\frac{\partial}{\partial\boldsymbol{q}}\cdot(\varrho_a\boldsymbol{U}_a)\right)=0,\tag{24.8}$$

$$\begin{aligned}\frac{\partial}{\partial t}\,\varrho_a U_i^a+\frac{\partial}{\partial q_j}\,\varrho_a U_i^a U_j^a &= -\frac{1}{m_a}\cdot\frac{\partial}{\partial q_i}(\varrho_a\varkappa T)\\ &+\frac{e_a}{m_a}\,\varrho_a\left(\boldsymbol{E}+\frac{1}{c}\,[\boldsymbol{U}_a\wedge\boldsymbol{B}]\right)_i\\ &-\frac{n_a}{m_a}\sum_b n_b\int\frac{\partial}{\partial q_i}\cdot\frac{e_a e_b}{|\boldsymbol{q}-\boldsymbol{q}'|}\,\gamma_{ab}(\boldsymbol{q},\boldsymbol{q}',t)\,d^3\boldsymbol{q}'\\ &-\nu_{an}\varrho_a U_i^a.\end{aligned}\tag{24.9}$$

To form equations for the functions γ_{ab}, $\boldsymbol{W}_a^b$ and $\boldsymbol{W}_b^a$, we use eqn. (5.35) for the function g_{ab}, supplemented by terms analogous to (24.6 and 7).

The equations for γ_{ab} and $\boldsymbol{W}_a^b$ are

$$\frac{\partial\gamma_{ab}}{\partial t}+\left(\frac{\partial}{\partial\boldsymbol{q}}\cdot\gamma_{ab}\boldsymbol{W}_a^b\right)+\left(\frac{\partial}{\partial\boldsymbol{q}'}\cdot\gamma_{ab}\boldsymbol{W}_b^a\right)=0.\tag{24.10}$$

$$\frac{\partial}{\partial t}(\gamma_{ab}W_{ai}^b)+\frac{\partial}{\partial q_j}(\gamma_{ab}W_{ai}^b W_{aj}^b)=-\frac{1}{m_a}\cdot\frac{\partial}{\partial q_i}(\gamma_{ab}\varkappa T)$$

$$+\frac{e_a}{m_a}\gamma_{ab}\left(\boldsymbol{E}+\frac{1}{c}\,[\boldsymbol{W}_a^b\wedge\boldsymbol{B}]\right)_i-\frac{\varrho_a\varrho_b}{m_a n_a n_b}\cdot\frac{\partial}{\partial q_i}\cdot\frac{e_a e_b}{|\boldsymbol{q}-\boldsymbol{q}'|}$$

$$-\frac{1}{m_a}\sum_c n_c\int\frac{\partial}{\partial q_i}\cdot\frac{e_a e_c}{|\boldsymbol{q}-\boldsymbol{q}''|}\gamma_{cb}(\boldsymbol{q}'',\boldsymbol{q}',t)\,d^3\boldsymbol{q}''$$

$$-\nu_{an}\gamma_{ab}\boldsymbol{W}_a^b. \tag{24.11}$$

The equation for the function $\boldsymbol{W}_b^a$ is obtained from (24.11) by the substitution $a\rightleftarrows b$, $\boldsymbol{q}\rightleftarrows\boldsymbol{q}'$.

Equations (24.8–11) form a closed set of equations for the functions ϱ_a, $\boldsymbol{U}_a$, γ_{ba}, $\boldsymbol{W}_a^b$ and $\boldsymbol{W}_b^a$.

If the following inequalities are satisfied

$$\frac{\partial}{\partial t}(\varrho_a\boldsymbol{U}_a)\ll\nu_{an}\varrho_a\boldsymbol{U}_a;\quad\frac{\partial}{\partial t}(\gamma_{ab}\boldsymbol{W}_b^a)\ll\nu_{an}\gamma_{ab}\boldsymbol{W}_a^b. \tag{24.12}$$

and the terms containing the functions $\varrho_a U_i^a U_i^b$ and γ_{ab}, $\boldsymbol{W}_{ai}^b$, $\boldsymbol{W}_{aj}^b$ are small, one can eliminate the functions $\boldsymbol{U}_a$, $\boldsymbol{W}_a^b$, $\boldsymbol{W}_b^a$ from eqns. (24.8–11) and so obtain a simpler set for the ϱ_a and γ_{ab}, which coincides with the corresponding set of equations in the theory of electrolytes [Klimontovich and Ebeling (1963) and Falkenhagen and Ebeling (1963)].

Consider two examples.

(1) For a spatially homogeneous electron plasma ($\varrho_e = n_e$), in the absence of external fields ($\boldsymbol{E}=\boldsymbol{B}=0$), and if the conditions (24.12) are fulfilled, in lieu of the set of eqns. (24.8–11) we have one equation for the spatial correlation function of the electrons

$$\gamma_{ee}(\boldsymbol{q}-\boldsymbol{q}',t)=\gamma_{ee}(\boldsymbol{r},t),$$

$$\nu_{en}\frac{\partial\gamma_{ee}}{\partial t}+\frac{\partial^2\gamma_{ee}}{\partial t^2}=\frac{2\varkappa T}{m_e}\left(\nabla^2\gamma_{ee}-\frac{1}{r_d^2}\gamma_{ee}\right)-\frac{2\omega_L^2}{n_e}\,\delta(\boldsymbol{r}), \tag{24.13}$$

where

$$\omega_L^2=\frac{4\pi e^2 n_e}{m_e},\quad r_d^2=\frac{\varkappa T}{4\pi e^2 n_e}.$$

In the equilibrium case eqn. (24.13) yields an expression for the Debye correlation function. From (24.13) it follows that the equilibration time of the Debye function depends on the relation between ω_L and ν_{en} and the initial distribution $\gamma_{ee}(\boldsymbol{r}, t=0)$.

If the condition (24.1) is satisfied and the initial correlation is non-zero for distances $r > r_d$, the equilibration time is

$$\tau_r = \frac{\nu_{en}}{\omega_L^2} > \frac{1}{\nu_{en}}. \tag{24.14}$$

Alternatively, this may be written as

$$\tau_r = \frac{r_d^2}{V_T\lambda} = \frac{r_d^2}{D},$$

where $D = V_T\lambda$ is the appropriate diffusion coefficient. Hence τ_r is of the same order of magnitude as the time required for a charged particle to diffuse over the distance r_d.

(2) We use eqns. (24.8–11) to calculate the conductivity and diffusion coefficients in a weakly ionized plasma which is in constant electric and magnetic fields.

It is assumed that

$$\boldsymbol{B} \parallel z, \quad \boldsymbol{E} \parallel x, \quad \varrho_a = \varrho_a(x), \quad \boldsymbol{U}_a = \boldsymbol{U}_a(x),$$
$$T = \text{const}, \quad \gamma_{ab} = \gamma_{ab}(\boldsymbol{r}, x). \tag{24.15}$$

On these conditions eqns. (24.8, 9) yield the following expressions for the components of the average velocity:

$$U_x^a = \frac{\nu_{an}}{\nu_{an}^2 + \Omega_a^2} \cdot \frac{e_a}{m_a\varrho_a} \left\{ -\frac{\varkappa T}{e_a} \cdot \frac{\partial \varrho_a}{\partial x} + \varrho_a E - \frac{n_a}{2\pi^2} \int \frac{k_x}{k^2} \operatorname{Im} \gamma_a(\boldsymbol{k}, x)\, d^3\boldsymbol{k} - \frac{\Omega_a n_a}{\nu_{an} 2\pi^2} \times \int \frac{k_y}{k^2} \operatorname{Im} \gamma_a(\boldsymbol{k}, x)\, d^3\boldsymbol{k} \right\}, \tag{24.16}$$

$$U_y^a = -\frac{\Omega_a}{\nu_{an}} U_x^a - \frac{e_a n_a}{2\pi^2 m_a \nu_{an} \varrho_a} \int \frac{k_y}{k^2} \operatorname{Im} \gamma_a(\boldsymbol{k}, x)\, d^3\boldsymbol{k}, \tag{24.17}$$

$$U_z^a = -\frac{e_a n_a}{2\pi^2 m_a \varrho_a \nu_{an}} \int \frac{k_z}{k^2} \operatorname{Im} \gamma_a(\boldsymbol{k}, x)\, d^3\boldsymbol{k}, \tag{24.18}$$

where $\Omega_a = e_a B/m_a c$ is Larmor's frequency and $\gamma_a(\boldsymbol{k}, x) = \sum_b e_b n_b \times \gamma_{ab}(\boldsymbol{k}, x)$ is the spatial Fourier component of the correlation function.

Without the correlation ($\gamma_{ab} = 0$), eqn. (24.16) yields a well-known expression for the diffusion and conductivity coefficients.

$$D_a = \frac{\varkappa T \nu_{an}}{m_a(\nu_{an}^2 + \Omega_a^2)}; \qquad \sigma_a = \frac{e_a^2 \varrho_a \nu_{an}}{m_a(\nu_{an}^2 + \Omega_a^2)}. \tag{24.19}$$

In having regard to the correlation in these expressions one needs to find, using eqns. (24.10, 11), the non-equilibrium addition to the Debye function due to the action of the external fields and the presence of the concentration gradient.

Performing the appropriate calculations (see Klimontovich and Ebeling, 1963; and Falkenhagen and Ebeling, 1963), we get the following expressions for the diffusion coefficient of the electrons:

$$D_e = \frac{\varkappa T}{m_e \nu_{en}} \left(1 - \frac{\sqrt{2}}{6(1+\sqrt{2})} \cdot \frac{e^2}{r_d \varkappa T}\right), \quad \text{if} \quad \boldsymbol{B} = 0; \tag{24.20}$$

$$D_e = \frac{\varkappa T \nu_{en}}{m_e \Omega_e^2} \left(1 + \frac{\pi}{8} \cdot \frac{\sqrt{2}}{1+\sqrt{2}} \cdot \frac{\Omega_e}{\nu_{en}} \cdot \frac{e^2}{r_d \varkappa T}\right), \quad \text{if} \quad \Omega_e \gg \nu_{en}. \tag{24.21}$$

The second terms in the brackets determine the additions due to the correlation of the charged particles. In a strong magnetic field the relative addition is greater than for $\boldsymbol{B} = 0$ by a factor of Ω/ν_{en}. Here the supplementary term depends on the magnetic field as $1/B$, i.e. it is less than the first term, which is determined by the collisions and so depends on the field as $1/B^2$.

If condition (24.1) is replaced by the less rigorous condition (24.1a), so permitting the equations to hold also for $\omega_L > \nu_{en}$ (though $\varepsilon\omega_L \sim \nu_{ab} \ll \nu_{an}$), the second term in (24.21) may be comparable with the first.

In the papers by Klimontovich and Ebeling (1963) and Falkenhagen and Ebeling (1963) eqns. (24.8–11) have been solved for variable external fields also.

It must be emphasized that the substantiation of approximation (24.3), and thus of eqns. (24.8–11) too, still remains an open question.

The results of the present section are given to illustrate the variety of possibilities for hydrodynamic descriptions of processes in a plasma.

In conclusion, note that in calculating the kinetic coefficients by the equations of §§ 16–18 (or by more general equations taking into account higher moments) the coefficients of diffusion, electrical conductivity, viscosity, and so forth, can each be represented in two parts as in (22.20, 21).

Their first part is determined by the "collisions". This implies that this part is expressed in terms of the integrals of the spatial spectral functions over the short-wave region of wave numbers—the "collision region".

The other part is determined by the spectral functions for the radiation region. For a non-stable plasma the contribution from the radiation region may considerably exceed that from the collision region.

Naturally, the hydrodynamic methods of describing the processes in a plasma, considered in this book, do not exhaust all the possibilities. For instance, by using the results of § 18, two other hydrodynamic approximations can be considered. Firstly, the hydrodynamic equations can take coherent interaction of waves into account. Secondly, one can construct the hydrodynamics from a consideration of eqns. (18.51–53), which provides a description of the turbulent state with regard to the interaction of three waves and so on.

References

ABRIKOSOV, A. A., L. P. GOR'KOV and I. YE. DZYALOSHINSKII (1965) *Quantum field theoretical methods in statistical physics*. Pergamon Press, Oxford.

AKHIEZER, A. I., I. A. AKHIEZER and A. G. SITENKO (1962) A contribution to the theory of fluctuations in a plasma, *Soviet Phys.—JETP* **17,** 462.

AKHIEZER, I. A., I. A. DANELIYA and N. L. TSINSADZE (1964) A contribution to the theory of transformation and dispersion of electromagnetic waves in a plasma. *Soviet Phys.—JETP* **19,** 208.

AKHMANOV, S. A. and R. V. KHOKHLOV (1964) *Non linear optics* (Electromagnetic waves in non-linear dispersive media). English translation to be published by North-Holland.

BALESCU, R. (1960) Irreversible process in ionized gases. *Phys. Fluids* **4,** 85.

BELYAYEV, S. T. (1958) Kinetic equation for rarefied gases and strong fields in plasma physics and the problem of controlled thermo-nuclear reactions, vol. 3. *Izd. Akad. Nauk SSSR*, p. 50, Moscow.

BELYAYEV, S. T. and G. BUDKER (1957) Relativistic kinetic equation. *Soviet Phys.—Doklady* **1,** 361.

BOGOLYUBOV, N. N. (1962) Problems of a dynamical theory in statistical physics. *Studies in statistical mechanics*, **1,** 1.

BONCH-BRUEVICH, V. L. and S. V. TYABLIKOV, (1962) *The Green function method in statistical mechanics*. North Holland, Amsterdam.

BRAGINSKII, S. I. (1958) Transport phenomena in a completely ionized plasma. *Soviet Phys.—JETP* **6,** 358.

DRUMMOND, W. E. and D. PINES (1961) Non-linear stability of plasma oscillations. Report to the conference on plasma physics, Salzburg.

FADDEYEVA, V. N. and N. M. TERENT'EV (1954) *Tables of values of the probability integral*. Gostekhizdat, Moscow. English translation published by Pergamon Press,

FALKENHAGEN, H. and W. EBELING (1963) Zur kinetischen Theorie schwach ionisierter Plasmen in Magnetfeld. *Ann. der Phys.* **10,** No. 7–8.

GINZBURG, V. L. (1964) *Propagation of electromagnetic waves in a plasma*. Pergamon Press, Oxford.

GORBUNOV, L. M., V. V. PUSTOVALOV and V. P. SILIN (1964) On the non-linear interaction of electromagnetic waves in a plasma (in Russian). Pre-print Lebedev Institute of U.S.S.R. Academy of Sciences.

GORBUNOV, L. M. and V. P. SILIN (1964) Theory of transport phenomena in a non-isothermic plasma. *Soviet Phys.-Tech. Phys.* **9,** No. 3–4.

GRAD, H. (1949) On the kinetic theory of rare gases. *Comm. Pure and Appl. Phys.* **2,** 331.

HERDAN, R. and B. LILEY (1960) Dynamical equations and transport relationships for a thermal plasma. *Rev. Mod. Phys.* **32,** 731.

References

IORDANSKII, S. V. and A. G. KULIKOVSKII (1964a) On the stability of higher correlation functions in a plasma. *Soviet Phys.—Doklady* **8**, 969.

(1964b) Quasi-linear approximation and correlation functions in a plasma. *Soviet Phys,—JETP* **19**, 499.

KADOMTSEV, B. B. and V. I. PETVIASHVILI (1963) A weakly turbulent plasma in a magnetic field. *Soviet Phys.—JETP* **16**, 1578.

KARPMAN, V. I. (1964) A contribution to the theory of a weakly turbulent plasma. *Soviet Phys.—Doklady* **8**, 919.

KLIMONTOVICH, YU. L. (1958a) On the method of "second quantization" in phase space. *Soviet Phys.—JETP* **6**, 753.

(1958b) On the space-time correlation functions of a system of particles with electromagnetic interaction. *Soviet Phys.—JETP* **7**, 119.

(1959) Charged particle energy losses in the excitation of oscillations in a plasma *Soviet Phys.—JETP* **9**, 999.

(1960) Relativistic kinetic equations for a plasma I, II. *Soviet Phys.—JETP* **10**, 524; **11**, 876.

(1961) Some aspects of the statistical theory of non-equilibrium processes in a plasma (in Russian). Doctor's thesis, Moscow State University.

(1962) On the kinetic description of quasi-equilibrium turbulent processes in a plasma. *Soviet Phys.—Doklady* **7**, 530.

(1963a) A contribution to the statistical theory of turbulence in a plasma (in Russian). *PMTF* **1**, 14.

(1963b) A contribution to the statistical theory of homogeneous isotropic turbulence in a relativistic plasma. *Soviet Phys.—Doklady* **7**, 1122.

(1965a). Allowing for non-linear interaction of waves in the kinetic equations for a plasma. *Soviet Phys.—Doklady* **9**, No. 4.

(1965b) On the non-linear interaction of waves in a plasma. *Soviet Phys.—JETP* **21**, No. 2.

(1966) Approximation of "free" and "bound" charges for a plasma. Self-consistent equations for second distribution functions. *Soviet Phys.—Doklady* **10**, No. 6.

KLIMONTOVICH, YU. L. and W. EBELING (1962) Hydrodynamische Näherungen in der Theorie stark oder schwach ionisierter Plasmen. Wiss. Univ. Rostock, issue 2, 355.

(1963) Hydrodynamic description of the motion of charged particles in a weakly ionised plasma. *Soviet Phys.—JETP* **16**, 104.

KLIMONTOVICH, YU. L. and V. V. LOGVINOV (1966) Stationary solutions of the equations in the quasi-linear approximation for a plasma with collisions. *PMTF* (in course of publication).

KLIMONTOVICH, YU. L. and V. P. SILIN (1961) Concerning magnetohydrodynamics for a non-isothermic plasma without collisions. *Soviet Phys.—JETP* **13**, 852.

(1962) A contribution to the theory of fluctuations of the particle distribution in a plasma. *Soviet Phys.—JETP* **15**, 199.

(1963) On the fluctuations in a plasma without collisions. *Soviet Phys.—Doklady* **7**, 698.

KONSTANTINOV, O. V. and V. I. PEREL' (1961) Particle collisions in a high-temperature plasma. *Soviet Phys.—JETP* **12**, 597.

KOVRIZHNYKH, L. M., A. A. RUKHADZE and V. P. SILIN (1963) On the oscillations of a low-pressure inhomogeneous plasma. *Soviet Phys.—JETP* **17**, 1314.

KOVRIZHNYKH, L. M. and V. N. TSYTOVICH (1964) A contribution to the non-linear theory of beam interaction in a plasma with transverse waves (in Russian). Pre-print. Lebedev Institute of U.S.S.R. Academy of Sciences.

KULIKOVSKII, A. G. and G. A. LYUBIMOV (1960) *Magnetohydrodynamics*. Fizmatgiz, Moscow.

LANDAU, L. D. (1937) The transport equation in the case of Coulomb interactions. *Zh. eksp. i teor. fiz.* **7**, 203. In *Collected Papers of L. D. Landau*, p. 163, Pergamon Press, Oxford, 1965.

LANDAU, L. D. and E. M. LIFSHITZ (1960) *Electrodynamics of continuous media*. Pergamon Press, Oxford.

(1962) *Theory of fields*. Pergamon Press, Oxford.

LENARD, A. (1960) On Bogolyubov's kinetic equation for a spatially homogeneous plasma. *Ann. of Phys.* **10**, 390.

LEONTOVICH, M. A. (ed.) (1963) *Questions in plasma theory*. Atomizdat. Moscow.

LEONTOVICH, M. A. and O. M. RYTOV (1952) On the differential law for the intensity of electric fluctuations and also how they influence the skin-effect (in Russian). *Zh. eksp. i teor. fiz.* **23**, 246.

LOVETSKII, YE. YE. and A. A. RUKHADZE (1962) On the hydrodynamics of a non-isothermic plasma. *Soviet Phys.—JETP* **14**, 1312.

MAZUR, P. (1958) On statistical mechanics and electromagnetic properties of matter. *Adv. in Chem. Phys.*, Vol. I, p. 309.

PINES, D. and J. SCHRIEFFER (1962) Approach to equilibrium of electrons, plasmons and phonons in quantum and classical plasmas. *Phys. Rev.* **125**, 804.

ROMANOV, YU. A. and G. F. FILIPPOV (1961) Interaction of streams of fast electrons with longitudinal plasma waves. *Soviet Phys.—JETP* **13**, 87.

ROSTOKER, N. (1960) Kinetic equation with a constant magnetic field. *Phys. Fluids* **3**, 922.

(1961) Fluctuations of a plasma. *Nuclear Fusion* **1**, 101.

RUKHADZE, A. A. and V. P. SILIN (1964) Method of geometric optics in the electrodynamics of an inhomogeneous plasma. *Soviet Phys.—Uspekhi* **7**, 1.

RYTOV, S. M. (1953) *Theory of electric fluctuations and thermal radiation*. Izd. Akad. Nauk SSSR, Moscow.

SHAPIRO, V. D. (1963) A contribution to the non-linear theory of interaction of "mono-energetic" beams with a plasma. *Soviet Phys.—JETP* **17**, 416.

SILIN, V. P. (1960) Kinetic equations for fast varying processes. *Soviet Phys.—JETP* **11**, 1277.

(1961, 1962a) On the collision integral for charged particles. *Soviet Phys.—JETP* **13**, 1244, *FMM* **13**, 180.

(1962b) On high frequency dielectric constant of a plasma. *Soviet Phys.—JETP* **14**, 617

(1963a) Triple correlations in a plasma and also the "collision integral" for a paired correlative function (in Russian). Pre-print, Lebedev Institute of U.S.S.R. Academy of Sciences.

SILIN, V. P. (1963b) Oscillations of a weakly homogeneous plasma. *Soviet Phys.—JETP* **17,** 857.

(1964) A contribution to the kinetic theory of the interaction of plasma waves (in Russian). *PMTF,* No. 1.

(1965) Non-linear high-frequency conduction of a plasma *Soviet Phys.—JETP* **20,** No. 6.

SILIN, V. P. and A. A. RUKHADZE (1961) *Electromagnetic properties of a plasma and plasma-like media.* Atomizdat, Moscow. English translation published by Consultants Bureau.

STRATONOVICH, R. L. (1961) *Selected questions in the theory of fluctuations in radio engineering.* Sov. radio, Moscow.

VEDENOV, A. A. (1962) Quasi-linear theory of a plasma [theory of a weakly turbulent plasma]. (English translation in *J. Nucl. Energy,* part C.) *Atomnaya energiya* **13,** 5.

VEDENOV, A. A. and YE. P. VELIKHOV (1963) Quasi-linear approximation in the kinetics of a rarefied plasma. *Soviet Phys.—JETP* **16,** 682.

VEDENOV, A. A., YE. P. VELIKHOV and R. Z. SAGDEYEV (1961) Stability of a plasma. *Soviet Phys.—Uspekhi* **4,** 332.

VLASOV, A. A. (1938, 1950) On the vibrational properties of electron gas (in Russian). *Zh. eksp. i teor. fiz.* **8,** 291. *Theory of many particles.* Gordon and Breach, New York.

YELEONSKII, V. M., P. S. ZYRYANOV, and V. P. SILIN (1962) Collision integral of charged particles in a strong magnetic field. *Soviet Phys.—JETP* **15,** 619.

ZHDANOV, V. M. (1962) Transport phenomena in a partially ionized gas. *Prikl. mat. i mekh.* **26,** 280.

ZUBAREV, D. N. (1960) Two-temperature Green functions in statistical physics. *Soviet Phys.—Uspekhi* **3,** 320.

ZYRYANOV, P. S. and G. G. TALUTS (1963) On non-equilibrium systems of electrons and phonons in an external magnetic field. *Soviet Phys.—JETP* **16,** 1510.

Index

Absorbing medium 25
Absorption 105, 267
Absorption of electromagnetic waves 25
Adiabatic invariant 197

Background 216, 226
Boltzmann equation ix, 62, 130, 135
Bound charges 3, 4
Bound charge approximation 237, 239

Capacitance 26
Cauchy integral 16
Central moments 59, 62
Chapman – Enskog method 248
Charge density 2, 81
Circular polarization 108
Coherent interaction of waves 225
Collision frequency 208, 268, 270
Collision integral x, 130, 139, 180, 190, 191, 192, 229, 231, 235, 253, 257
Collision rate 235
Collision region 179, 185, 193, 197, 198, 199, 205, 207, 208, 216, 231
"Collisions" 116, 210, 211, 234, 235, 236, 243
Conductivity 8, 274, 275
Conductivity tensor 8, 21, 82, 102, 106
Conservation of energy 210, 262
Conservation laws 2, 130, 140
Conservation of momentum 71, 142
Conservation of number of particles 141, 251
Continuity equation 41, 49
Correlation of the fluctuations 161
Correlation functions x, 58, 60, 62, 65, 69, 121, 156, 160, 167, 169, 200, 231, 237
Correlation radius 137, 156, 233, 240
Correlation terms 144
Correlation velocities 271
Coulomb law 5
Coulomb plasma xi, 144, 182, 194, 206, 207, 230, 231, 238
Current density 2, 81

Damping coefficient 19
Damping decrement 36, 45, 94, 95, 98, 115, 116, 179, 197, 199, 203, 206, 210, 214, 236, 262
Damping increment 167
Debye correlation function 273
Debye radius x, 63, 126, 137, 156
Density matrix 240
Dielectric 6, 12
Dielectric constant dispersion 15
Dielectric constant function 15, 18, 19, 82, 88, 124, 129, 132, 182, 184, 191, 206, 236
Dielectric constant tensor 22, 83, 84, 103, 105, 114, 155, 177, 178
Dielectric susceptibility 8
Diffusion coefficient 129, 191, 274, 275
Diffusion constant 154
Dipole approximation 240, 241
Dipole moment 12
Dispersion 79
Dispersion equation 43, 45, 97, 115, 205, 218
Dispersion relations 17, 87, 88, 92, 93, 104, 107, 174

Index

Dispersive medium 25, 26, 30, 35
Displacement current 9
Dissipative medium 30
Dissipative processes 98, 105, 231, 266
Distribution function ix, 57, 62
Distribution function for quanta 37

Effective range 127
Electric charge density 72
Electric conductivity 176, 276
Electrical induction 6
Electrical stress tensor 74
Electrolytes 273
Electromagnetic energy 30
Electromagnetic field, energy density 75
Electromagnetic stress tensor 73, 142
Electromagnetic tensor 54
Electromagnetic wave 10
Electron–ion plasma 68, 127, 133
Electron temperature 95
Energy balance equation 75, 143
Energy density 35
Energy of electromagnetic field 24
Energy flux vector 35
Entropy 76, 98, 130, 132
Entropy density 42
Equation of continuity 263
Equation of motion of an electron 11
External charge 3
External current 3
Extraordinary wave 108

Faraday's law 5
Fluctuation spectrum 154
Fluctuations of the charge density 161
Fluctuations of electric field strength 154
Fokker–Planck equations 153, 190
Four-wave interaction 221, 225, 228, 229
Free-charge approximation 237
Free-charges 4
Free-path time 136, 247

Friction coefficient 129, 191, 208, 257
Fusion coefficient 208

Gas-dynamics equations 1, 38
Gas-dynamics functions 58
Green function method xii
Group velocity 36
Gyrotropic medium 105

Hamiltonian 47
Hamiltonian equations 47
Hydrodynamic approximation 226, 261
Hydrodynamic description 275
Hydrodynamic equations 116, 243, 248, 257, 258, 271, 276
Hydrodynamic functions 245, 247, 248
Hydrodynamic instability 226

Ideal liquid approximation 76
Induced charge 3
Induced current 3
Inductance 26
Induction vector 82
Instability condition 91
Interaction of waves 276
Ion-oscillations 97
Ion temperature 95
Irreversible processes 1, 117

Joule heat generation 42

Landau damping 94, 234, 236
Landau's equations ix, 135, 156, 157
Langmuir frequency 89
Larmor frequency 263, 274
Larmor radius 39, 112
Local equilibrium 39
Local Maxwell distributions 251, 271
Longitudinal dielectric constant 84, 122, 165
Longitudinal electrical field 60

Longitudinal excitations 145
Longitudinal permittivity 34
Longitudinal waves 34, 36, 88, 95, 104, 107
Long-wave region 216
Lorentz system of equations 50, 242
Lorentz transformations 53
Low-frequency waves 114

Magnetic field strength 4
Magnetic flux density 4
Magnetic susceptibility 8
Magnetization 6, 10
Magneto-active medium 105
Magnetohydrodynamic equations 42, 264, 266
Magnetohydrodynamic waves 42, 44, 45, 109, 111, 115
Magnetosonic waves 44, 111, 115, 116, 267
Material equations 8
Maxwell distribution 92, 210
Maxwell equation ix, 2, 50, 72, 79, 147, 177
Maxwell stress tensor 73
Mean free path 1, 136, 247
Metals 19, 39
Microscopic state 49
Momentum density 244
Momentum flux density tensor 71, 74

Navier–Stokes equation 41
Non-dispersive medium 25
Non-linear medium 30, 87
Nyquist's formula 176

Ohm's law 19, 39, 40, 82
Ordinary wave 108
Oscillating circuit 26

Pass-band 174, 180, 197
Permeability 8
Permeability tensor 8
Permittivity 8
Permittivity tensor 8
Phase-randomness 226
Phase velocity 18, 92
Plasma 46
Plasma frequency 89, 90, 94, 96, 97, 173, 203, 264
Plasma momentum 73
Plasma momentum density 244
Plasma parameter x
Plasma polarization x
Poisson equation 83, 138, 139, 195, 236
Polarization 6, 10, 12, 34, 108, 133, 156, 222, 223, 231
Poynting vector 25, 75
Principal value of an integral 17
Pulsations 216, 226

Quasi-equilibrium processes 1
Quasi-linear approximation 216, 226
Quasi-static processes 1

Radiation region 174, 175, 180, 193, 197, 198, 205, 207, 212, 216, 226
Radiation-temperature 210, 262
Random functions 58
Rarefied gases 62
Rarefied plasma, parameter for 120
Refractive index 18, 108
Relation functions 214
Relativistic invariance 54
Relativistic Maxwell distribution 159
Relativistic plasma 206, 211
Relaxation processes 195
Relaxation time 68, 116, 118, 120, 127, 136, 193, 197

Second distribution functions 240
Second moments approximation 64, 215
Self-consistent equations 237, 263

Index

Self-consistent field ix, 69, 87, 215
Self-consistent field approximation 69, 76, 118
Self-consistent field equations 116, 216
Shock waves 268, 269, 270
Short-wave region 216
Smoothed distribution functions 87
Sonic waves 44, 116
Sound velocity 97, 114, 265
Sound waves 97
Space–time correlation functions 171, 179
Space–time correlations 161, 163
Space–time spectral functions 165, 193, 194
Spatial correlation function 271
Spatial dispersion 24, 27
Spatial spectral functions 118, 120, 121, 124, 147, 165, 188, 205
Spectral functions 119, 154, 180
Stop-band 179, 193, 197
Stress tensor 72, 244

Thermal conductivity 256
Thermal flux vector 245, 252
Thermodynamic functions 258
Thermodynamic parameters 1
Three-wave interaction 221, 225, 227, 228, 229
Transverse dielectric constant 84, 148, 165
Transverse excitations 145
Transverse magnetosonic waves 45
Transverse permittivity 34
Transverse waves 34, 36, 97, 104, 107
Triple correlation function 64
Turbulence 262, 276
Two-component electron-ion plasma 52
Two-component plasma 237

Unstable states 92

Velocity of sound 42
Viscosity 276
Viscosity coefficient 256
Viscous stress tensor 244, 252
Vlasov equations ix, 70, 215, 226, 240

Wave attenuation 114
Wave dispersion 95
Waves in cold plasma 104

PRINTED IN HUNGARY